ARCHAEOLOGY 96/97

Second Edition

Editor

Linda L. Hasten

Linda Hasten received both her B.A. and M.A. from UCLA. Her background is in archaeology, and she has done fieldwork in several areas including California, the southwest United States, Peru, Europe, Mexico, and British Columbia. She taught anthropology and archaeology full-time as a professor at Pasadena City College from 1971 to 1991. She has also taught experimental anthropology classes to children at UCLA. Currently, she is continuing her career as an author of fictional works, and she is a member of the Author's Guild of America.

A Library of Information from the Public Press

Cover illustration by Mike Eagle

**Dushkin Publishing Group/
Brown & Benchmark Publishers**
Sluice Dock, Guilford, Connecticut 06437

The Annual Editions Series

Annual Editions is a series of over 65 volumes designed to provide the reader with convenient, low-cost access to a wide range of current, carefully selected articles from some of the most important magazines, newspapers, and journals published today. Annual Editions are updated on an annual basis through a continuous monitoring of over 300 periodical sources. All Annual Editions have a number of features designed to make them particularly useful, including topic guides, annotated tables of contents, unit overviews, and indexes. For the teacher using Annual Editions in the classroom, an Instructor's Resource Guide with test questions is available for each volume.

VOLUMES AVAILABLE

Abnormal Psychology
Africa
Aging
American Foreign Policy
American Government
American History, Pre-Civil War
American History, Post-Civil War
American Public Policy
Anthropology
Archaeology
Biopsychology
Business Ethics
Child Growth and Development
China
Comparative Politics
Computers in Education
Computers in Society
Criminal Justice
Developing World
Deviant Behavior
Drugs, Society, and Behavior
Dying, Death, and Bereavement
Early Childhood Education
Economics
Educating Exceptional Children
Education
Educational Psychology
Environment
Geography
Global Issues
Health
Human Development
Human Resources
Human Sexuality

India and South Asia
International Business
Japan and the Pacific Rim
Latin America
Life Management
Macroeconomics
Management
Marketing
Marriage and Family
Mass Media
Microeconomics
Middle East and the Islamic World
Multicultural Education
Nutrition
Personal Growth and Behavior
Physical Anthropology
Psychology
Public Administration
Race and Ethnic Relations
Russia, the Eurasian Republics, and Central/Eastern Europe
Social Problems
Sociology
State and Local Government
Urban Society
Western Civilization, Pre-Reformation
Western Civilization, Post-Reformation
Western Europe
World History, Pre-Modern
World History, Modern
World Politics

Cataloging in Publication Data
Main entry under title: Annual Editions: Archaeology. 1996/97.
    1. Archaeology—Periodicals. I. Hasten, Linda L., comp. II. Title: Archaeology.
ISBN 0–697–31522–3   930.1′05

Second Edition

Printed in the United States of America

Printed on Recycled Paper

To the Reader

In publishing ANNUAL EDITIONS we recognize the enormous role played by the magazines, newspapers, and journals of the *public press* in providing current, first-rate educational information in a broad spectrum of interest areas. Within the articles, the best scientists, practitioners, researchers, and commentators draw issues into new perspective as accepted theories and viewpoints are called into account by new events, recent discoveries change old facts, and fresh debate breaks out over important controversies.

Many of the articles resulting from this enormous editorial effort are appropriate for students, researchers, and professionals seeking accurate, current material to help bridge the gap between principles and theories and the real world. These articles, however, become more useful for study when those of lasting value are carefully *collected, organized, indexed,* and *reproduced* in a *low-cost format,* which provides easy and permanent access when the material is needed. That is the role played by ANNUAL EDITIONS. Under the direction of each volume's *Editor,* who is an expert in the subject area, and with the guidance of an *Advisory Board,* we seek each year to provide in each ANNUAL EDITION a current, well-balanced, carefully selected collection of the best of the public press for your study and enjoyment. We think you'll find this volume useful, and we hope you'll take a moment to let us know what you think.

The second edition of *Annual Editions: Archaeology 96/97* consists of a number of articles specifically selected to present a lively overview of the field of archaeology as it is practiced today. Each article was chosen to make the old bones, shards of pottery, and stone tools *pop* into the living cultural context in which they once existed. The *pop* or sensuality of doing a thing is not to be found in the typical archaeology textbook.

The guiding concept behind this book is to present a *show me* approach in which archaeologists can speak for themselves of their own special experiences. Thus, the student will be exposed to a holistic perspective about archaeology as a living and applied science. In good writing, an author does not say "Darwin was a very tall man" but rather that "Darwin had to duck his head to pass through his seven-foot-tall library door." A *show me* literature can energize the necessary basics and enable the student to transform passive learning into active learning in a way in which information is both conceptualized and perceptualized. In other words, the "light bulb" goes on.

This book is organized into seven units, each of which contains several articles on various aspects of practicing archaeology. At the beginning of the book, a *table of contents* provides a short synopsis of each article. This is followed by a *topic guide* that cross-references general areas of interest as they appear in the various articles. At the end of the book is a comprehensive *index*. Each unit is introduced by an *overview* that provides commentary on the unit topic, and *challenge questions* are offered to provoke thought and discussion.

The organization of this book is both suggestive and subjective. The articles may be assigned or read in any fashion that is deemed desirable. Each article stands on its own and may be assigned in conjunction with or in contrast to any other article. The book may serve as a supplement to a standard textbook used in introductory archaeology classes. Or it might be used with other books to replace the standard textbook altogether. This anthology would be useful in general courses in anthropology and to an interested lay public.

Unlike most academic texts, this book will be updated annually to keep pace with its rapidly changing subject matter and to allow for greater exposure to the vast literature available in the field of archaeology. Those involved in the production of this volume wish to make each edition a valuable and provocative teaching tool. We welcome your criticisms, advice, and suggestions in order to carefully hone this book into a finer artifact of education. *Please use the form at the end of the book for your comments.*

It is humbling to realize that today is tomorrow's past and that evidence abounds of truths whose questions we have not yet asked.

Linda L. Hasten
Editor

Contents

Unit 1

About Archaeology

Six articles present overviews of the history and definition of archaeology and how archaeologists view themselves and each other.

The concepts in bold italics are developed in the article. For further expansion please refer to the Topic Guide and the Index.

Unit 2

Thinking Like an Archaeologist

Three selections illustrate a variety of approaches to understanding and authenticating archaeological information.

Unit 3

Problem-oriented Archaeology

Seven articles examine the contemporary goal of archaeology, which is to solve problems rather than to make discoveries. Problems range from the discovery of art by prehistoric human beings to general issues when earliest peoples first migrated to the New World.

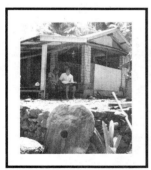

Unit 4

Experimental Archaeology

Five selections demonstrate how modern archaeologists
purposely set up experiments to reenact past events.
Whatever the experiments, a whole new body of
fundamental information about archaeological
processes is generated.

Unit 5

History and Ethnoarchaeology

Eight articles consider the use of the studies of contemporary societies, including but not limited to primitive societies, to extrapolate back to the past in order to recreate a kind of living social archaeology.

Unit 6

The New Politics of Archaeology: A Trowel for Your Thoughts

Seven selections examine who has what rights and responsibilities with respect to archaeological sites. Nationalistic politics as well as local politics come into play in attempting to meet these various and often conflicting demands.

The concepts in bold italics are developed in the article. For further expansion please refer to the Topic Guide and the Index.

Unit 7

Contemporary Archaeology

Nine articles explore the expanding roles of archaeologists as they move into the areas of salvage, private business, cultural resource management, preservation of sites, and public archaeology, all underscored by significantly reduced funding.

The concepts in bold italics are developed in the article. For further expansion please refer to the Topic Guide and the Index.

Topic Guide

This topic guide suggests how the selections in this book relate to topics of traditional concern to students and professionals involved with the study of archaeology. It can be very useful for locating articles that relate to each other for reading and research. The guide is arranged alphabetically according to topic. Articles may, of course, treat topics that do not appear in the topic guide. In turn, entries in the topic guide do not necessarily constitute a comprehensive listing of all the contents of each selection.

TOPIC AREA	TREATED IN	TOPIC AREA	TREATED IN
African American Archaeology	26. Bones and Bureaucrats 27. Earth Is Their Witness	Ethics and Laws	2. Golden Marshalltown 5. 'Reverse Archaeologists' 30. Antiquities Market 33. Anthropological Culture Shift 34. My Grandmother Is Your Database 35. Archaeology Division 36. Indians, Archaeologists, and the Future 37. Tales from a Peruvian Crypt 38. Damming the Past 39. Before the Deluge 41. Saving our World's Heritage 42. Proving Ground of the Nuclear Age 45. Preservation of the Past
Antiquities, Antiquarians, and Amateur Archaeologists	1. Quest for the Past 5. 'Reverse Archaeologists' 30. Antiquities Market 31. Who Owns the Spoils of War? 32. Politics and Archaeology 44. Boom in Volunteer Archaeology		
Art and Religion	14. Weaving Preceded Settled Life 15. Ancient Odysseys 18. Moving the Moai 19. Paleolithic Paint Job 22. Red Feathers from the South 30. Antiquities Market 31. Who Owns the Spoils of War? 32. Politics and Archaeology 37. Tales from a Peruvian Crypt	Ethnographic Analogy and Ethnoarchaeology	22. Red Feathers from the South 23. Post-Mortem at the Little Big Horn 24. Past as Propaganda 25. Murders from the Past 26. Bones and Bureaucrats 27. Earth Is Their Witness 28. Colorful Cotton! 29. Living through the Donner Party 43. Sentinels of Stone
Burials, Reburials, and Skeletal Remains	1. Quest for the Past 4. Enlightened Archaeologist 13. Egil's Bones 16. Thailand's Good Mound 23. Post-Mortem at the Little Big Horn 26. Bones and Bureaucrats 27. Earth Is Their Witness 30. Antiquities Market 33. Anthropological Culture Shift 34. My Grandmother Is Your Database 36. Indians, Archaeologists, and the Future 37. Tales from a Peruvian Crypt 45. Preservation of the Past	Experimental Archaeology	17. Yes, Wonderful Things 18. Moving the Moai 19. Paleolithic Paint Job 20. Bushmen 21. Ancient Indians 42. Proving Ground of the Nuclear Age
		Forensic Archaeology	23. Post-Mortem at the Little Bighorn 25. Murders from the Past
Cannibalism	29. Living through the Donner Party	Frauds	7. Epistemology 24. Past as Propaganda
Contract Archaeology	5. 'Reverse Archaeologists' 33. Anthropological Culture Shift 40. Archaeology Meets the 104th Congress 41. Saving Our World's Heritage 43. Sentinels of Stone 45. Preservation of the Past	Gender and Sex Roles	1. Quest for the Past
		History and Historical Archaeology	1. Quest for the Past 5. 'Reverse Archaeologists' 20. Bushmen 22. Red Feathers from the South 23. Post-Mortem at the Little Big Horn 24. Past as Propaganda 25. Murders from the Past 26. Bones and Bureaucrats 27. Earth Is Their Witness 28. Colorful Cotton! 29. Living through the Donner Party 31. Who Owns the Spoils of War? 38. Damming the Past 39. Before the Deluge 42. Proving Ground of the Nuclear Age 45. Preservation of the Past
Cultural Resource Management (CRM) and Conservation	26. Bones and Bureaucrats 27. Earth Is Their Witness 30. Antiquities Market 38. Damming the Past 39. Before the Deluge 40. Archaeology Meets the 104th Congress 41. Saving Our World's Heritage 43. Sentinels of Stone 44. Boom in Volunteer Archaeology 45. Preservation of the Past		
Epistemology	2. Golden Marshalltown 3. How Archaeology Works 7. Epistemology 8. Mysterious Fall of the Nacirema		

TOPIC AREA	TREATED IN	TOPIC AREA	TREATED IN
Hunter-Collectors	9. Rhinos and Lions and Bears (Oh, My!) 10. Coming to America 14. Weaving Preceded Settled Life 19. Paleolithic Paint Job 20. Bushmen 30. Antiquities Market 36. Indians, Archaeologists, and the Future 38. Damming the Past	**Professional Archaeologists**	1. Quest for the Past 2. Golden Marshalltown 3. How Archaeology Works 4. Enlightened Archaeologist 5. 'Reverse Archaeologists' 8. Mysterious Fall of the Nacirema 30. Antiquities Market 33. Anthropological Culture Shift 34. My Grandmother Is Your Database 35. Archaeology Division 36. Indians, Archaeologists, and the Future 40. Archaeology Meets the 104th Congress 41. Saving Our World's Heritage 45. Preservation of the Past
Looters, Grave Robbers, and Pot Hunters	1. Quest for the Past 30. Antiquities Market 31. Who Owns the Spoils of War? 32. Politics and Archaeology 37. Tales from a Peruvian Crypt 41. Saving our World's Heritage 45. Preservation of the Past	**Public Archaeology**	44. Boom in Volunteer Archaeology 45. Preservation of the Past
Myths and Legends	8. Mysterious Fall of the Nacirema 13. Egil's Bones 22. Red Feathers from the South 37. Tales from a Peruvian Crypt 43. Sentinels of Stone	**Repatriation**	26. Bones and Bureaucrats 31. Who Owns the Spoils of War? 32. Politics and Archaeology 33. Anthropological Culture Shift 34. My Grandmother Is Your Database 35. Archaeology Division 36. Indians, Archaeologists, and the Future 42. Proving Ground of the Nuclear Age
Native Americans	4. Enlightened Archaeologist 5. 'Reverse Archaeologists' 10. Coming to America 21. Ancient Indians 23. Post-Mortem at the Little Big Horn 26. Bones and Bureaucrats 28. Colorful Cotton! 30. Antiquities Market 33. Anthropological Culture Shift 34. My Grandmother Is Your Database 35. Archaeology Division 36. Indians, Archaeologists, and the Future 37. Tales from a Peruvian Crypt 38. Damming the Past 40. Archaeology Meets the 104th Congress 44. Boom in Volunteer Archaeology	**Ritual and Myth**	8. Mysterious Fall of the Nacirema 13. Egil's Bones 18. Moving the Moai 22. Red Feathers from the South 27. Earth Is Their Witness 29. Living through the Donner Party 37. Tales from a Peruvian Crypt
Paleolithic	9. Rhinos and Lions and Bears (Oh, My!) 10. Coming to America 15. Ancient Odysseys 14. Weaving Preceded Settled Life 19. Paleolithic Paint Job	**Salvage Archaeology**	4. Enlightened Archaeologist 33. Anthropological Culture Shift 37. Tales from a Peruvian Crypt 38. Damming the Past 39. Before the Deluge 40. Archaeology Meets the 104th Congress 41. Saving Our World's Heritage 42. Proving Ground of the Nuclear Age 45. Preservation of the Past
Politics	6. Kentucky Memoir 18. Moving the Moai 24. Past as Propaganda 26. Bones and Bureaucrats 27. Earth Is Their Witness 28. Colorful Cotton!	**Science, the Scientific Method, and Hypotheses**	4. Enlightened Archaeologist 7. Epistemology 9. Rhinos and Lions and Bears (Oh, My!) 10. Coming to America 14. Weaving Preceded Settled Life 15. Ancient Odysseys 18. Moving the Moai 19. Paleolithic Paint Job 29. Living through the Donner Party
Politics in Archaeology	30. Antiquities Market 31. Who Owns the Spoils of War? 32. Politics and Archaeology 33. Anthropological Culture Shift 34. My Grandmother Is Your Database 35. Archaeology Division 36. Indians, Archaeologists, and the Future 40. Archaeology Meets the 104th Congress 41. Saving Our World's Heritage 42. Proving Ground of the Nuclear Age 43. Sentinels of Stone 45. Preservation of the Past	**Techniques and Methods**	5. 'Reverse Archaeologists' 9. Rhinos and Lions and Bears (Oh, My!) 12. Dead Sea DNA 17. Yes, Wonderful Things 18. Moving the Moai 19. Paleolithic Paint Job 20. Bushmen 25. Murders from the Past
		Underwater Archaeology	3. How Archaeology Works

About Archaeology

What is the difference between archaeology and anthropology? Would the archaeologist or anthropologist who has *not* been asked this question please stand up and be counted!

If human behavior were a baseball game, the anthropologist would be in the broadcaster's booth. But long before the game was over, in a seeming paradox, the anthropologist would run into the stands to be a spectator, chow down on a good mustard-covered hot dog, then rush onto the field to be a player and catch a high fly to right field. This is the eccentric nature of anthropology. This is why anthropologists are so interesting.

If one compares anthropology, psychology, sociology, and history as four disciplines that study humankind, anthropology is the study of humankind that takes the biggest step back and uses a panoramic camera that gives a 360° view. The psychologist stands nose-to-nose with the individual person, the sociologist steps back for the group shot, and the historian steps back in time as well as space. However, the anthropologist does all these things standing well behind the others, watching and measuring, in a sense using the data of all these disciplines but weaving them into the uniqueness of the anthropological perspective.

Anthropology is the science of human behavior that studies all humankind, starting with our biological and evolutionary origins into cultural beings and the continuation and diversification of our cultural selves. Humankind is the single species that has evolved culture as a unique way of adapting to the world.

Academically, anthropology is divided into the two major fields of physical and cultural anthropology. Cultural anthropologists hold a generally shared concept of culture. The basic question that cultural anthropologists address is how to explain the differences and similarities between cultures. In order to achieve this, cultural anthropologists view people with a cross-cultural perspective. This encompasses comparing all cultures, present and past, with each other. A grand task, indeed.

What is culture? Culture is the unique way in which our species adapts to its total environment. Total environment includes everything that affects human beings—the physical environment, plants, animals, the weather, beliefs, values, a passing insult, or an opportunistic virus. Everything! Human beings are both created by culture and are the creators of culture.

Culture is the human adaptive system in which all people live in groups defined by time, space, and place, pass on shared values and beliefs through a common language(s), and manipulate things in the environment through tool use and tool making. Cultures change and evolve through time. And perhaps most important, cultures, all cultures, whether they are high civilizations or small tribes, eventually cease to exist.

And it is archaeology as a subfield of cultural anthropology that studies these extant cultures. Archaeologists dig up the physical remains, the tools, the houses, the rubbish of these once-living cultures. From from this spare database, archaeologists are the anthropologists who try to reconstruct these past cultures. Is this important to anthropology? Yes. Because these once-living cultures represent approximately 98 percent of all cultures that have ever existed. They tell us where we have been, when we are there again, and where we might go in the future. Let us proceed now to see how these archaeologists ply their trade.

Looking Ahead: Challenge Questions

What is the general relationship between anthropology and archaeology?

What does it mean to say that archaeology started as an "underground" science?

When was archaeology recognized as a science? Why?

Is an archaeologist's reputation based on the excellence of his or her fieldwork?

Describe how archaeology raises questions of ethics.

In what measurable ways have archaeological methods changed over time?

Characterize the relationship between amateur and professional archaeologists.

What is the range of variation in the scale of archaeological digs? Give some examples.

How was archaeology. used during the Great Depression to create jobs?

The Quest for the Past

Brian M. Fagan

Archaeologists are commonly thought to be eccentric people who wear rumpled khaki shorts and sun helmets and spend their lives unearthing crumbling ruins in the shadow of mighty pyramids. They live in a world of lost civilizations and buried treasure, deep mysteries and unexplained phenomena. The archaeologist of novel and television seems to be continually off on a "dig," searching for missing links and unwrapping innumerable Ancient Egyptian mummies. Sometimes, too, the angry mummies chase the unfortunate archaeologists, intoning dreadful curses that lead to their premature deaths. Many of us, at one time or another, have dreamed of pursuing such a romantic—if, in fact, mythical—career.

This is . . . about actual archaeological discoveries, about remarkable archaeologists whose explorations have dramatically expanded our understanding of human history. It is . . . about the excitement of archaeological discovery, about a scientific world that many consider to be one of the most engrossing frontiers of science. Its heroes are archaeologists of extraordinary ability who have made fascinating discoveries, often after years of patient effort. Each was a pioneer who pursued a dream, a conviction that spectacular archaeological finds awaited his or her spade.

The face of archaeology has changed considerably in recent years. Archaeologists of the 1840s, and even as late as the 1930s, could hope to uncover hitherto unknown civilizations: the Assyrians and Sumerians of Mesopotamia surfaced in the mid-nineteenth century, the Maya of Mexico in the 1840s, the Mycenaeans of Greece in the 1870s, the Shang civilization of China in the late 1920s. All of these discoveries captured the public imagination, for they were made under conditions of great difficulty, conditions that often required near-heroic efforts, The early archaeologists had few resources and no advanced excavation techniques. By constant improvisation, by drawing on their own wealth, and by acute political maneuvering, they frequently achieved miracles. They learned digging the hard way, made brilliant finds, and, regrettably, sometimes irreparably damaged vital clues to the past.

Some of our archaeologists belong to this heroic era, others to our own generation, where there are simply no lost civilizations left to find. But today's archaeologists still make remarkable discoveries, often as a result of applying such advanced tools as the computer to archaeological data. Modern archaeology is big business; thousands of people all over the world are currently involved in digging up the past. Practically every nation now employs a few archaeologists—as museum curators, university professors, or conservators of national culture. All of these archaeologists use excavation techniques that have evolved over generations of archaeological discovery. The newer techniques enable them to tackle problems that would have boggled the mind even a few years ago.

One of Mexico's earliest cities, Teotihuacán, is a case in point. Early archaeologists could only gasp at the size of Teotihuacán, sample a portion of a pyramid or a few houses, then turn away in despair. They simply did not have the technology needed to carry their explorations further. It has taken a team of modern archaeologists over a decade to map the entire twelve-and-a-half square miles of Mexico's largest prehistoric city. Their task would have been impossible without a mosaic of air photographs and highly sophisticated computer programs that enabled them to store inventories of archaeological finds and millions of other items of information on computer tape. When the time came to put the data together, the archaeologists could recall and classify thousands of data items in a few seconds. The result: a whole new picture of Teotihuacán.

How do archaeologists dig up the past? What makes archaeological excavation different from ditch digging or the treasure-hunting activities of our mythical, sun-helmeted archaeologist? To get some idea of just how far the field of archaeology has progressed, let's look back over its colorful history.

Archaeology has a long and disreputable line of descent: its ancestors were, quite literally, grave robbers and adventurers. A century and a half ago, even serious archaeological excavation was little more than licensed treasure hunting. Everyone, whether archaeologist or treasure hunter, had the same objective—to recover as many valuable objects as possible in the shortest time. Serious archaeologists would not hesitate to use gunpowder to blast their way into a burial chamber or a pyramid. Everything was cast aside in a frantic search for the valuable and spectacular. As a result, most excavations resembled untidy vegetable gardens.

Mummy hunters in Egypt literally waded through piles of discarded coffins to reach their prey. The famous Italian collector Giovanni Belzoni, who worked in Egypt from 1817 to 1820, would crawl hundreds of yards into the rocky hillsides behind Thebes in search of mummies and papyri. Exhausted, he would perch in the darkness for a few minutes on a convenient mummy. Once his perch collapsed in a cloud of smelly dust. "I sank altogether among the broken mummies, with a crash of bones, rags, and wooden cases," he remembered. It was a good quarter of an hour before Belzoni could extricate himself.

Belzoni and his contemporaries were quite open about their efforts to "rob the Egyptians of their papyri." No one thought this either eccentric or wrong. Rather, Belzoni's audiences would be agog as he related his eerie experiences in the dark burial chambers, where, in the flickering lamplight, the mummies seemed almost to converse with one another and the naked Arab workmen, coated in layers of dust, resembled mummies themselves. The audiences would gasp as Belzoni produced pieces of desiccated ancient Egyptians, remarking casually that "mummies are rather unpleasant to swallow."

In general, the nineteenth century was a time of frantic search for ancient sculptures and fine artifacts, whether from Egypt, Greece, Mesopotamia, or the Americas. Everyone wanted items for their collections and no one had any scruples about the means used to dig up their pet acquisitions. All too often we read in their early reports that such and such a find "crumbled to dust" on discovery or that exposure to the open air caused the finds to "dissolve before our very eyes."

One cannot entirely blame Belzoni and his successors. Basically, they were ignorant. No one had ever tried to dig a large archaeological site at all systematically. Even today, the technology of conservation is in relative infancy and modern archaeologists are still at a loss as to how to preserve

many delicate finds satisfactorily. Considering the state of the art, it's a miracle that so much is preserved from early excavations. But the archaeological price of filling the British Museum, the Louvre, and other great museums was simply enormous: witness Austen Henry Layard's excavations in Mesopotamia at ancient Nineveh and Nimrud from 1845 to 1851.

Layard started digging Nimrud with precious little money and absolutely no archaeological experience. He simply tunneled into the huge mounds reputed to be the remains of these ancient cities and went on digging until he hit a fine sculpture or a stone-walled palace room. At Nimrud he was lucky enough to find two palaces. But, as he dug through mud-brick walls and houses, he failed to recognize invaluable inscribed tablets of unbaked clay. To his unskilled eyes, the bricks and tablets were indistinguishable from the brown soil of the mound. Later excavators recovered thousands of these tablets from areas of Nimrud that Layard left untouched. They had developed the skills and techniques to find them.

The deep tunnels that Layard dug along walls or lines of sculptured slabs at least sheltered him from the merciless sun and sweeping winds of the open plains. He would shovel out the contents of each room with dispatch, then sit down to record the intricate details of prancing horsemen and fighting warriors that flickered in the somber shadows. When his trenches were open to the elements, clouds of blinding dust stirred by savage gale-force winds would bombard the workmen. Layard himself would take refuge behind a giant sculpture until the sandstorm subsided. Under the circumstances, it is remarkable that he succeeded in excavating at all.

Austen Henry Layard shifted thousands of tons of soil, discovered nearly two miles of bas-reliefs, and cleared seventy rooms in the Palace of Sennacherib at Kuyunjik alone. Although he did keep some records, he more or less shoveled his way into the past. He tore Nimrud and Nineveh apart and, in the process, wiped out priceless archaeological information—data on

daily life and ancient diet, details of houses and storerooms, and, above all, the complex sequence of layers that made up the occupation mounds.

Every Mesopotamian city mound was formed over centuries of occupation through complex processes of rebuilding houses, dumping garbage, and the natural actions of rain and wind. Many years before Layard came to Nineveh, geologists studying railway cuttings and canal excavations in Europe and America had observed the layered strata of the earth and established the classic principle of superposition. Very simply stated, this means that the lower levels of a succession of geological horizons were laid down earlier than the higher levels. The law of superposition had obvious applications to great city mounds like Nimrud or Nineveh, for every site started as a small settlement on a low ridge. The first occupation levels were soon covered by later settlements built in the same place. A thousand years later, the same city could look down from the top of a high mound of age-old occupation debris. The archaeologist wishing to understand the history of the city would have to dissect this mound layer by layer.

Layard himself was well aware that his mounds had gone through many changes. He knew that many kings had ruled his cities. But his excavation methods were simply too crude to permit him to dig the mounds period by period. One cannot blame Layard. If anything, he was more conscientious than his contemporaries, for he at least wrote popular accounts of his findings.

Many excavations of Layard's time were little more than picnic parties. Wealthy country gentlemen would open Indian burial mounds or Bronze Age earthworks for the sheer fun of it. When the English antiquarian Thomas Wright attended the opening of an ancient burial mound in 1844, he found a large party of interested gentry assembled for the sport. While the workmen opened eight burial mounds, the ladies and gentlemen "continued to spend [their] time, at intervals between digging and picnicking, in games of various descriptions . . . and in other amusements. The weather was fortunately exquisitely fine." When a sudden shower threatened to drench the party, they took refuge in the trench under a shield of umbrellas. The burial mounds contained "skeletons, more or less entire, with the remains of weapons in iron, bosses of shields, urns, beads, armlets, and occasionally more vessels." All of these finds vanished into the landowner's private collection, which the party inspected after partaking of a "sumptuous repast." This burial-mound dig was in no way exceptional; rather, it was typical of thousands.

The techniques of excavation were still in their infancy when Heinrich Schliemann began work on the great Hissarlik mound, site of ancient Troy. Schliemann, a millionaire, attacked archaeological problems with the same single-minded intensity he applied to business ventures. His wealth gave him the means to work on a truly grand scale, with resident experts and hundreds of workmen. He arrived on the site in 1871 with the vague notion that the mound contained many different settlements. So he set out to dig to bedrock, on a scale that almost beggars description. In 1872, for example, he borrowed a railroad engineer and employed three overseers to direct over a hundred men. They sliced into Hissarlik with a cutting over 230 feet wide that eventually penetrated over 40 feet into the huge mound. The city walls found in the upper-most strata were ruthlessly cleared away as Schliemann dug his way down through the centuries, toward his Homeric city.

Eventually, Schliemann identified the remains of seven cities, one above the other. His excavations exhibited a notable lack of finesse. In his books, he refers to the clearance of entire ancient streets, to the removal of "older walls which I am also having broken through," and to thousands upon thousands of potsherds, ornaments, and other small finds that were shoveled out as thousands of tons of soil were dug out of Hissarlik. At one point, he boasted that he had removed 325,000 cubic yards of soil from ancient Troy.

Schliemann's motto was speed, more speed, and yet still more. When he dug, he cleared an entire landscape. Every day he described his findings in a comprehensive diary, which he eventually published. Unlike many of his contemporaries, Schliemann kept his finds and recorded all of them, not just the spectacular pieces. And, although he has been castigated as little more than a treasure hunter, he in fact undertook the first large-scale dissection of a city mound where, unlike the situation at Nineveh or Nimrud, there were no sculptures to guide the way to ancient structures. As his digging experience increased, Schliemann began to rely more heavily on expert diggers, who were able to refine his methods drastically.

While Schliemann was working at Troy, German archaeologists had begun a quiet revolution in excavation methods that was to affect both the Troy excavations and many other digs as well. The Austrian archaeologist Alexander Conze dug at the site of Samothrace in Greece between 1873 and 1875. He dug with the help of architects and a photographer, who recorded the progress of the excavations. The Samothrace report was a beautiful production, the first to be illustrated with photographs. Conze's example was not lost on the German Archaeological Institute, which started work at Olympia in 1875. For six winters, Ernst Curtius directed a brilliant campaign of excavations on the site of the original Olympic Games. The Kaiser himself paid for part of the dig. Every find was carefully preserved and housed in a special museum built at the site. No artifacts were exported. Curtius and Wilhelm Dörpfeld worked out every detail of the stratigraphy at Olympia with the aid of new and very precise record-keeping methods. The Olympia excavations set new standards that the ever-energetic Dörpfeld took with him to Troy. In his later years at Hissarlik, Schliemann became what one authority has called "a constitutional monarch among expert ministers." Dörpfeld refined Schliemann's seven cities into the complex history of a mound that, he said, flourished from

about 3000–700 B.C., the Homeric city dating from 1500–1000 B.C.

Curtius and Dörpfeld were concerned with the trivial as well as the spectacular. Their excavations were far more meticulous than those of their predecessors, although still crude by-modern standards. A retired British general named Augustus Pitt-Rivers revolutionized the art of excavation even further. The general, a formidable personality, spent much of his military career working on the development of army rifles. His experimental research involved him in the history of firearms and the study of different types of primitive artifacts from all over the world. Pitt-Rivers was deeply interested in the evolution of human technology. He became an avid collector of artifacts of all types—masks, shields, weapons, even canoes. His collections became so large that he donated them to Oxford University, where they are to this day.

In 1880, Pitt-Rivers inherited an enormous estate in southern England, an estate littered with ancient burial sites and earthworks. The general decided to devote the rest of his life to investigation of the sites on his property. He did so with ruthless efficiency, diverting enormous sums from his fortune into leisured excavations that lasted twenty years, until his death in 1901. Pitt-Rivers had a mania for records and detail. "Every detail should be recorded in the manner most conducive to facility of reference," he wrote. "I have endeavored to record the results of these excavations in such a way that the whole of the evidence may be available for those who are concerned to go into it." He had realized a cardinal point: all archaeological excavation is permanent destruction and all objects found in a site have a vital context in time and space that is just as important a piece of information as the find itself.

The learned general was far ahead of his time. He trained archaeological assistants, had "before" and "after" models of his sites constructed, built a special museum to display his finds, and even marked his filled-in trenches with special medallions that said, in effect, "Pitt-Rivers was here." His ideas were revolutionary. Consider some of his basic principles of digging: "No excavation ought to ever be permitted except under the immediate eye of a responsible and trustworthy superintendent." "Superfluous precision may be regarded as a fault on the right side." "Tedious as it may appear to some to dwell on the discovery of odds and ends that have, no doubt, been thrown away by the owners as rubbish . . . yet it is by the study of such trivial details that archaeology is mainly dependent for determining the date of earthworks."

Hundreds of man-hours went into each of Pitt-Rivers's sumptuous reports. Each was published privately, complete with detailed plans, accurate measurements of every artifact, and precise information on every aspect of the site from pottery to hut foundations, stratigraphy to animal bones. It was to be years before anyone would equal or surpass Pitt-Rivers's painstaking work. He deplored the destruction of earthworks by plowing, laid out picnic grounds for people visiting his museum, and urged his fellow landowners to follow his example. The general was not a particularly endearing gentleman, but his legacy to archaeology is unquestioned. An interesting glimpse into the man comes from a photograph of the excavations which is tersely captioned: "The figure standing at attention in the foreground gives the scale." Evidently Pitt-Rivers was a military man, as well as an archaeologist, to the very end.

Few people followed Pitt-Rivers's example. One could still become an excavator without any training at all, although well-known archaeologists like Wilhelm Dörpfeld and the immortal Egyptologist Flinders Petrie were busy training students to follow in their footsteps. Petrie begged his colleagues to be quit of "the brandy-and-soda young man . . . of the adventurous speculator. Without the ideal of solid continuous work, certain, accurate, and permanent, archaeology is as futile as any other pursuit." He went on to urge informal attire: "To attempt serious work in pretty suits, shiny leggings or starched collars, would be like mountaineering in evening dress." "It is sickening to see the rate at which everything is being destroyed," he once remarked, "and the little regard paid to preservation."

Some of the better digging that stemmed from Pitt-Rivers's work took place on Roman sites in Britain. Still, to modern eyes, the efforts appear to have been terribly amateurish and the excavators incredibly ill-equipped. Young Leonard Woolley, for example, later to become famous for his skilled excavations of royal graves at Ur-of-the-Chaldees in Mesopotamia, found himself in charge of a major Roman excavation without any experience at all or the least idea of how to survey a site or make plans.

The early part of this century also seems to have been a difficult period for female archaeologists. When a little-known archaeologist named J. P. Droop wrote a small manual on excavation in 1915, he spent a lot of time worrying about male/female roles. "I have never seen a trained lady excavator at work," he admitted. "Of a mixed dig, however, I have seen something, and it is an experiment that I would be reluctant to try again." His reasons were twofold. "In the first place, there are the proprieties." Excavators should respect the etiquette and mores of the countries they are working in. Droop's other reasons were more personal. It seems that, in his experience, the "charm" of ladies vanishes during an excavation, for the dig lays on its mixed participants "a bond of closer daily intercourse than is conceivable." Droop found this irritating. "The ordinary male at least cannot stand it," he added. He cited the strain of "self-restraint in moments of stress, moments that will occur on the best regulated dig, when you want to say just what you think without translation, which before ladies, whatever their feelings about it, cannot be done." Droop was never to know of the key roles played by twentieth-century women in major archaeological excavations the world over.

Nevertheless, there were a handful of women who carried out important work in the field long before female excavators became Commonplace. One pioneer was the English novelist Amelia Edwards, a Victorian lady in the classic sense of the word, who embarked on a two-month journey up the Nile in 1874. She traveled in genteel company aboard a sailing ship complete with upright piano and proper chaperones. Edwards was horrified by the looting and destruction of Ancient Egyptian sites on every side, at the blatant forgery of antiquities, and the "black-robed, grave men, who always lay in wait ready to sell you anything." Nevertheless, she was entranced by the Pyramids, the Temple of Karnak, and Abu Simbel, by the columns of ancient temples which she compared to groves of redwood trees. Her *Thousand Miles Up the Nile* (1877) is one of the classics of early archaeological travel and still bears reading today. Edwards devoted the rest of her life to lecturing and writing about the destruction in Egypt and was instrumental in the founding of the Egypt Exploration Society, which works in the Nile Valley to this day.

Harriet Boyd Hawes, a Smith graduate who met Amelia Edwards while in college, was even more remarkable. In 1897, she traveled to Athens to study archaeology, one of the first women to do so. Archaeology soon took a back seat to nursing when Turkey declared war on Greece. For months, Hawes cared for wounded Greek soldiers within sound of artillery barrages, developing a passion for humanitarian causes that guided much of her life. Much to her surprise, she won a fellowship at the American School in Athens from Yale University, but was not allowed to excavate, this being considered a male domain. The British were more encouraging and she went over to Crete, where she combed the countryside for archaeological sites on the back of a mule. Her persistence was rewarded and she became the first woman to excavate a Minoan town. Hawes's monograph on Gournia is one of the classics of early Mediterranean archaeology. Not that Harriet did much more fieldwork, for she threw herself into humanitarian work among Serb soldiers in Corfu and served as a ward aid in American hospitals in France during World War I. But she opened doors into the narrow archaeological world for many talented women that followed in her footsteps.

There were other talented women pioneers, too, among them the redoubtable Gertrude Bell, who became an expert desert traveler and founded the Iraq Museum; Gertrude Caton-Thompson, who discovered what were then the earliest farmers in the world in Egypt's Fayum in the 1920s; and Dorothy Garrod, the first woman Professor of Archaeology anywhere in Europe, who excavated the Stone Age caves on Mount Carmel in the Levant in the 1930s. For the most part, they worked on shoestring budgets and often with few companions. But the discoveries they made contributed to the revolution in archaeological methods that took hold after World War I, in the hands of several capable excavators. Indeed the lax standards of Pitt-Rivers's contemporaries and successors were assaulted by archaeologists of the 1920s and 1930s. "There is no right way of digging but there are many wrong ones," wrote one of Pitt-Rivers's most avid disciples—Mortimer Wheeler. Wheeler, who was ten years old when Pitt-Rivers died, came to archaeology through the good offices of Arthur Evans, discoverer of the ancient palace of King Minos on Crete. Wheeler spent his lifetime digging large sites with meticulous precision and training new generations of archaeologists in methods that owed their inspiration to the Victorian general.

Wheeler worked first on Roman forts, then on the famous Iron Age fortress at Maiden Castle in southern Britain. From archaeological evidence, he was able to reconstruct a blow-by-blow account of the Roman storming of that fort. After a distinguished military career in World War II, Wheeler was asked to head up the Archaeological Survey of India. With characteristic and flamboyant energy, he took up the task of organizing archaeology out of chaos. He found Roman imported pottery in southern India and dug deeply into the ancient city mounds of Harappa and Mohenjo-daro in the In-

dus Valley. There he sketched a fascinating picture of a long-extinct Indian civilization that had traded with Mesopotamia and developed its own distinctive, and still undeciphered, script. Mortimer Wheeler's excavations were, quite simply, meticulous, and the results remarkable. Most modern excavations build on the basic principles that he and Pitt-Rivers, as well as a handful of other pioneers, set out.

"The archaeologist is not digging up things, he is digging up people," Wheeler would begin. Good excavation takes imagination, an ability to understand what one is digging up. According to Wheeler, people who do not have this kind of imagination should collect bus tickets instead of digging. He believed the key to excavation was accurate observation and recording of occupation levels and architectural features, of the layout of burials and minute artifacts. The relationship between different objects in the ground can tell one much about the behavior of their makers, he taught his students. Wheeler's excavations were models of tidiness, with straight walls and carefully swept trenches to make the tasks of observation and discovery more precise. The observation of superimposed layers and the features and artifacts in them would give one an accurate chronology to work with, an essential framework for studying the numerous pot fragments and other finds from the dig. He pointed out how buildings should be dissected with great care, so that the foundations could be related to the underlying, dated strata and the contents isolated from those in other parts of the site. The burials Wheeler found were exposed bone by bone and carefully photographed in position before removal.

All of Wheeler's excavations were carefully designed not only to find artifacts but to answer specific questions about chronology or other matters. These questions were formulated in advance or as the dig was in progress. The staff of the excavation was organized into a hierarchy of specialists, led by the director himself, whose task was to "cultivate a scrupulous accuracy and completeness in the observation

and record of his factual evidence." Wheeler's ideal director had "the combined virtues of the scholar and the man of action," an ability to achieve accuracy "not for accuracy's sake, but as a basis for using his imagination to interpret his finds." "Archaeology," wrote Wheeler, "is primarily a fact-finding discipline." But, he would always add, we have to dig sites as a means to an end, the end being the understanding of humanity's complex and changing relationship with its environment.

Schliemann dug up the past of Troy. He and many other early archaeologists taught us that archaeological sites contain many treasures. Curtius, Dörpfeld, Pitt-Rivers, and Wheeler developed techniques for recording the contents of each site in meticulous detail. And Wheeler himself threw down the gauntlet to his successors—he challenged them to apply these recording methods to such complex problems as "estimating the density and social structure of populations." His words were prophetic, for that is what leading archaeologists are now trying to achieve.

Mortimer Wheeler died in 1976 after witnessing a revolution in digging methods all over the world, a revolution whose impact is still being felt. His students and their students, as well as those of other pioneering archaeologists, have refined his methods even further. Some idea of the complexity of a modern excavation can be gained by a brief look at the investigation of an ancient site at Olduvai Gorge in Tanzania. The site dates to about 1.75 million years ago.

"Archaeology," wrote British archaeologist Stuart Piggott some years ago, "is the science of rubbish." And rubbish is precisely what Louis and Mary Leakey had to dissect when they excavated the scatters of bones and stone artifacts in the lowest levels of Olduvai Gorge. All that remained were small scatters of discarded animal bones, stone tools, and waste chips, lying in irregular concentrations on the very land surfaces ancient people once trod. Often the scatter of artifacts and bones was only a few inches thick and was sealed under dozens of feet of sterile sand and lake clay. How old were these scatters? What activities took place there? Could any information on prehistoric diet and food-getting methods be obtained from the scatters? These and many other questions came to mind as the Leakeys began clearing these small but complicated sites. They had no doubt as to the importance of their excavations: these were probably among the earliest traces of human behavior in the world. To avoid damaging any human fossils and to prevent disturbance of the artifacts from their original positions, only the most delicate methods could be used.

Each scatter lay within a major geological horizon of Olduvai Gorge, one that the Leakeys knew dated to the earliest millennia of the human experience. But dating samples had to be obtained, that is, lumps of lava that could be dated by laboratory tests for their radioactive content. These samples had to come from the scatters themselves, from lava fragments that had actually been carried to the site by those who had lived there. The Leakeys had no choice: they knew they must excavate each entire site, plot all the objects on them, and obtain dating samples from among the finds in the scatter.

One site yielded the famous skull of *Zinjanthropus* in 1959. . . . Mary Leakey originally found a portion of the fossil outcropping from the lower lake beds of the Gorge. A small excavation was immediately undertaken at the site of this discovery to aid both in the removal of the precious skull and in establishing the exact level from which the fossil came. The immediate surroundings of the skull were sifted carefully in case additional fragments had already fallen down the slope on which it was found. The trial excavation yielded broken animal bones, some rodent fragments, and a few stone tools that lay in place near the skull. There seemed a strong possibility that the skull was directly associated with the tools—indeed, its owner might have made them.

It was seven months before Mary Leakey could return to the site, for the skull had been found at the very end of the 1959 season. When the time came for larger-scale excavations, she did not attack the site at once. Her task was to establish the precise position of the artifact scatter in the Olduvai geological strata. To determine this, she dug a six-foot trial trench in steps through the entire forty feet of the geological bed the skull had come from, right down to bedrock. She found that the scatter was halfway up the bed.

Once the stratigraphical position of the fossil skull was established, Mary Leakey set out to determine the extent of the scatter itself. The workmen removed the sterile over-burden of lake bed from the area around the trial trench. This unproductive soil was removed with picks and shovels in rough levels. When they reached a whitish-yellow volcanic-ash zone that Mary Leakey knew directly overlay the precious scatter, they stepped aside. The trench was now divided into four-foot-wide strips that were worked one by one with great care. Skilled workers carefully pared away the volcanic ash to within a few inches of the underlying artifacts and bones. Sometimes bones and other finds protruded through into the ash. So dry was the soil that the excavators had to dampen it before removal to guard against damaging valuable fossils underneath.

The scatter proved to be about a foot thick. With great care, Mary Leakey worked each strip of the trench from one side of the floor to the other. Whenever possible, every find was cleared from the surrounding soil with dental probes and small paintbrushes. Every find of any size, whether a stone tool or an animal bone, was marked with black or white ink and plotted on the floor plan before being lifted. A complete photographic record of the site was maintained as well. Once the larger finds had been removed, the soil was wet- or dry-sifted through one-sixteenth-inch screens so that even the tiniest stone chips and bone fragments were recovered for laboratory analysis. As a result of this painstaking excavation, the position of every significant find on the site was known to within an inch or less. What a contrast

to Belzoni's burial chambers or Layard's palaces!

The man-hours expended on the *Zinjanthropus* site were well worth the expense. The amount of detail about early human lifeways that came from the *Zinjanthropus* floor was truly astonishing, all of it the result of meticulous excavation. In addition to the dating samples gathered—which proved the site to be 1.75 million years old—the Leakeys obtained data on the dimensions and layout of one of the earliest archaeological sites in the world. Mary Leakey found and took apart a concentration of stone tools and flakes and over a thousand broken bone fragments covering an area twenty-one feet by fifteen feet near the spot where *Zinjanthropus* was found. This central zone was separated from another concentration of bones by a less densely covered area that she felt might have been the site of a crude shelter. We know that the inhabitants used crude stone choppers and many flakes in the preparation of food and the butchering of small animals. They smashed the limb bones of antelope and zebra and broke open the skulls to remove the brain. But large scavengers like hyenas visited the site as well and chewed up some of the freshly broken bones—presumably after the inhabitants left. None of this information could have been obtained without rigorous excavation techniques. The Leakeys literally drained the site of information. . . .

Archaeology has come a long way since Leonard Woolley performed miracles with plaster at Ur. Today, it is a sophisticated science that calls on experts from dozens of academic disciplines. It owes much to the natural and physical sciences, to revolutionary dating techniques . . . that enable us to date 2.5-million-year-old archaeological sites or tiny fragments of a wooden spear shaft extracted from the socket of a bronze spearhead used three thousand years ago. Computers enable archaeologists to manipulate vast data bases of artifacts and food remains, to plot intricate jigsaw puzzles of waterlogged timbers that once formed a prehistoric house. We can trace the sources of volcanic rock used to make mirrors in three-thousand-year-old Mexican villages, establish whether stone workers making tools in a Belgian hunting camp ten thousand years ago were left- or right-handed. Using minute pollen grains, we can reconstruct the landscape around twenty-thousand-year-old Stone Age winter camps. Thousands of bison bones from an ancient mass kill on the American Plains can be reassembled so precisely that we know exactly how bison hunters of eight thousand years ago butchered their prey.

But the greatest advances of all have not been in the field or the laboratory, where all the hi-tech wizardry of archaeology comes into play. They have been in the ways in which we think of archaeology and plan our research. Much early archaeology was designed to recover as many spectacular objects as possible. This is what Layard strove for at Nimrud and Nineveh, and Schliemann at Hissarlik. Today's archaeology has three much more sophisticated goals: to construct the culture history of the past, to reconstruct ancient lifeways, the ways in which people made their living, and, most important of all, to explain how and why ancient human cultures changed through prehistoric times. This is where the most important advances in archaeology have been made—in seeking to explain why humans took up farming and abandoned hunting and gathering, or what caused people to congregate in cities, develop writing, and establish a literate civilization. Studying such topics has involved the development of sophisticated theoretical models for explaining and interpreting the past, models that owe much to evolutionary and ecological theory. Science now realizes that archaeology is about the only discipline that enables us to study human biological and cultural evolution over long periods of time. The development of the tools to do so ranks among the greatest scientific triumphs of this century. Not that archaeology is confined to such topics, for in recent years there has been an explosion of interest in such issues as gender roles in ancient societies, and in such fascinating problems as social inequality in the past. One of the great fascinations of modern archaeology is its sheer range and diversity that accommodates archaeologists who study everything from foraging camps that are millions of years old to Mayan cities and abandoned railroad stations from the Industrial Revolution.

. . . there is a tremendous satisfaction and excitement in searching out the past. Even today, most talented archaeologists, at one time or another, feel they are in touch with the people they are studying. They seem to have an instinct for discovery, to know where to search and dig, and a sense of identity with their subjects. This sense seems to have been highly developed in Louis Leakey, Heinrich Schliemann, and Howard Carter. Carter experienced an almost eerie bond with Tutankhamun. He summed it up well when he wrote: "I stood in the presence of a king who reigned three thousand years ago." One suspects Carter was not speaking strictly figuratively: he felt he *really had*. Sometimes, as I have stood gazing over a long-deserted prehistoric settlement, silent on a cool evening as the sun casts long shadows over earthworks and eroding occupation deposits, I have experienced a sudden collapse of time. The site comes to life: thatched huts rise from the ground, scented wood smoke ascends in the evening still, dogs bark and children laugh in play. Outside their huts, old men sit and gossip quietly for a brief evening hour. Then, just as quickly, the image recedes and the village once again becomes a deserted archive of archaeological information, a silent complex of mud-hut foundations, dusty pot fragments, and broken food bones. For a moment, the ancient inhabitants of that village sprang to life, shedding their cloaks of anonymity to reach out across the millennia. Heady emotions, perhaps, but, for a moment, one understands why archaeology is so much more than just a set of techniques and tools for digging up the past.

The Golden Marshalltown: A Parable for the Archeology of the 1980s

Kent V. Flannery

Kent V. Flannery is Professor of Anthropology and Curator of Environmental Archeology, Museum of Anthropology, University of Michigan, Ann Arbor, MI 48109. He presented the Distinguished Lecture to the American Anthropological Association at the national meetings in Los Angeles on December 5, 1981.

I am happily too busy *doing* science to have time to worry about philosophizing about it. [Arno Penzias, Nobel Laureate, 1978]

This is a story about archeological goals and rewards, and no one should look for anything too profound in it. It's really just the story of a ride I took on an airplane from San Diego to Detroit. That may not sound very exciting to those of you who fly a lot, but this particular trip was memorable for me. For one thing, it was my first time on a 747. For another, I met someone on the plane who became one of the most unforgettable characters I've ever run across.

The flight was taking me home to Ann Arbor after the Society for American Archaeology meetings in May of 1981. I was leaving San Diego a day early because I had endured all the physical stress I could stand. I didn't particularly feel like watching the movie, so as soon as the plane was airborne and the seat belt sign had been turned off, I went forward to the lounge area of the plane. There were only two people there, both archeologists, and both recognized me from the meetings. So I had no choice but to sit down and have a beer with them.

I want to begin by telling you a little about my two companions, but you have to understand, I'm not going to give their actual names. Besides, their real identities aren't important, because each considers himself the spokesman for a large group of people.

The first guy, I suppose, came out of graduate school in the late 1960s, and he teaches now at a major department in the western United States. He began as a traditional archeologist, interested in Pueblo ruins and Southwestern prehistory, and he went on digs and surveys like the rest of us. Unlike the rest of us, he saw those digs and surveys not as an end in themselves, but as a means to an end, and a means that proved to be too slow. After a few years of dusty holes in hot, dreary valleys he was no closer to the top than when he had started, and in fact, he was showing signs of lamentable fallibility. In 50 tries at laying out a 5-ft square, he had never come closer than 4 ft 10 in by 5 ft 3 in, and he'd missed more floors than the elevator in the World Trade Center. And then, just when all seemed darkest, he discov-

ered Philosophy of Science, and was born again.

Suddenly he found the world would beat a path to his door if he criticized everyone else's epistemology. Suddenly he discovered that so long as his research design was superb, he never had to do the research; just publish the design, and it would be held up as a model, a brass ring hanging unattainable beyond the clumsy fingers of those who actually survey and dig. No more dust, no more heat, no more 5-ft squares. He worked in an office now, generating hypotheses and laws and models which an endless stream of graduate students was sent out to test; for he himself no longer did any fieldwork.

And it was just as well, for as one of his former professors had said, "That poor wimp couldn't dig his way out of a kitty litter box."

In all fairness to the Born-Again Philosopher, he was in large measure a product of the 1960s, and there are lots more like him where he came from. And let us not judge him too harshly until we have examined my other companion in the lounge, a young man whose degree came not from 1968, but from 1978. I will refer to him simply as the Child of the Seventies.

Like so many of his academic generation, the Child of the Seventies had but one outstanding characteristic: blind ambition. He had neither the commitment to culture history of my generation nor the devotion to theory of the generation of the 1960s. His goals were simple: to be famous, to be well paid, to be stroked, and to receive immediate gratification. How he got there did not matter. Who he stepped on along the way did not matter. Indeed, the data of prehistory did not matter. For him, archeology was only a vehicle—one carefully selected, because he had discovered early that people will put up with almost anything in the guise of archeology.

As a graduate student, the Child of the Seventies had taken a course in introductory archeology from a man I will simply refer to as Professor H. Professor H. worked very hard on the course, synthesizing the literature, adding original ideas and a lot of his own unpublished data. The Child of the Seventies took copious notes. Sometimes he asked questions to draw the instructor out, and sometimes he asked if he could copy Professor H.'s slides. When the professor used handouts, he bound them in his notebook.

At graduation, the Child of the Seventies went off to his first job at Springboard University. The day he arrived, he went directly to Springboard University Press and asked if they would like a textbook on introductory archeology. Of course they did. The Child polished his notes from Professor H.'s course and submitted them as a book. It was published to rave reviews. Today it is the only textbook on the subject that Professor H. really likes, and he requires it in his course. The faculty at Springboard U overwhelmingly voted the Child of the Seventies tenure. Professor H., on the other hand, has been held back because he hasn't published enough. "He's a great teacher," his colleagues say. "If only he could write more. Like that student of his at Springboard U."

To his credit as an anthropologist, the child had merely discerned that our subculture not only tolerates this sort of behavior, it *rewards* people for it. But the story doesn't end there.

The Child of the Seventies had written a six-chapter doctoral dissertation. Now he xeroxed each chapter and provided it with an introduction and con-

clusion, making it a separate article. Each was submitted to a different journal, and all were published within a year. He then persuaded Springboard University Press to publish a reader composed of his six reprinted works. In that reader, the chapters of his dissertation were at last reunited between hard covers. He added an overview, recounting the ways his perspective had changed as he looked back over the full sweep of his 18 months as a professional archeologist.

His publisher asked him to do another reader. This time, he invited six colleagues to write the various chapters. Some were flattered. Some were desperate. All accepted. He wrote a three-page introduction and put his name on the cover as editor. The book sold. And suddenly, his path to the top was clear; he could turn out a book a year, using the original ideas of others, without ever having an original idea himself. And in the long run, he would be better known and better paid than any of his contributors, even though they worked twice as hard.

I ordered a Michelob, and paid my buck-fifty a can, and sat wondering exactly what I could say to these two guys. It isn't easy when you know that one will criticize any idea you put forth, and the other will incorporate it into his next book. Fortunately I never had to say anything, for it was at exactly that moment that the third, and most important, character of this story entered the lounge.

He stood for a moment with his battered carryon bag in his hand, looking down at the three of us. He was an Old Timer—no question about that—but how old would have been anybody's guess. When you're that tanned and weather-beaten you could be 50, or 60, or even 70, and no one could really tell. His jeans had been through the mud and the barbed-wire fences of countless field seasons, his hat had faded in the prairie sun, and his eyes had the kind of crow's feet known locally as the High Plains squint. I could tell he was an archeologist by his boots, and I could tell he was still a good archeologist by the muscle tone in his legs.

(You see, I have a colleague at Michigan—an ethnologist—who claims that since archeologists have strong backs and weak minds, when an archeologist starts to fade, it's the legs that go first. On the other hand, his wife informs me that when an ethnologist starts to fade, the first thing to go is not his legs.)

The Old Timer settled into the seat next to me, stowed his carryon bag, and turned to introduce himself. I failed to catch his name because the stewardess, somewhat out of breath, caught up with him at that moment and pressed a bourbon and water into his hand. "Thank you, ma'am," he said, sipping it down; and he stared for a moment, and said, "I needed that. And that's the God's truth."

"I know what you mean," I said, "The meetings can do that to you. Six hundred people crammed into the lobby of a hotel. Two hundred are talking down to you as if you're an idiot. Two hundred are sucking up to you as if you're a movie star. Two hundred are telling you lies, and all the while they're looking over your shoulder, hoping they'll meet somebody more important."

"This year it was worse than that, son. Last night my department retired me. Turned me out to pasture."

"I wouldn't have guessed you were retirement age," I lied.

"I'm not. I had two years to go. But they retired me early. Mostly because of an article in the *New York Times Sunday Magazine* by an ethnologist, Eric Wold. You remember that one?"

"I read it," I said, "but I don't remember him calling for your retirement."

The Old Timer reached into his pocket, past a half-empty pouch of Bull Durham, and brought out a yellowed clipping from the Sunday *Times* of November 30, 1980. I caught a glimpse of Wolf's byline, and below it, several paragraphs outlined in red ink. "See what he says here," said the Old Timer.

An earlier anthropology had achieved unity under the aegis of the culture concept. It was culture, in the view of anthropologists, that distinguished humankind from all the rest of the universe, and it was the possession of varying cultures that differentiated one society from another. . . . The past quarter-century has undermined this intellectual sense of security. The relatively inchoate concept of "culture" was attacked from several theoretical directions. As the social sciences transformed themselves into "behavioral" sciences, explanations for behavior were no longer traced to culture; behavior was to be understood in terms of psychological encounters, strategies of economic choice, strivings for pay-offs in games of power. Culture, once extended to all acts and ideas employed in social life, was now relegated to the margins as "world view" or "values." [Wolf 1980]

"Isn't that something?" said the Old Timer. "The day that came out my department called me in. The chairman says, 'It has come to our attention that you still believe in culture as the central paradigm in archeology.' I told him yes, I supposed I did. Then he says, 'We've talked about it, and we all think you ought to take early retirement.' "

"But that's terrible. You should have fought it."

"I *did* fight it," he said. "But they got my file together and sent it out for an outside review. Lord, they sent it to all these distinguished anthropologists. Marvin Harris. Clifford Geertz. And aren't there a couple of guys at Harvard with hyphenated names?"

"At least a couple." I assured him.

"Well, they sent my file to one of them. And to some Big Honcho social anthropologist at the University of Chicago. And the letters started coming back.

"Harris said he was shocked to see that in spite of the fact that I was an archeologist, I had paid so little attention to the techno-eco-demo-environmental variables. Geertz said as far as he could tell, all I was doing was Thick Description. The guy from Harvard said he wasn't sure he could evaluate me, because he'd never even heard of our department."

"And how about the guy from Chicago?"

"He said that he felt archeology could best be handled by one of the local trade schools."

There was a moment of silence while we all contemplated the heartbreak of an archeologist forced into early retirement by his belief in culture. In the background we could hear our pilot announcing that the Salton Sea was visible off to the right of the aircraft.

"They sure gave me a nice retirement party, though," said the Old Timer. "Rented a whole suite at the hotel. And I want to show you what they gave me as a going-away present."

His hand groped for a moment in the depths of his battle-scarred overnight bag, and suddenly he produced a trowel. A trowel such as no one had ever seen. A trowel that turned to yellow flame in the rays of the setting sun as he held it up to the window of the 747.

"This was my first Marshalltown trowel," he said. "You know what an archeologist's first Marshalltown is like? Like a major leaguer's first Wilson glove. I dug at Pecos with this trowel, under A. V. Kidder. And at Aztec Ruin with Earl Morris. And at Kincaid with Fay-Cooper Cole. And at Lindenmeier with Frank Roberts. Son, this trowel's been at Snaketown, and Angel Mound, and at the Dalles of the Columbia with Luther Cressman.

"And then one night, these guys from my department broke into my office and borrowed it, so to speak. And the next time I saw it, they'd had that sucker plated in 24-karat gold.

"It sure is pretty now. And that's the God's truth."

The trowel passed from hand to hand around our little group before returning to the depths of the Old Timer's bag. And for each of us, I suppose, it made that unimaginably far-off day of retirement just a little bit less remote.

"What do you think you'll do now?" asked the Child of the Seventies, for whom retirement would not come until the year 2018.

"Well," said the Old Timer, "so far the only thing that's opened up for me are some offers to do contract archeology."

The Born-Again Philosopher snickered condescendingly.

"I take it," said the Old Timer, "you have some reservations about contract archeology."

"Oh, it's all right, I suppose," said the Philosopher. "I just don't think it has much of a contribution to make to *my* field."

"And what would that field be?"

"Method and theory."

"No particular region or time period?"

"No. I wouldn't want to be tied down to a specific region. I work on a higher level of abstraction."

"I'll bet you do," said the Old Timer. "Well, son, there are some things about contract archeology I don't like either. Occasional compromises between scientific goals and industrial goals. Too many reports that get mimeographed for the president of some construction company, rather than being published where archeologists can read them. But in all fairness, most of the contract archeologists I know express just as strong an interest in method and theory as you do."

"But they're law *consumers,*" said the Philosopher. "I'm committed to being a law *producer.*"

The Old Timer took a thoughtful drag on his bourbon. "Son," he said, "I admire a man who dispenses with false modesty. But you've overlooked what I see as one of the strengths of contract archeologists: they still deal directly with what happened in prehistory. If I want to know what happened in Glen Canyon, or when agriculture reached the Missouri Basin, or how long the mammoth hunters lasted in Pennsylvania, often as not I need to talk to a contract archeologist. Because the answers to the cultural-historical questions don't always lie on a 'higher level of abstraction.' "

"No," said the Born-Again Philosopher. "Only the *important* questions lie on that level."

"There was an interruption as the stewardess reappeared before us, pushing an aluminum beverage cart. We ordered another round of beer, and she picked up our empty cans, depositing them in a plastic trash bag attached to the cart.

"I'd like to ask a favor," said the Born-Again Philosopher. "Before our 10-minute stopover in Tucson, I'd like to examine the contents of that bag."

"Now I've heard everything," said the stewardess.

"No, it's not a come-on," said the Philosopher. "It's a favor for a friend. I have a colleague, Bill Rathje, who's doing a study of garbage disposal patterns in the city of Tucson [Rathje 1974]. He's got the internal system pretty well mapped out, but he realizes that Tucson is not a closed system: garbage enters and leaves via planes, cars, and backpacks. I promised him if I were ever on a plane landing or taking off from Tucson, I'd sample the refuse on board."

The stewardess struggled to remove all trace of emotion from her face. "Well," she said, "I suppose if you clean up everything when you're done—."

"I'll be checking the refuse in the tourist-class cabin," said the Philosopher, "while my friend here" (indicating the Child of the Seventies) "will be checking the first-class cabin, and coauthoring the paper with me."

"And what do you call your profession?" she asked.

"Archeology."

"You guys are weird," she called over her shoulder as she and the cart disappeared down the aisle.

The Born-Again Philosopher settled back in his seat with a pleased smile on his face. "Now there's a perfect example of why archeologists should not restrict themselves to the study of ancient objects lying on the surface or underneath the ground. If we're to develop a truly universal set of covering laws, we must be free to derive them from any source we can.

"In my opinion," he said, "the greatest legacy we can leave the next generation is a body of robust archeological theory."

"Well, son, I'll give you my opinion," said the Old Timer. "I don't believe there's any such thing as 'archeological theory.' For me there's only *anthropological* theory. Archeologists have their own methodology, and ethnologists have theirs; but when it comes to theory, we all ought to sound like anthropologists."

"My God, are you out of it!" said the Born-Again Philosopher. "For ten years we've been building up a body of purely archeological laws. I myself have contributed 10 or 20."

"I'd love to hear a few," I said. And I could see I was not the only one: the Child of the Seventies was getting ready to write them down unobtrusively on his cocktail napkin.

"Number One," said the Philosopher: "Prehistoric people did not leave behind in the site examples of everything they made. Number Two: Some of the things they did leave behind disintegrated, and cannot be found by archeologists."

"I don't want to sound unappreciative," I said, "but I believe Schliemann already knew that when he was digging at Troy."

"If he did," and the B.A.P. ," he never made it *explicit*. I have made it *explicit*."

"Son," said the Old Timer, "I guess we can all sleep easier tonight because of that."

"I also came up with the following," the Philosopher went on. "Number Three: Objects left on a sloping archeological site wash downhill. Number Four: Lighter objects wash downhill farther than heavy objects."

"Hold it right there, son," said the Old Timer, "because you've just illustrated a point I was hoping to make. So often these things you fellows call archeological laws turn out not to be laws of human behavior, but examples of the physical processes involved in the formation of sites. And son, those are no more than the products of *geological* laws."

The Born-Again Philosopher's face lit up in a triumphant smile. "That objection has been raised many times before," he said, "and it was disposed of definitively by Richard Watson, who is both a geologist and a philosopher. In his 1976 *American Antiquity* article, Watson (1976:65) makes it clear (and here I am paraphrasing) that even when hypotheses are directly dependent on laws of geology, they are specifically archeological *when they pertain to archeological materials*."

Now it was the Old Timer's turn to smile "Oh. Well. That's different," he said. "In that case, I guess, archeology just barely missed out on a major law."

"How's that?" asked the Child of the Seventies earnestly, his pencil at the ready.

"Well, following your argument, the Law of Uniform Acceleration could have been an archeological law if only Galileo had dropped a metate and mano from the Leaning Tower of Pisa."

"I don't think you're taking this seriously," the Born-Again Philosopher complained.

"Son," said the Old Timer. "I'm taking it fully as seriously as it deserves to be taken. And as far as I'm concerned, so far the only legitimate archeological law I know of is the Moss-Bennett Bill."

The Born-Again Philosopher drew himself erect. "I think I'd better go back and start my inventory of the tourist-class trash," he said, and he began working his way down the aisle toward the galley.

"You're being awfully hard on him," said the Child of the Seventies. "You have to remember that he's the spokesman for a large number of theoretical archeologists who hope to increase archeology's contribution to science and philosophy."

The Old Timer took a long, slow pull on his bourbon. "Son, do you watch Monday Night Football?" he asked.

"Occasionally," said the Child. "When I'm not correcting page proofs."

"I have a reason for asking." said the Old Timer. "I just want to try out an analogy on you.

"During Monday Night Football there are 22 players on the field, 2 coaches on the sidelines, and 3 people in the broadcast booth. Two of the people in the booth are former players who can no longer play. One of the people in the booth never played a lick in his life. And who do you suppose talks the loudest and is the most critical of the players on the field?"

"The guy who never played a lick," I interrupted. "And the guys with him, the former players, are always saying things like, 'Well, it's easy to criticize from up here, but it's different when you're down on the field.' "

"Well said, son," the Old Timer chuckled. "And I want you to consider the symbolism for a moment. The field is lower than everything else; it's physical, it's sweaty, it's a place where people follow orders. The press box is high, detached, Olympian, cerebral. And it's verbal. Lord, is it verbal.

"Now football is a game of strategy, of game plans (or 'research designs,' if you will), and what are called differing philosophies. In our lifetime we've witnessed great innovations in strategy: the nickel defense, the flex, the shotgun, the wishbone—and the list goes on. How many of them were created in the press box?"

"None," I said. "They were created by coaches."

"By coaches, many of them former players, who are still personally involved in the game, and who diligently study their own mistakes, create new strategies, and return to the field to test them in combat," said the Old Timer.

"I think I see what you're driving at," said the Child of the Seventies, but we knew he was lying.

"There are estimated to be more than 4,000 practicing archeologists in the United States," said the Old Timer. "Most of them are players. Sure, many of us are second- or third-string, but when we're called upon to go in, we do the best we can. And we rely on the advice and strategy of a fair number of archeological 'coaches'—veterans, people we respect because they've paid their dues the same as we have.

"What's happening now is that we're getting a new breed of archeologist. A kind of archeological Howard Cosell. He sits in a booth high above the field, and cites Hempel and Kuhn and Karl Popper. He second-guesses our strategy, and tells us when we don't live up to his expectations. 'Lew Binford,' he says, 'once the fastest mind in the field, but frankly, this season he may have lost a step or two.' Or, 'It's shocking to see a veteran like Struever make a rookie mistake like that.'

"What I worry about, son, is that every year there'll be fewer people down on the field and more up in the booth. There's a great living to be made in the booth, but it's a place that breeds a great deal of arrogance. No one in the booth ever fumbles a punt or, for that matter, misclassifies a potsherd or screws up a profile drawing. They pass judgment on others, but never expose themselves to criticism. The guys in the booth get a lot of exposure, and some even achieve celebrity status. What rarely gets pointed out is that the guys in the booth have had little if any strategic and theoretical impact on the game, because they're far removed from the field of play.

"But the players know that. Especially the contract archeologists, and those of us who perennially work in the field. Because we have the feeling the guys in the booth look down on us as a bunch of dumb, sweaty jocks. And we're damn sick of it, son, and that's the God's truth."

"But you surely don't deny the importance of theory in archeology," said the Child of the Seventies. "I'm sure you've used what Binford [1977] calls middle-range theory in your own work."

"Of course," said the Old Timer. "I've used it to organize and make sense out of my data. Which is, when you stop to think about it, one of the main purposes for theory. The problem came when the guys in the booth began to think of 'archeological theory' as a subdiscipline in its own right—a higher and more prestigious calling than the pursuit of data on prehistory, which they see as a form of manual labor. As if that weren't bad enough, some of them are now beginning to think of themselves as philosophers of science."

"I find that exciting," said the Child of the Seventies.

"Son," said the Old Timer, "it would be exciting, if they were any good at it. Unfortunately, in most cases, it's the only thing they're worse at than field archeology."

"But some are establishing a dialogue with philosophers," said the Child.

"That's right," said the Old Timer. "Now we're going to have philosophers who don't know anything about archeology, advising archeologists who don't know anything about philosophy."

"They want archeology to make a contribution to philosophy," said the Child.

"I'll tell you what," said the Old Timer. "I'd settle for making a contribution to *archeology*. I guess I'd rather be a second-rate archeologist than a third-rate philosopher."

"But doesn't archeology have more to offer the world than that?"

The Old Timer leaned back in his seat and sipped at his bourbon. "That's a good question," he said. "We hear a lot about archeology's relevance to anthropology in general. To the social sciences. To the world. And of course, we're all waiting for our recently departed friend to come up with his first Great Law. But I'd like to turn the question around and ask What does the world really want from archeology?

"If I turn on television, or walk through a paperback bookstore, I'll tell you what I see. I see that what the world wants is for archeology to teach it something about humanity's past. The world doesn't want epistemology from us. They want to hear about Olduvai Gorge, and Stonehenge, and Macchu Picchu. People are gradually becoming aware that their first three million years took place before written history, and they look at archeology as the only science—the *only one*—with the power to uncover the past.

"I remember Bill Sanders telling me once that the only legitimate reason to do archeology was to satisfy your intellectual curiosity. And I suspect that if we just try to do a good job at that, the more general contributions will follow naturally. I don't think Isaac Newton or Gregor Mendel ran around saying 'I'm a law producer.' Their laws grew unself-consciously out of their efforts to satisfy their own curiosity.

"Son, if the world wants philosophy, it will surely turn to philosophers, not archeologists, to get it. I'd hate to see us get so confused about what the world wants from archeology that we turn our backs on what we do best. In my opinion, our major responsibility to the rest of the world is to do good, basic archeological research."

"You know," said the Child of the Seventies, "as I listen to you talk, I'm thinking how nice it would be to have you write an overview for the book I'm editing right now. A book on future directions in archeology."

"I'm not sure how excited I am about some of the future directions," said the Old Timer.

That's why your overview would give us needed balance," said the Child. "Why, you're our link with the past. You've stepped right out of the pages of archeology's rich, much maligned empiricist tradition."

"You overestimate me, son."

"No. You're too modest," said the Child, who was not used to being turned down. "I feel that you may well be the most significant figure of your generation, and I'd consider myself deeply honored to have your overview in my book."

"Horsefeathers," said the Old Timer.

The Child of the Seventies stood up with a gesture of frustration. "I've got to inventory the trash in the first-class cabin, or I won't get to coauthor that article," he said. "But think over what I said. And don't say anything important until I get back."

We watched him disappear through the curtain into the first-class section.

"You must have been inoculated against soft soap." I told the Old Timer.

"Son," he said, "if that young fellow's nose were any browner, we'd need a Munsell Soil Color Chart to classify it."

"If you think he's at all atypical," I suggested, "take a good look around you at the next archeology meeting."

"And you know," said the Old Timer, "we're partly to blame for that. All of us in academic departments.

"We hire a young guy, right out of graduate school, and we give him all our introductory courses to teach. Then we tell him it's publish or perish. His only choices are to write something halfbaked, or make an article out of an attack on some already established figure. You take those two kinds of papers out of *American Antiquity,* and you got nothing left but the book review."

"What we *ought* to do, if we really want these young people to grow, is give them their first year off, so they can go collect their own data and make their own positive contribution. How can we give them eight courses to teach and then put pressure on them to publish?"

"You're right," I said. "But our two friends here have discovered how to beat the system. One has created a specialty that never requires him to leave his office, and the other has figured out how to get other people to write his books for him. And we reward both of them for it."

"But not without some reservations," said the Old Timer. "You know, archeologists don't really like having a colleague who's so ambitious he'd kick his own grandmother's teeth in to get ahead. Businessmen, or perhaps showbusiness people, will tolerate it. They'll say, 'He's a real S.O.B., but he gets things done.' But archeologists don't want a colleague who's a real S.O.B. They're funny that way."

The stewardess with the beverage cart paused by our seats for a moment to see if we needed a refill. We did. And I took that opportunity to ask how our friends were coming with their inventory of her garbage.

"The one in the aft cabin seems to have hit a snag," she said thoughtfully. "I think he ran into a couple of airsickness bags."

"Well," said the Old Timer, "nobody said fieldwork was easy."

"What are those guys trying to find out, anyway?" she asked.

"As I understand it," I said, "they're trying to provide us with a better basis for archeological interpretation. Since archeologists study the garbage of ancient peoples, they hope to discover principles of garbage discard that will guide us in our work."

The Old Timer's eyes followed the stewardess as she passed through the curtain into the next cabin.

"Son," he said, "I want to hit you with a hypothetical question. Let's say you're working on a 16th-century Arikara site in South Dakota. There's lots of garbage—bison scapula hoes, Catlinite pipes, Bijou Hills quartzite, cordmarked pottery—you know the kind of stuff. You got to interpret it. You got an 18th-century French account of the Arikara, and you got a report on Tucson's garbage in 1981. Which would you use?"

"I think you already know the answer to that one," I smiled.

"Then why do I have the distinct impression that these two kids would use the report on Tucson's garbage?" he demanded.

"Because *you* still believe in *culture*," I said, "and these kids are only concerned with *behavior.*"

"I guess that's right," he said thoughtfully. "I guess I believe in something called 'Arikara culture,' and I think you ought to know something about it if you work on Arikara sites."

"But suppose, as Eric Wolf suggests in that *Times* article, you're one of those people who no longer looks to culture as an explanation for behavior," I suggested. "Suppose you believe that behavior is explained by universal laws, or psychological encounters, or strategies of economic choice. Then it really doesn't matter whether your interpretive framework comes from tribal ethnohistory or 20th-century industrial America, does it?"

"Nope. And that's sure going to simplify archeology," said the Old Timer. "For one thing, we can forget about having to master the anthropological literature."

He fell silent as the Born-Again Philosopher and the Child of the Seventies returned to their seats, their notebooks filled with behavioral data and their faces flushed with success.

"Did we miss much?" asked the Child.

"Not much," said the Old Timer. "I was just fixing to ask my friend here where he thinks anthropology will go next, now that it no longer has culture as its central paradigm."

"I'm kind of worried about it," I admitted. "Right now I have the impression that anthropology is sort of drifting, like a rudderless ship. I have the feeling it could fragment into a dozen lesser disciplines, with everybody going his own way. Somehow it's not as exciting as it used to be. Enrollments are down all over the country. The job market sucks. I suspect one reason is that anthropology is so lacking in consensus as to what it has to offer, it just can't sell itself compared to more unified and aggressive fields."

"Doesn't Wolf tell you in his *Times* article what the next central paradigm will be?" asked the Child of the Seventies. He was hoping for a title for his next book.

"No," said the Old Timer. "He mentions other things people have tried, like cultural materialism, cultural ecology, French structuralism, cognitive and symbolic anthropology, and so on. But you know, none of those approaches involves more than a fraction of the people in the field."

"But it's useful to have all those approaches," I suggested.

"That's the God's truth," he agreed. "But what holds us all together? What keeps us all from pursuing those things until each becomes a separate field in its own right? What is it that makes a guy who works on Maori creation myths continue to talk to a guy who works mainly on Paleoindian stone tools?"

"In my department," I said, "they *don't* talk any more."

"Nor in mine," he said. "But they used to. And they *used* to talk because however obscure their specialties, they all believe in that 'integrated whole,' that 'body of shared customs, beliefs, and values' that we called culture."

"That's right," I said. "But now the Paleoindian archeologist would tell you his stone tools were best explained by Optimal Foraging Strategy. And the Maori ethnologist would tell you his creation myths are the expression of a universal logic inside his informants' heads."

"You know," said the Old Timer, "we've got an ethnologist like that on our faculty. He told me once, 'I'm not interested in anything you can feel, smell, taste, weigh, measure, or count. None of that is real. What's real is in my head.' Kept talking and talking about how what was in his head was what was important. For a long time, I couldn't figure it out.

"Then one day he published his ethnography, and I understood why what was in his head was so important. He'd made up all his data."

The Born-Again Philosopher stirred restlessly in his seat. "It's incredible to me," he said, "that you people haven't realized that for more than a decade now the new paradigm has been Logical Positivism. It's hard to see how you can do problem-oriented archeology without it."

Slowly the Old Timer rolled himself a cigarette. The Child of the Seventies sat up momentarily, leaned forward to watch, then slumped back in his seat with disappointment when he realized it was only Bull Durham.

"Have you considered," said the Old Timer deliberately, "the implications of doing problem-oriented archeology without the concept of culture?"

"Now you're putting us on," said the Philosopher.

For just a moment, the Old Timer allowed himself a smile. "Consider this," he said. "An ethnologist can say, 'I'm only interested in myth and symbolism, and I'm not going to collect data on subsistence.' He can go to a village in the Philippines and ignore the terraced hillsides and the rice paddies and the tilapia ponds, and just ask people about their dreams and the spirits of their ancestors. Whatever he does, however selective he is in what he collects, when he leaves the village, it's still there. And next year, if a Hal Conklin or an Aram Yengoyan comes along, those terraces and paddies and fish ponds will still be there to study.

"But suppose an archeologist were to say, 'I'm only interested in Anasazi myth and symbolism, and I'm not going to collect data on subsistence.' Off he goes to a prehistoric cliff dwelling and begins to dig. He goes for the pictographs, and figurines, and ceremonial staffs, and wooden bird effigies. What, then, does he do with all the digging sticks, and tumplines, and deer bones that he finds while he's digging for all the other stuff? Does he ignore them because they don't relate to his 'research problem?' Does he shovel them onto the dump? Or does he pack them up and put them in dead storage, in the hope that he can farm them out to a student some day to ease

his conscience? Because, unlike the situation in ethnology, no archeologist will be able to come along later and find that stuff in its original context. It's *gone,* son."

"It's as if—well, as if your Philippine ethnologist were to interview an informant on religion, and then kill him so no one could ever interview him on agriculture," I ventured.

"Exactly, son," he said. "Archeology is the only branch of anthropology where we kill our informants in the process of studying them."

"Except for a few careless physical anthropologists," I said.

"Well, yes, except for that."

"But hasn't that always been the conflict between 'problem-oriented' archeology and traditional archeology?" asked the Born-Again Philosopher. "Surely you have to have a specific hypothesis to test, and stick pretty much to the data relevant to that hypothesis, rather than trying to record everything."

"And what about other archeologists with other hypotheses," I asked. "Don't you feel a little uncomfortable destroying data relevant to their problem while you're solving yours?"

"Well, *I* don't, because I really don't do any digging now," said the Philosopher. "I see my role as providing the hypotheses that will direct the research efforts of others. There are lots of archeologists around who can't do anything *but* dig. Let *them* do the digging.

"Look," he said, "I can't say it any better than Schiffer [1978:247] said it in Dick Gould's 1978 volume on ethnoarcheology. To paraphrase him: I feel free to pursue the study of laws wherever it leads. I do *not* feel the need to break the soil periodically in order to reaffirm my status as archeologist."

"Son," said the Old Timer, "I think I just heard 10,000 archeological sites breathe a sigh of relief."

There was a moment of air turbulence, and we all reached for our drinks. The sleek ribbon of the Colorado River shimmered below us, and over the audio system we could hear the captain advise us to keep our seat belts loosely fastened. Hunched in his seat, reflective, perhaps just a little sad, the Old Timer whispered in my ear: "That's what the ethnologists will never understand, son. There's a basic conflict between problem-oriented archeology and archeological ethics. Problem orientation tells you to pick a specific topic to investigate. Archeological ethics tell you you *must* record everything, because no one will ever see it in context again. The problem is that except for certain extraordinary sites, archeological data don't come packaged as 'cognitive' or 'religious' or 'environmental' or 'economic.' They're all together in the ground—integrated in complex ways, perhaps, but integrated. That's why the old concept of culture made sense as a paradigm for archeology. And it still does, son. That's the God's truth."

I wish I could tell you how the rest of the conversation went, but at this point I could no longer keep my eyes open. After all, you wear a guy out at the meetings, and then give him six beers and start talking archeological theory, and that guy's going to fall asleep. So I slept even through those bumpy landings in the desert where the Child of the Seventies and the Born-Again Philosopher retired to their respective universities, and then somewhere between St. Louis and Detroit, I started to dream.

Now, I don't know whether it was because of the beer or the heated discussion we'd had, but my dream was a nightmare. I don't really know what it means, but my friends who work with the Walbiri and the Pitjandjara tell me that Dream Time is when you get your most important messages. So let me talk about it for a minute.

In this dream, I'd been released by the University of Michigan—whether for moral turpitude or believing in culture is really not clear. No job had opened up anywhere, and the only work I could find was with Bill Rathje's Garbage Project in Tucson. And not as a supervisor, just as a debagger. Sorting through the refuse of a thousand nameless homes, Anglo and Chicano, Pima and Papago, hoping against hope for that discarded wallet or diamond ring that could underwrite my retirement program.

And then, one day, I'm standing on the loading dock with my gauze mask on, and my pink rubber gloves, and my white lab coat with "Le Projet du Garbage" embroidered on the pocket, and this *huge* garbage truck pulls up to the dock and unloads a 30-gallon Hefty Bag. The thing is heavy as the dickens, and I wrestle it onto a dolly, and wheel it inside the lab; and we dump it onto the lab table, where the thing splits under its own weight and its contents come out all over the place.

And you know what's in it?

Reprints.

Reprints of *my* articles. Every single reprint I ever mailed out. All of them. And I'm not just talking reprints; I'm talking *autographed* reprints. The kind where I'd written something in the upper right-hand corner like, "Dear Dr. Willey, I hope you find this of interest."

You know, you can mail 'em out, but you never know whether they *keep* 'em or not.

And I suddenly realize that my whole career—my entire professional output—is in that Hefty Bag. Along with a couple of disposable diapers, and a pair of pantyhose, and a copy of *Penthouse* with the Jerry Falwell interview torn out.

But that's not the worst part.

The worst part is that the form Rathje's people fill out doesn't have a space for "discarded reprints." So my whole career, my entire professional output, simply has to be recorded as "other."

And that's where the nightmare ended, and I woke up on the runway at Detroit. I was grabbing my carryon bag as I bumped into the stewardess on her way down the aisle. "The Old Timer who was sitting next to me," I said. "What stop did he get off at?"

"What Old Timer?" she asked.

"The old guy in the boots and the faded hat with the rattlesnake hatband."

"I didn't see anybody like that," she said. "The only 'old guy' in the lounge was you."

"Have a nice day," I said sweetly. And I caught the limousine to Ann Arbor, and all the way home to my front door I kept wondering whether I had dreamed the whole thing.

Now I'll bet some of you don't think this all really happened. And I was beginning to doubt it myself until I started to unpack my carryon bag, and I was almost blinded by a gleam. A 24-karat gleam.

And there, hastily stuffed into my bag with a note wrapped around the handle, was the golden Marshalltown.

And the note read: "Son, where I'm going, I won't be needing this. I know you and I see eye to eye on a lot of things, so I'm going to ask a favor. I want you to save it for—well, just the right person.

"First off, I don't see any paradigm out there right now that's going to replace culture as a unifying theme in archeology. If some ethnologists want to go their separate ways—into sociobiology, or applied semeiotics, or social psychology—well, fine, they can call themselves something else, and let *us* be the anthropologists. I sort of felt that the concept of culture was what distinguished us from those other fields and kept us all from drifting apart for good.

"Because of the way our data come packaged in the ground, we pretty much have to deal with all of them to deal with any of them. It's harder for us to abandon the traditional concerns of anthropology, and we can't afford sudden fads, or quixotic changes in what's 'in' this year. We need long-term stability. And because we kill our informants as we question them, we have to question them in ways that are less idiosyncratic and more universally interpretable. And we have to share data in ways they don't.

"Because of that, we have to have a kind of integrity most fields don't need. I need your data, and you need mine, and we have to be able to trust each other on some basic level. There can't be any backstabbing, or working in total isolation, or any of this sitting on a rock in the forest interpreting culture in ways no colleague can duplicate.

"That's why we can't afford too many S.O.B.s. We can't afford guys whose lives are spent sitting in a press box criticizing other people's contributions. Son, all of prehistory is hidden in a vast darkness, and my generation was taught that it was better to light one tiny candle than curse the darkness. Never did I dream we'd have people whose whole career was based on cursing our *candles.*

"In the old days we mainly had one kind of archeologist: a guy who scratched around for a grant, went to the field, surveyed or excavated to the best of his ability, and published the results. Some guys labored patiently, in obscurity, for years. And one day, their colleagues would look up and say, 'You know, old Harry's doing good, solid work. Nothing spectacular, mind you, but you know—I'd trust him to dig on my site.' I believe that's the highest compliment one archeologist can pay another. And that's the God's truth.

"Now that doesn't sound like much, son, but today we got archeologists that can't even do that. What's more, they're too damn ambitious to labor in obscurity. So they've decided to create a whole new set of specialties around the margins of the field. Each defines himself (or herself) as the founder of that specialty, and then sets out to con the rest of us into believing that's where all the action is.

"And because archeologists will believe *anything,* pretty soon you've got a mass migration to the margins of the field. And pretty soon that's where the greatest noise is coming from.

"Now, don't get me wrong. A lot of these kids are shrewd and savvy, and they'll make a contribution one way or another. But that's one out of ten. The other nine are at the margins because things weren't moving fast enough for them in the main stream. You know,

some of these kids think archeology is a 100-meter dash, and they're shocked and angry when no one pins a medal on them after the first 100 meters. But I'll tell you a secret: archeology is a marathon, and you don't win marathons with speed. You win them with character.

"Son, after our talk this afternoon, I got to wondering about what archeology needed the most.

"I decided there probably isn't an urgent need for one more young person who makes a living editing other people's original ideas. I decided there probably wasn't an urgent need for one more kid who criticizes everyone else's research design while he or she never goes to the field. And I decided we probably didn't need a lot more of our archeological flat tires recapped as philosophers. There seem to be enough around to handle the available work.

"What I don't see enough of son, is first-rate archeology.

"Now that's sad, because after all, archeology is fun. Hell, I don't break the soil periodically to 'reaffirm my status.' I do it because archeology is still the most fun you can have with your pants on.

"You know, there are a lot of awards in archeology. The Viking Fund Medal, the Kidder Medal, the Aztec Eagle, the Order of the Quetzal. But those awards are for intellectual contributions. I'd like to establish an award just for commitment to plain, old-fashioned basic research and professional ethics. And that's what this trowel is for.

"So, son, some day when you meet a kid who still believes in culture, and

in hard work, and in the history of humanity; a kid who's in the field because he or she loves it, and not because they want to be famous; a kid who'd never fatten up on somebody else's data, or cut down a colleague just to get ahead; a kid who knows the literature, and respects the generations who went before—you give the kid this golden Marshalltown."

And the note ended there, with no signature, no address, and no reply required.

So that, I guess, is what I'm really here for tonight: to announce an award for someone who may not exist. But if any of you out there know of such a kid coming along—a kid who still depends on his own guts and brains instead of everyone else's—a kid who can stand on the shoulders of giants, and not be tempted to relieve himself on their heads—have *I* got an award for *him.*

And that's the God's truth.

REFERENCES CITED

Binford, Lewis R., 1977. General Introduction. *In* For Theory Building in Archeology: Essays on Faunal Remains, Aquatic Resources, Spatial Analysis, and Systemic Modeling. Lewis R. Binford, ed. pp. 1–10. New York: Academic Press.

Rathje, William L., 1974. The Garbage Project: A New Way of Looking at the Problems of Archaeology. Archaeology 27:236–241.

Schiffer, Michael B., 1978. Methodological Issues in Ethnoarchaeology. *In* Explorations in Ethnoarchaeology. Richard A. Gould, ed. pp. 229–247. Albuquerque: University of New Mexico Press (for the School of American Research).

Watson, Richard A., 1976. Inference in Archaeology. American Antiquity 41(1):58–66.

Wolf, Eric, 1980. They Divide and Subdivide, and Call It Anthropology. The New York Times Sunday Magazine, Nov. 30, 1980.

How Archaeology Works

Wendy Ashmore and Robert J. Sharer

. . . We examine the information archaeologists work with and the ways it is acquired. You may have read about archaeologists "piecing together the past" by studying ancient pottery, "arrowheads," or other artifacts found by excavation. However, these artifacts represent only one of several categories of evidence with which archaeologists work, and excavation is only one of several means of collecting information about the past.

ARCHAEOLOGICAL DATA

The material remains of past human activity, from the microscopic debris produced by chipping stone tools to the most massive architectural construction, become *data* when the archaeologist recognizes their significance as evidence and collects and records them. The collection and recording of these material remains constitutes the acquisition of archaeological data. Here we are concerned with the three basic classes of data—artifacts, features, and ecofacts—and how they cluster into larger units. These categories are not inflexible. There is some overlap among them, but they illustrate the variety and range of information available.

Artifacts

Artifacts are portable objects whose form is modified or wholly created by

human activity (Fig. 3.1). Stone hammers or fired clay vessels are artifacts because they are either natural objects modified for or by human use, such as a hammer-stone, or new objects formed completely by human action, such as a pottery vessel. The shape and other traits of artifacts are not altered by removal from their place of discovery; both the hammerstone and the vessel

retain their form and appearance after the archaeologist takes them from the ground.

Features

Features are nonportable artifacts that cannot be removed from their place of discovery without altering or destroying their original form (Fig. 3.2). Some common examples of features

Figure 3.1

Artifacts are portable objects whose form is modified or wholly created by human activity, while ecofacts are nonartifactual remains that nonetheless have cultural relevance. Here a projectile point (an artifact) lies embedded among the bones (ecofacts) of an extinct form of bison at Folsom, New Mexico. (All rights reserved. Photo Archives, Denver Museum of Natural History.)

From *Discovering Our Past: A Brief Introduction to Archaeology* by Wendy Ashmore and Robert J. Sharer, 1988, pp. 30-54. © 1988 by Mayfield Publishing Company. Reprinted by permission.

Figure 3.2

Features are artifacts that cannot be recovered intact, in this case a partially excavated cremation burial pit.

are hearths, burials, storage pits, and roads. It is useful to distinguish between these simple features and composite features such as buildings and other multiple component remains. It is also useful to differentiate features that have been deliberately constructed from others, such as trash heaps, that have grown by simple accumulation. Features usually define an area where one or more activities once took place.

Ecofacts

Ecofacts are nonartifactual natural remains that nonetheless have cultural relevance (Fig. 3.1). Although they are neither directly created nor significantly modified by human activity, ecofacts provide information about past human behavior. Examples include remnants of both wild and domesticated animal and plant species (bones, seeds, pollen, and so forth). These and other ecofacts such as soils contribute to our understanding of the past because they reflect ancient environmental conditions, diet, and resource exploitation.

Sometimes the line between ecofacts and artifacts is blurred. For example, bones with cut marks from butchering might be considered artifacts (reflecting human technology) as well as ecofacts (yielding clues to the ancient environment).

Sites

Sites are spatial clusters of artifacts, features, and/or ecofacts. A site may consist of only one form of archaeological data—a surface scatter of artifacts, for example—or of any combination of the three different forms. Site boundaries are sometimes well defined, especially if features such as walls or moats are present. Usually, however, a decline in density or frequency of the material remains is all that marks the limits of a site. However boundaries are defined, the archaeological site is usually a basic working unit of archaeological investigation.

Sites can be described and categorized in a variety of ways, depending on the characteristics one wants to note. For instance, location—sites in open valley positions, cave sites, coastal sites, mountaintop sites, and so forth—may reflect past environmental conditions, concern for defense, or relative values placed on natural resources located in different areas. Sites

may be distinguished by one or more functions they served in the past. For example, one can speak of habitation sites, trading centers, hunting (or kill) sites, ceremonial centers, burial areas, and so on. Sites may also be described in terms of their age and/or cultural affiliation. For example, a Near Eastern site may be described as belonging to the Bronze Age, or a Mexican site may be described as Aztec.

The nature and depth of cultural deposits at a site can reveal the time span of activities: whether occupation was brief or extended. At some sites occupation (and deposition of artifacts) may have been continuous. Other sites may have had multiple occupations with periods of abandonment marked by naturally deposited (nonartifactual or "sterile") layers. Depth of accumulation is not an automatic indicator of length of occupation; at one spot a great deal of material can be deposited very rapidly, while elsewhere a relatively thin deposit of trash might represent layers laid down intermittently over hundreds of thousands of years. Whether thick or thin, the remains of sites may be visible on the ground surface or completely buried and invisible to the naked eye.

Some "buried" sites lie not underground but underwater, the most common being sunken ships. However, sites that were once on dry land may also become submerged because of changes in water level (sometimes resulting from human activity such as dam building) or land subsidence. A famous example of the latter is Port Royal, Jamaica, a coastal city that sank beneath the sea after an earthquake in 1692.

Regions

Regions are the largest and most flexible spatial clusters of archaeological data. The region is basically a geographic concept: a definable area bounded by topographic features such as mountains and bodies of water (Fig. 3.3). But the definition of an archaeological region may also consider ecological and cultural factors. For instance, a region may be defined as the area

Figure 3.3

An archaeological region is often defined by topographic features: In this case, hilly areas and seacoast define the limits of the Virú Valley, Peru, (After Willey 1953.)

used by a prehistoric population to provide its food and water. By considering whole regions the archaeologist can reconstruct aspects of prehistoric society that may not be well represented by a single site.

Obviously, the nature and scope of an archaeological region vary according to the complexity of the prehistoric society and its means of subsistence. Part of the archaeologist's task is to identify the factors that define a particular region under study, as well as to show how these factors changed through time. In other words, the archaeologist usually works within a convenient natural region defined by geographical boundaries and seeks to determine that region's ancient ecological and cultural boundaries as well.

these remains are *behavioral processes* comprising four consecutive stages: acquisition, manufacture, use, and disposal or deposition (Fig. 3.4). Artifacts such as tools are made from acquired raw materials, used for one or more specific purposes, and then discarded when broken or worn. Features such as houses are built from gathered materials, occupied, and then abandoned and destroyed or left to ruin. Ecofacts such as meat animals are hunted, butchered, cooked, eaten, and passed as waste products. The complex aggregate of these activities delineates the same stages in the life span of the site as a whole.

Thus the archaeologist can use all forms of archaeological data to reconstruct the acquisition, manufacture, use, and disposal stages of ancient

behavior. Clues to all four kinds of ancient behavior may be found in characteristics of the data themselves and in the circumstances of their deposition (Fig. 3.5).

These behavioral processes represent the first stage in the formation of archaeological data. The second step consists of *tranformational processes*. These processes include all conditions and events that affect material remains from the time ancient use stops (at any point in the behavioral process) to the time the archaeologist recognizes and acquires them as data. When the specific materials under study are plants or animals, the archaeologist draws on the field of *taphonomy*: the study of what happens to remains of plants and animals after they die. One important book on taphonomy is appropriately titled *Fossils in the Making*.

The tangible products of ancient human behavior are never completely indestructible, but some survive better than others. As a result the data recovered by the archaeologist always present a picture of the past that is biased by the effects of transformational processes (see Fig. 3.5). To gauge bias it is crucial to determine the processes that have been at work in each archaeological situation. Both natural and human events act either to accelerate or to retard destruction. Natural agents of transformation include climatic factors, which are usually the most basic influences acting on the preservation of archaeological evidence. Temperature and humidity are generally the most critical: Extremely dry, wet, or cold conditions preserve fragile or-

DEPOSITION AND TRANSFORMATION

Archaeological data are the result of two factors: behavioral processes and transformational processes. We will describe them in the order of their involvement with archaeological data.

All archaeological sites represent the products of human activity. While some human behavior, such as storytelling, leaves no tangible trace, many activities produce material remains. The activities responsible for

ACQUISITION **MANUFACTURE** **USE** **DEPOSITION**

Figure 3.4

Archaeological data represent at least one behavioral cycle of acquisition, manufacture, use and deposition.

ganic materials such as textiles and wooden tools, as well as bulkier perishable items such as human corpses. Organic remains have been preserved under these circumstances along the dry coast of Peru, in the wet bogs of Scandinavia, and in the frozen steppes of Siberia.

Natural destructive processes such as oxidation and decay and catastrophic events such as earthquakes and volcanic eruptions also have profound effects on the remains of the past. Underwater remains may be broken up and scattered by tidal action, currents, or waves. Catastrophes such as volcanic eruptions may either preserve or destroy archaeological sites; often the same event may have a multitude of effects. For example, around 1500 B.C. both an earthquake and a volcanic eruption struck the island of Thera in the Aegean Sea near Greece. Part of the island blew up; another part collapsed inward and was filled by the inrushing sea; and still other areas were immediately buried under a blanket of ash. The population abandoned the island, but the remains of its settlements were sealed beneath the ash. Recent excavations have disclosed well-preserved buildings, some intact to the third story—a rarity in more-exposed sites—as well as beautiful wall paintings and traces of fragile baskets.

One of the most decisive factors in the transformation process is subsequent human activity. Reoccupation of an archaeological site may destroy all traces of previous occupation. Earlier buildings are often leveled to make way for new construction or to provide construction materials. In other cases, however, later activity may preserve older sites by building over and thus sealing the earlier remains (see Fig. 3.5). Of course, large-scale human events such as war usually have destructive consequences for archaeological preservation, as does a flourishing market in antiquities, which encourages the looting and consequent destruction of archaeological sites.

In summary, archaeologists must determine what conditions and events have transformed the site before they

2000 years ago: Hunting camp (acquisition, manufacture, use, and deposition behavior)

1800 years ago: Flood covers remains of camp with silt (transformational process)

1500 years ago: Farming village built on silt (new cycle of acquisition, manufacture, use, and deposition behavior)

1000 years ago: New flood destroys farming village (transformational process); stone shrine built on new ground surface (new cycles of acquisition, manufacture, use, and deposition behavior)

500 years ago: Shrine is abandoned and begins to disintegrate, forming mound (depositional and natural transformational processes)

Today: Mound is mined for fill to be used in highway construction (cultural transformational process)

Figure 3.5

The characteristics of archaeological data and their deposition reflect both behavioral and transformational processes.

can consider reconstructing past human behavior. Obviously, the behavioral and transformational processes are specific to each site, so each must be evaluated individually. Archaeologists begin to reconstruct these processes from the circumstances under which the data are recovered, including their matrix, provenience, and association.

Matrix refers to the physical medium that surrounds, holds, and supports other archaeological data (Fig. 3.6). Most frequently it consists of combinations of soil, sand, gravel, or rock. The nature of a matrix is usually an important clue to understanding the artifacts, features, or ecofacts it contains. For instance, artifacts recovered from an alluvial matrix (deposited by

running water) may have been deposited by the natural action of a river. A matrix may also be produced by human activity, such as the deposition of immense amounts of soil in order to construct an earthen platform. In this case, the soil is not only a matrix for any artifacts or ecofacts contained in it and for other features constructed on it, but also a constructed feature.

Provenience simply refers to a three-dimensional location of any kind of archaeological data on or within the matrix. Horizontal provenience is usually recorded relative to a geographical grid system using known reference points. Vertical provenience is usually recorded as elevation above or below sea level. Provenience information allows the archaeologist to record (and

Figure 3.6

In this photograph, a human burial has been excavated from most of its matrix, but the relationship of the remains to the matrix is readily apparent. (Courtesy of the Ban Chiang Project, Thai Fine Arts Department/University Museum.)

later to reconstruct) association and context.

Association refers to two or more artifacts (or any other kind of data) occurring together in the same matrix (Fig. 3.7). The associations of various kinds of data are often crucial to the interpretation of past events. For instance, the artifacts found in association with a human burial, such as hunting weapons, may be clues to the individual's sex and livelihood.

Context is a summary evaluation of the significance of the provenience, association, and matrix for a given artifact or other bit of evidence, in light of effects of both behavioral and transformational processes. In other words, context is an assessment of where the evidence is, how it got there, and what has happened to it in the meantime.

There are two basic kinds of archaeological contexts: primary and secondary. Each of these may be divided into two further categories.

Primary context refers to conditions in which both provenience and matrix have been undisturbed since original deposition. Intact archaeological features are always in primary context, although later disturbance can remove portions of such features from primary context. There are two kinds of primary contexts:

1. *Use-related primary context* results from deposition in the place where the artifact was acquired, made, or used. The occurrence of two or more associated artifacts in use-related primary context ideally means that they were used and deposited at the same time. Such an occurrence allows the archaeologist to reconstruct the activity of which the artifacts were a part. Truly undisturbed archaeological contexts, however, are rare, the best examples being burials and tombs. Most contexts have been altered to some degree by transformational processes.

2. *Transposed primary context* is a more specific category since it results from behavior concerned with disposal of refuse (formation of trash heaps or *middens*). In other words, it is the product of the final stage in the behavioral cycle. The association of two or more artifacts in transposed primary context does not allow direct inferences about any ancient behavior other than waste disposal. However, association in transposed primary context does support the conclusion that the artifacts were made and used during the same general period. It can be seen, therefore, that use-related primary context represents a wider range of ancient activities, but archaeological data in primary contexts

Figure 3.7

A group of pottery vessels found in association as a result of intentional ritual deposition (primary context). This indicates there were used together as part of an ancient ceremony (ca. first century A.D., El Porton, Guatemala).

are more commonly found in transposed situations.

Secondary context refers to a condition in which provenience, association, and matrix have been wholly or partially altered by processes of transformation. There are two kinds of secondary contexts:

1. *Use-related secondary context* results from disturbances by subsequent human activity, ancient or modern.
2. *Natural secondary context* results from disturbance by a variety of nonhuman agents, such as burrowing animals, tree roots, erosion, decay, volcanic eruptions, or earthquakes.

The differences among the types of archaeological context and the significance of accurately determining context, can be illustrated by several examples. In the first place, any artifact may be modified to be reused for different purposes over its use span. Thus a pottery vessel may be manufactured for the transport of water but later modified to use as a container for food or other substances and then (when inverted) as a mold for the shaping of new pottery vessels. If this vessel were abandoned during, or immediately after, any of these activities—say its use as a pottery mold—and remained in an undisturbed matrix with its associated artifacts, ecofacts, and features, its archaeological context upon discovery would be primary (undisturbed) and use-related (as part of pottery making activity). Knowing the provenience, associations, and context (in this case reflected in the finding of an inverted vessel surrounded by other vessels in various stages of manufacture, along with clay-working tools and so forth), the archaeologist would be able to reconstruct both the type of activity and many specific techniques used in this instance of pottery making. Any prior uses, however, would not be directly detected.

As already noted, the survival of use-related primary contexts is relatively rare and depends on both the circumstances of the original behavior and transformation processes that ten-

Figure 3.8

This plan shows positions of bodies in the "Great Death-Pit" adjacent to the royal tombs at Ur. (From Woolley 1934; by permission of the University Museum, University of Pennsylvania.)

ded to preserve rather than destroy. Discoveries of chipped stone projectile points in clear association with bones of animals have been important keys to the reconstruction of early human activities in the New World. In the mid-1920s, discoveries at Folsom, New Mexico, revealed such points in undisturbed use-related contexts associated with bones of a species of bison that has been extinct for at least 10,000 years (Fig. 3.1). The dates have been supplied by paleontological study, but archaeological association and context were critical in establishing the cultural meaning of these finds.

Many kinds of activity can disturb or erase earlier use-related primary contexts. In some cases, however, subsequent human activity can preserve them—as in the building of a new

structure over the recently abandoned pottery workshop described above. In other cases the manner of original deposition may tend to secure use-related primary contexts from disturbance. One of the best examples of such deposition is provided by the preparation of burials and tombs. In many areas of the world ancient people developed elaborate funerary customs. When found undisturbed the resultant tombs provide opportunities to reconstruct ancient ritual activity and belief systems.

A good illustration of this reconstruction can be seen in the Royal Tombs of Ur, an ancient Mesopotamian site in Iraq, excavated by Sir Leonard Woolley in the late 1920s (Fig. 3.8). Careful recording of provenience and associations enabled Woolley to reconstruct a nearly complete funerary scene, including elaborate grave goods and sacrificed victims. From the reconstructions Woolley was able to infer a great deal about royal customs of the time, as well as specific details such as court costume. Only the chamber of the king himself, which had been looted, could not be reconstructed; the rest had been protected and preserved by interment.

Other examples of use-related primary context have been preserved by natural events. The deposition of soil by wind and water has buried countless sites under deep layers of earth; a famous example of a buried site is the ancient Roman city of Pompeii, which was covered by volcanic ash from the eruption of Mount Vesuvius in A.D. 79.

Not all primary contexts are use related, however. People in most societies discard items after they are damaged, broken, or no longer useful. Middens are specialized areas for rubbish disposal; they contain artifacts that are usually undisturbed from the moment of their deposition. Furthermore, if used over long periods of time, middens may become stratified or layered, with each layer corresponding to a period of rubbish deposition. Middens are thus in primary context, but because of the nature of their deposition, the only past behavior directly reflected by this context is the general practice of rubbish accumulation and disposal. For this reason, material recovered from middens is in *transposed primary context*. If a midden is used over a long period of time, relative position within the deposit (or within a particular layer of the midden) can be used to assess relative chronological position (Fig. 3.9).

The identification of use-related secondary context can often help the archaeologist understand how artifacts came to be associated. Of course, if the disturbed context is not recognized as such, the interpretation can be badly in error. For example, the contents of a heavily disturbed tomb might include not only some portion of the original furnishings, but also materials such as tools and containers that were brought

in and left behind by the looters. During the excavation of the tomb of the Egyptian Pharaoh Tut-ankh-amun, ancient looting was recognized by evidence of two openings and reclosings of the entry; the final sealings of the disturbed areas were marked by different motifs from those on the undisturbed portions. If the disturbance had not been recognized, the associations and arrangements of recovered artifacts might be wrongly interpreted as representing burial ritual behavior.

Natural secondary context, which might occur, for example, when burrowing animals have placed later artifacts in apparent association with earlier features, can also make interpretation difficult. At Ban Chiang, a site in northern Thailand, ancient burials are juxtaposed in a very complex fashion, with later pits intruding into or overlapping earlier ones. The job of segregating distinct units was made even more difficult by the numerous animal burrows, including those of worms, crisscrossing the units, so that tracing pit lines and other surfaces was exacting and intricate work.

The archaeologist uses the foregoing kinds of information along with the products of past behavior—archaeological data—to reconstruct both the behaviors and the cultural systems by

which they were produced. As the first step in linking the data to a past cultural system, the archaeologist must assess the effects on the data of the processes we have discussed: the kinds of ancient behavior that produced the evidence (behavioral processes), and the natural or human events that have affected the evidence from the time of deposition to the moment of archaeological recovery (transformational processes).

A point to be emphasized is that any kind of excavation—by archaeologists or anyone else—*destroys* matrix, association, and context. The only way to preserve the information these factors convey is in drawings, photographs, and written records. Without them, even the most painstakingly controlled excavation is no more justifiable or useful than a looter's pit.

ACQUIRING DATA

Archaeologists are concerned with gathering evidence of past human behavior as a first step toward understanding that ancient behavior and toward meeting both the specific objectives of their research and the general goals of archaeology. Realizing these objectives requires discovery of

Figure 3.9

Cross-section drawing of a stratified midden representing nearly 2000 years of accumulation at Chalchuapa, El Salvador. One of the characteristics of transposed primary context, such as this midden, is that the artifacts from a given layer are contemporaneous but cannot be assumed to represent the same set of ancient activities.

Figure 3.10

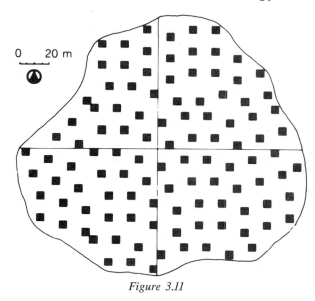

Figure 3.11

A universe with nonarbitrary units: In this case, rooms in a prehistoric Southwestern pueblo. The shaded rooms were the ones excavated. (By permission from Broken K Pueblo, Prehistoric Social Organization in the American Southwest, *by James N. Hill, University of Arizona Anthropological Paper #18, Tucson: University of Arizona Press, copyright 1970.)*

A universe with arbitrary units at Girik-i-Haciyan, Turkey: the black areas were the units investigated. (After Redman and Watson, reproduced by permission of The Society for American Archaeology, adapted from American Antiquity 35: 281–282, 1970.)*

as much as possible about the characteristics of the data. Ideally archaeologists seek to recover the full range of variation in the archaeological data relevant to their research questions. What was the range of activities carried on at a site? What was the range of places chosen for location and settlement? What was the range of forms and styles of artifacts? To the extent that such variation existed but is not known, the picture of ancient life is unnecessarily incomplete and any inferences drawn may be wrong. In a sense archaeological data are always unrepresentative; not all behavior produces tangible evidence, and not all the evidence will survive. The ideal goal is seldom realized, but understanding the processes that affected the production and preservation of the evidence can compensate to some extent for the unevenness in the availability of data. At this point we need to consider how the archaeologist chooses data acquisition strategies to maximize the usefulness of the evidence that *is* available.

The first step in data acquisition is to define the limits of the region under investigation. This will impose a practical limit on the amount of evidence to be collected. A bounded research area may be referred to as a *data universe.* An archaeological data universe is bounded both in time and geographical space. An investigator may define a data universe as a single site or even a portion of site. In a regional situation the research area corresponds to a much larger universe, such as an entire valley or a coastal area containing many sites. The archaeologist may also draw temporal boundaries to seek data corresponding to a relatively short era, such as the Pueblo II period of the American Southwest (ca. A.D. 900–1100), or a much longer span, such as a period of several thousand years corresponding to an entire interglacial period of the Pleistocene (Ice Age).

Once defined, the data universe is subdivided into *sample units.* A sample unit is the unit of investigation; it may be defined by either arbitrary or nonarbitrary criteria. *Nonarbitrary sample units* correspond either to natural areas, such as microenvironments, or to cultural entities, such as rooms,

houses, or sites (Fig 3.10). *Arbitrary sample units* are spatial divisions with no inherent natural or cultural relevance (Fig. 3.11). Examples of the latter include sample units defined by a grid system (equal-sized squares). *Sample units should not be confused with data:* If an archaeologist is looking for sites, the sample units will be geographical areas where sites might be located. If sites are the sample units, the data to be gathered will be artifacts, ecofacts, and features within the site.

The choice between arbitrary and nonarbitrary sample units is made by the investigator; it reflects the specific objectives of the study and the nature of the data (see below). But in any case all sample units are (or are assumed to be) comparable. That is, nonarbitrarily defined units are assumed to yield similar or complementary information about ancient behavior. For example, if sites are the sample units, one "cemetery" site will give information similar to that from another cemetery site and complementary to information from "habitation" sites and other sample units within the data population. Arbitrarily defined units, on the other hand, are comparable because they are always regular in size and/or shape.

The aggregate of all sample units is the *population*. Note that when the universe is a region and the sample units correspond to all the known sites, the population will not include unknown sites or locations in the region without sites, even though these areas are part of the universe. Nevertheless, conclusions drawn about the population are often inferred to be "true" of the research universe as well.

Total data acquisition involves investigation of all the units in the population. Of course the archaeologist never succeeds in gathering every shred of evidence from a given data universe; we are constantly developing new techniques of recovery and analysis that broaden the very definition of archaeological data. A change in the research problem also alters the definition of what materials and relationships are considered appropriate data. It is nonetheless important to distinguish between investigations that attempt to collect all available evidence (by investigation of all sample units) and those that set out to collect only a portion of the available data. Something approaching total data acquisition is often attempted in salvage situations, as when a site or region is threatened with immediate destruction by construction of a new highway or dam.

Sample data acquisition refers to situations in which only a portion or sample of the data can be collected from a given archaeological data pool. The limits of the sample recovered are often influenced by economic constraints: The archaeologist seldom has the funds to study all potential units. Nor is research time unlimited; seasonal weather conditions, scheduling commitments, and other factors often determine the time available to gather evidence. Access to archaeological data may be restricted by natural barriers, lack of roads or lack of permission from property owners. Even when there are no restrictions to access, however, it is still desirable to collect only

part of the available archaeological data. Except in situations of threatened site destruction, most archaeologists recommend that a portion of every site be left untouched to allow future scientists a chance to work with intact sources of archaeological evidence using techniques more sophisticated than today's. In this way future research can check and refine the results obtained with present methods.

RESEARCH DESIGN

Whether total or sample coverage is used, research must be planned to ensure that its goals will be addressed and met. Traditionally, archaeological research has been "site-oriented." The major goal was to excavate a particular site and, in many cases, collect spectacular remains. With the emergence of archaeology as a scientific discipline, more systematic approaches have become the rule. Today, regional and problem-oriented investigations are increasingly the norm. This kind of research aims at solving specific problems or testing one or more hypotheses by using controlled and representative samples of data.

Archaeological research design refers to a sequence of stages that guides the conduct of investigation (Fig. 3.12) to ensure the validity of results and make efficient use of time, money, and effort. Each stage has one or more specific purposes. Although the stages may be ideally portrayed as a series of steps, the process is flexible in practice. Aspects of two or more stages may be carried out simultaneously, or the stages may be accomplished in a different order, depending on circumstances. Furthermore, since each research situation is unique, this generalized research design must be capable of adapting to a wide variety of specific applications.

Formulation involves definition of the research problem, background investigations, and feasibility studies. Decisions regarding the problem to be investigated and the geographical area of study both limit and guide further work. Once these choices are made,

the archaeologist conducts background research to locate and study any previous work that may be relevant to the investigation. Useful information at this point may include geographical, geological, climatological, ecological, and anthropological studies, when available. Such data may be found in publications, archives, laboratories, and so on and through consultations with individual experts. Because archaeological research usually requires fieldwork, the archaeologist must usually do a feasibility study involving a trip to the region or sites to be investigated to evaluate the archaeological situation and local conditions such as accessibility, availability of supplies, and so forth.

Thorough background investigations facilitate the actual research by refining the problem under investigation and defining specific research goals. The goals of most archaeological research include testing one or more specific hypotheses. Some of these may come from previously proposed models, while others may arise during the formulation of the basic research problem. As the research progresses, of course, new hypotheses may be generated and tested. It is important to remember, however, that the initial formulation of research problem(s) leads the archaeologist to look for particular kinds of data and thus sets the course for the entire study.

Implementation involves completing all the arrangements necessary for the success of the planned fieldwork. These arrangements may be complex, especially if the research is to be done in a foreign country. The first step in implementing a study may be to secure the necessary permits for conducting research, usually from government agencies responsible for overseeing archaeological work. The owners of the land on which the work will take place must also grant permission before investigations can proceed. The laws governing archaeological work vary from country to country and from state to state within the United States, so the archaeologist must be aware of the relevant regulations and customs within the area being investigated.

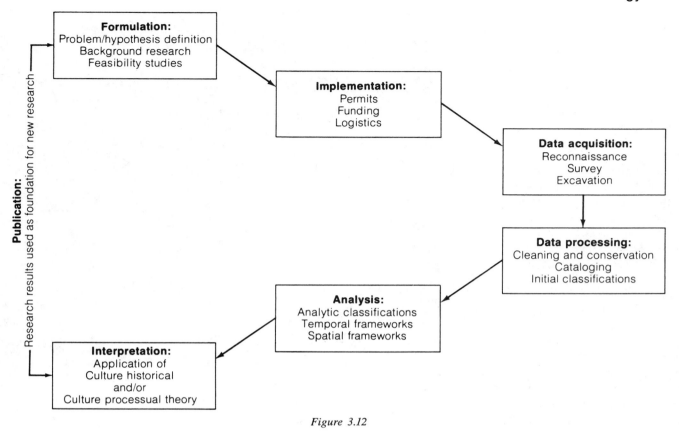

Figure 3.12

Diagram of stages of archaeological research.

At some point the archaeologist must find funds to finance the research. In some cases this involves submitting a research proposal to private or governmental agencies that fund archaeological investigations. In many CRM situations the agency issuing the contract provides the funding for the research.

When funding and permit have been secured, the archaeologist can turn to making logistic arrangements. Research equipment and supplies must be acquired. In most cases field facilities must be rented or built for safekeeping of the equipment and for laboratory processing and storage of artifacts and field records. Many projects require a staff that must be recruited, transported, housed, and fed, and these arrangements must be completed before the work can begin.

Acquisition involves three basic procedures for the collection of data: reconnaissance, survey, and excavation. . . . Reconnaissance is the means for identifying and locating archae-ological sites, accomplished by on-the-scene visual search and by remote sensors. Survey is undertaken to record as much as possible about archaeological sites without excavation, through photography, mapping, remote sensors, and collection of surface artifacts. Excavation is undertaken to expose the buried characteristics of archaeological sites, using a variety of techniques to retrieve and record the data revealed.

Data processing refers to the manipulation of raw data (artifacts and ecofacts) and the creation and manipulation of records. Portable remains are usually processed in a field laboratory to insure that they are recorded, preserved, and stored to be available for further analysis. Records referring to these data (descriptions, photographs, and scaled drawings) are also completed and filed to be accessible for later use.

Analysis provides a variety of information useful for archaeological interpretations. For artifacts these studies include classification, determination of age, and various technical analyses designed to identify sources of raw materials, methods of manufacture, and uses. Some of these procedures can be done in the field laboratory, but the more technical or complex analyses are usually undertaken at specially equipped permanent scientific facilities.

Interpretation involves the synthesis of all the results of data collection, processing, and analysis as a means of answering the original goals of the investigation. The use of the scientific method in these procedures is an important characteristic of modern professional archaeology. A variety of models are used in the interpretive process, including both specific and general historical and anthropological frameworks.

Publication completes the research cycle and makes the findings fully accessible so that the results can be used and retested by fellow archaeologists and any other interested individuals. This ensures that any research contributes to the broadest objectives of archaeology and of science in general.

ARCHAEOLOGICAL RESEARCH PROJECTS

Scientific archaeology demands a broad range of expertise. Today's archaeologist must be a theoretical scientist, a methodologist, a technician, an administrator, and more. In reality, of course, it is nearly impossible for one individual to do everything necessary for a particular project; usually the archaeologist must bring together specialists from a wide variety of disciplines. Doing so requires an interdisciplinary approach and coordination of the efforts of many scientists, each of whom focuses on a particular aspect of the research. Scientific teams—usually led by an archaeologist but including botanists, ecologists, geologists, and other specialists—are often created to conduct thorough fieldwork on a research question. Only by depending on others can the archaeologist ensure that the data collected are used to the maximum degree possible. In some cases the archaeologist may find most of the required support specialists housed under one roof, as in the larger museums and research institutions in many parts of the world. In the United States, the Smithsonian Institution provides one of the most complete support facilities for archaeology.

The size and duration of archaeological research projects depend on the scale of the problems being investigated. A few months' work by a single individual may be all that is required to plan and conduct the data-gathering stages of the research. But even the single individual will need some form of assistance from outside specialists in processing and analyzing the results. Archaeological research concerned with complex civilizations, such as the work being done at large urban sites in the Near East and Mexico, usually calls for a large archaeological staff and a huge labor force (Fig. 3.13). Projects in these and simi-

Figure 3.13

The modern large-scale archaeological excavation at Quiriguá, Guatemala, involved over 100 people and continued over a six-year period. (Quiriguá Project, University Museum, University of Pennsylvania.)

lar areas have employed teams of on-site specialists in research extending over many years.

Like most activities, archaeological research is limited by the availability of time and money. A far greater problem, however, is one that threatens the very existence of archaeological research: the increasing destruction wrought by our rapidly expanding world. The destruction of archaeological remains has reached such proportions that we may well ask, "Does the past have a future?"

SUMMARY

The material remains from the past become archaeological data once they are recognized, collected, and recorded. The direct products of past human activity are either artifacts (portable) or features (nonportable). Indirect products of past human activity are called ecofacts. Archaeologists usually examine distributions of data within sites (clusters of data), or, as is increasingly common today, within re-

gions (clusters of sites). Further information is gleaned from recording the specific location (provenience), associations, and matrix (surroundings) of data. The context of data—their behavioral significance—is revealed by evaluation of all these factors. The understanding of context, with care to discriminate among the various kinds of context, is the crucial link that allows the archaeologist to reconstruct the kinds of ancient behavior the recovered data represent.

The material record ideally reflects four major categories of human activity—acquisition, manufacture, use, and deposition—which together constitute behavioral processes. But archaeologists can never recover data representing all kinds of past behavior. Some activity leaves no tangible trace, and the evidence of other kinds of ancient behavior may be altered over time by human and natural transformational processes. These processes act selectively either to preserve or to destroy archaeological evidence. Thus the data available to the archaeologist constitute a sample determined first by ancient human activity (behavioral processes) and then by human or natural forces acting after the remains are deposited (transformational processes).

The resulting data form the base that the archaeologist attempts to recover, either totally (by collection of all available evidence) or by sampling methods. Whatever collection method is used, the archaeologist seeks data that represent, as much as possible, the full range of ancient human activity. With very few exceptions (such as when a site is about to be destroyed), it is generally practical and desirable to collect only a sample of the data.

Archaeological research is usually aimed at solving specific problems or testing specific hypotheses. To guide such investigations, most archaeologists follow a similar research design that begins with formulation of the problem, based on background and feasibility studies, followed by implementation, which includes fund-raising, securing permits, and making logistical arrangements. The next stage is data acquisition, which often includes reconnaissance (locating unknown sites), survey (mapping and collecting surface data), and excavation (removal of matrix to reveal buried data). This is followed by data processing and analysis, leading to interpretation (reconstruction of the past to address the specific research goals) and publication of the research.

To be a successful researcher, today's archaeologist must command a broad range of expertise. He or she must have knowledge of field methods, theory, administration, and a range of technical skills. Seldom can one individual perform all the tasks demanded by the complexity of archaeological investigation, so in almost all cases the archaeologist calls on a variety of specialists for assistance.

The scale of archaeological research ranges from the study conducted by a single person in a few weeks to the work of large research teams over several years or decades. The practical limits to such research are usually determined by time and money, but the severest threat to our understanding of the past is posed by our expanding world's destruction of archaeological data.

The Enlightened Archaeologist

Thomas Jefferson's exploration of an Indian burial mound was, for its time, an extraordinary achievement. Recent excavations in Virginia offer new insights into his goals and interpretations.

Jeffrey L. Hantman and Gary Dunham

Jeffrey L. Hantman, an associate professor of anthropology at the University of Virginia, has conducted research on the prehistory of the Pueblo Southwest and the late prehistoric and contact periods in Virginia. He is currently writing a book on Monacan archaeology and ethnohistory.
Gary Dunham, a doctoral candidate in anthropology at the University of Virginia, directed the excavations at the Rapidan Mound.

Thomas Jefferson's excavation of an Indian burial mound near Charlottesville, Virginia, has earned him the title "Father of American Archaeology." Jefferson described his dig on the South Fork of the Rivanna River in his book, *Notes on the State of Virginia.* He also reported that "many [mounds] are to be found all over this country [though] cleared of their trees and put under cultivation [they] are much reduced in their height, and spread in width, by the plough, and will probably disappear in time." In fact, the mound excavated by Jefferson has disappeared from view, despite several attempts to locate it earlier in this century. Jefferson's description of it remains the sole documentation that it existed at all.

In 1988, an opportunity arose to study a burial mound quite similar to the one dug by Jefferson. Known as the Rapidan Mound, it is located just 14 miles from the one Jefferson excavated. It had been placed on the endangered sites list of the Virginia Department of Historic Resources, and money was available to help excavate and preserve the remaining portions of it. Once prominent in the middle of a floodplain, it had been steadily eroded by the shifting course and destructive flooding of the Rapidan River. Early nineteenth-century accounts of the Rapidan Mound suggest it was then a 12- to 15-foot-high conical mound with a diameter of some 50 feet. In 1892, the Smithsonian's Gerard Fowke, who had been an assistant to Cyrus Thomas on the great mound surveys of the late nineteenth century, recorded the mound as being reduced to six feet in height, though the width had remained stable. Fowke dug a large trench through the mound, even then severely eroded by the river and partially leveled by farmers. In 1979, Archaeological Society of Virginia members Charlton G. Holland, Sandra Spieden, and David van Roijen opened two small excavation units on the river's edge and described apparently random deposits of human bone and a submound pit. By 1988 those units had been washed away, and only a small fragment of the mound's south edge remained. The rate of destruction had quickened even in the past few years, and there was no way possible to secure the site without flooding farm fields downstream.

On a cold spring day, we met with archaeologists Keith Egloff, David Hazzard, Randy Turner, and Catherine Slusser from the Virginia Department of Historic Resources and discussed the possibility of salvaging the site. Because preservation was simply not possible, we decided to record what was left of the mound, in accordance with Virginia's new burial laws that include a commitment to rebury human remains.

Initially we were skeptical that there would be anything left within the mound to record. Although respectfully protected in recent years by the family that owned the land on which it was located, the mound's condition was rapidly deteriorating. Recent floods had eroded the north face exposed to the river; a few abandoned cars buried off the south edge of the mound acted as a makeshift flood wall. Despite the erosion, we felt a season of testing was worth the effort. Funds from the Virginia Department of Historic Resources provided for a professional staff to oversee the excavation; students from the University of Virginia's summer field school joined in the dig after receiving extensive training at nearby sites. It would be three years before we finished our work.

Most of our first season was spent clinging to the riverbank, our feet in small rests cut into the submound soils, cleaning off flood debris and roots to reveal the mound's inner levels. We could see the clear outline of the trench that Fowke had made. Having located the old trench, we could focus our attention on undisturbed areas. What we discovered was an astonishing similarity between the profiles of our mound and the one excavated by Jefferson—layers of dark stained soil with bone in it, interrupted by lighter colored soils brought to the site. Where Jefferson had seen seven such levels near the center of his mound, we could see three.

Jefferson had actually employed two excavation strategies. One was trenching, which allowed him to look at the internal structure of the mound and its stratigraphy. In this he was about 100 years ahead of his time. But he also wrote: "I first dug superficially in several parts of it, and came to collections of human bones, at different depths, from six inches to three feet below the surface. These were lying in the utmost confusion, some vertical, some oblique, some horizontal, and directed to every point of the compass, entangled, and held together in clusters by the earth. Bones of the most distant part were found together. . . ." What Jefferson could not see or fully appreciate with his narrow trenching and random digging was the internal structure of each of the separate burial features he had carefully identified.

In 1989 and 1990 we excavated the Rapidan River mound by exposing broad horizontal areas in an effort to study the spatial relationships among the mound's burial features, as well as the internal configuration of each burial. We were able to identify six burial features, three of which we excavated completely. We found that the bones were not "lying in utmost confusion," as Jefferson described them, nor were they random placements as posited by later excavators. Instead, the bones, after an initial burial or exposure of the body to remove the flesh, had been recovered and reburied as part of a mortuary ritual. The skulls had been placed in concentric circles with long bones distributed around them in linear arrangements. Our excavations also revealed a pattern of change in burial practice over time from earlier individual or small multiple burials in pits, to later secondary

burials containing up to 20 individuals. Jefferson did not record any submound pits, although they are common in most Virginia mounds, and we, as well as Fowke, found them at Rapidan Mound. Like the careful arrangement of bones, Jefferson probably missed them because he dug only narrow trenches and excavation pits.

We estimate that between 1,000 and 1,500 people were buried in the Rapidan Mound. Remarkably, with considerably less information in hand, Jefferson wrote of the Rivanna River mound, "I conjectured that in this barrow might have been a thousand skeletons." Based on our study of the Rapidan Mound, we now have good reason to believe his conjecture was accurate. The central Virginia mounds may not be extraordinary in terms of size, but the number of burials they contained and the generations it took for them to accumulate, is quite extraordinary.

A page from Jefferson's personal copy of the 1787 edition of Notes on the State of Virginia includes comments in his own hand, mostly in Greek, which he hoped to include in a new edition to be published in his lifetime. They stress his interest in the similarities in Greek, Roman, and Native American burial practices.

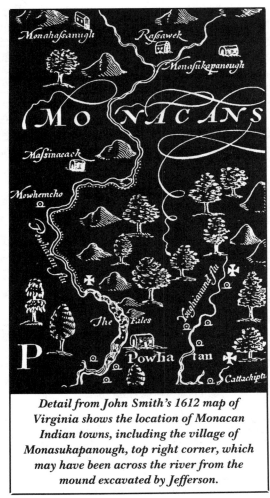

Detail from John Smith's 1612 map of Virginia shows the location of Monacan Indian towns, including the village of Monasukapanough, top right corner, which may have been across the river from the mound excavated by Jefferson.

Analysis of bones from Rapidan Mound has provided interesting new insights. Sandra Olsen, an archaeologist at the Carnegie Museum of Natural History, who was then on the staff of the Virginia Museum of Natural History, performed a scanning electron microscope analysis of five detached skull caps and two skulls missing caps that were found in a single burial feature. Separating skulls from skull caps, presumably with a sharp instrument, was a practice described in local histories relating to the treatment of an enemy prisoner after death. Of further interest was an intact cranium that had an unusual depressed fracture and V-shaped linear groove indicating a blow to the head with a sharp weapon. We inferred from this that some of those buried in the mound may have been killed in warfare. Such evidence, though tentative, contrasts with Jefferson's finding that "no holes were discovered in any of them, as if made by

bullets, arrows or other weapons." In the absence of scanning electron microscopy, Jefferson may well have missed some tell-tale signs of violent death.

On so many other points, however, it is quite remarkable how well Jefferson's interpretations hold up in the late twentieth century. His reading of the stratigraphy of the mound has been well supported by excavations at other mounds in Virginia. Our own work also sheds light on the question of why Jefferson didn't mention any artifacts, and didn't appear to keep any from his excavation. At Rapidan Mound we found very little in the way of artifacts. Using screens and flotation, we did find small potsherds that appear to have been intentionally broken into small pieces as part of the burial ritual, and some stone tools including triangular projectile points. It is not likely that a trenching operation like Jefferson's, without screening, would have turned up such inconspicuous items.

Jefferson accurately described the variety of mounds in central Virginia, noting how they were of different sizes, some built of loose earth and others of stone. More than many twentieth-century archaeologists, he was aware of how the mound he was excavating fit into a regional archaeological perspective. He was also fairly accurate in describing the function of the mounds as community burial places, and the development of the mounds over an unstated period of time. He wrote: "Appearances certainly indicate that [the mound] has derived both origin and growth from the accustomary collection of bones, and deposition of them together; that the first collection had been deposited on the common surface of the earth, a few stones put over it, and then a covering of earth, that the second had been laid on this, had covered more or less of it in proportion to the numbers of bones, and was then also covered with earth, and so on."

To what extent did Jefferson's excavation contribute to an understanding of Native American history? The area in which his mound was located was the territory of the Monacan Indians. He noted that the mound was located across the river from an Indian town, most likely the Monacan town of Monasukapanough, or any one of a number of Late Woodland and possibly early contact period villages identified in archaeological surveys along the Rivanna. But of the Monacans, Jefferson only wrote that he thought they had merged with the Tuscarora and were now part of the Iroquois Confederacy to the north. He did not connect the mound to local Indian history. In fact, in his description of the excavation in *Notes,* Jefferson did not use archaeology to comment on Indian history at all. His focus was not on time, or cultural history, but on the inner construction of an odd feature on the landscape.

Why did he describe the mound at all? Because he was asked to do so. In 1780, a French diplomat in Philadelphia, François Marbois, circulated a letter to representatives of all the newly formed states requesting information on 22 separate topics such as their natural history, resources, population, climate, Indian population, etc. Jefferson was the Virginian who elected to answer this questionnaire, and his response became *Notes on the State of Virginia.* When Jefferson wrote *Notes,* he abbreviated the Indian question put to him by the Frenchman as: "A description of the Indians established in that state." In fact, Marbois' letter had requested: "A description of the Indians established in the state before the European settlements and of those who are still remaining. An indication of the Indian Monuments in that state."

Jefferson's chapter on Indians in *Notes,* titled "Aborigines," is in answer to these three questions posed by Marbois. First, he described the Indians established in the state before the Europeans, but he based this discussion entirely on his reading of colonist John Smith's account of Indians in the Jamestown area at the beginning of the seventeenth century—not on archaeological evidence. He then described the current distribution of the Indian tribes in Virginia, but argued that most had moved away, been greatly reduced in number or now "have more negro than Indian blood in them." Then he added, "I know of no such thing existing as an Indian monument for I would not honour with that name arrow points, stone hatchets, stone pipes, and halfshapen images." Jefferson then described his mound excavation. His archaeology was done in response to the request for information on Indian monuments, and was not undertaken as a matter of historical interest. In fact, in the section on Indian history in *Notes* he did not even mention the mounds. Jefferson concluded, however, with a moving personal memory that must have dated to his childhood: "But on whatever occasion they may have been

made, they are of considerable notoriety among the Indians: for a party passing, about thirty years ago, through the part of the country where this barrow is, went through the woods directly to it, without any instructions or inquiry, and having staid about it some time, with expressions of sorrow, they returned to the high road, which they had left about half a dozen miles to pay this visit, and pursued their journey."

There is little reason to doubt the veracity of this account. We know that Indians were still living in central Virginia into the eighteenth century, even if they had relocated away from the Charlottesville area. The moundbuilder myth that would soon sweep the country and which denied any tie between ancient mounds and contemporary Indians was apparently not a temptation to Jefferson. Such myths are often attributed to the period of American expansion and the pushing west of American Indians, and Jefferson was, as governor of Virginia and later president, a prominent agent in such forced relocation. In 1781, the very year he wrote *Notes,* he was also authorizing and closely monitoring the removal of the Cherokees from the western part of Virginia. Difficult as it is to comprehend such contradictory sides of Jefferson, we simply note here that he apparently did not rationalize his actions by manipulating his archaeological writing as some nineteenth-century scholars did.

At the time he wrote *Notes,* Jefferson did not see archaeological research as the key to understanding Native American origins. In *Notes* he followed the description of his archaeological excavation with a consideration of Indian origins based on linguistics, and suggested a close tie between Asians and Indians. However, seven years after publishing *Notes,* he wrote in a

letter to a colleague that he would be interested in hearing more of his colleague's linguistic theory of the descent of the Creek Indians from the Carthaginians, noting that he "saw nothing impossible in this conjecture." Clearly, his archaeological excavations had not dissuaded him from considering rather spectacular theories of Indian origins. But his opinions were subject to change. By 1813, in a lengthy letter to John Adams, he dismissed as "really amusing" notions of Indian origins in a distant Trojan or Hebrew past, concluding that "the question of origins was so unresolved that it could not be deciphered; Thus it was not a very practical question to ask."

Jefferson's excavation stands as one of many original scientific achievements in a lifetime of remarkable achievements. That it was intended to answer a particular question, not merely to collect relics, is notable, although Jefferson *was* a notable relic collector. And the publication of his excavation strategy, hypotheses, observations, and conclusions was extraordinary for his time. In moving from speculation to empirical observation, his concern was with the inner construction of a man-made phenomenon. In this regard, as in his interest in architecture, landscape, and so much else, Jefferson was particularly concerned with form and function rather than history. Yet, in his sympathetic depiction of the mound visit by Indians, he hinted at a continuity between present and past Indian cultures. And his description of the mound excavation preserved information that would otherwise have been lost, and provides a comparative base for our own excavations and interpretations of the prehistoric and early historic period in Virginia.

'Reverse Archaeologists' Are Tracing the Footsteps of a Cowboy-Explorer

A century ago rancher Richard Wetherill found the remnants of an ancient culture; finally his efforts are being recognized.

David Roberts

David Roberts is at work on his next book, a personal narrative of his travels throughout Anasazi country.

It was a bitter day in December 1888, with snow on the wind. Across the top of the remote Mesa Verde in southwestern Colorado, Richard Wetherill and his brother-in-law Charlie Mason rode horse-back, tracking cattle that had strayed from the family ranch in the Mancos Valley. Twenty-five miles from home, the ranchers faced a cold bivouac under the pines before they could bring the cattle in.

A looping track drew the two men near the mesa's edge, where the sandstone cliff dropped sheer to the talus below. They dismounted, walked to the rim and gazed east across a canyon they had never explored. Suddenly Wetherill blurted out a cry of astonishment.

Half a mile away, in the cliff forming the canyon's opposite wall, loomed an overhang that sheltered a natural cavern fully 400 feet long by 90 feet deep. Inside it stood the pristine ruins of an ancient city, more than 200 rooms built of stone and mud, dominated by a round three-story tower. "It looks just like a palace," murmured Mason.

Wetherill named the ruin Cliff Palace. The two men forgot about their cattle. Roping together dead trees with their lariats, they improvised a ladder to descend the cliff, then scrambled down to the canyon floor and up the opposite slope to enter the majestic ruin.

A PASSION FOR DISCOVERY YIELDS STILL MORE RUINS

It was as if the vanished inhabitants had walked off a few hours before, leaving everything in place. The rooms were strewn with intact ceramic pots sitting in the dust. On one floor the ranchers found a heavy stone ax, still hafted to its wooden handle. A perfunctory dig in the rubble uncovered three skeletons.

Wild with the passion of discovery, the men split up to search for other ruins in the few hours of daylight they had left. Wetherill headed north and west across the mesa top and stumbled upon another great ruin, which he named Spruce Tree House. He rejoined Mason at dusk; they built a fire and talked into the night.

In the morning, the pair found yet a third village, whose most startling feature was a soaring four-story tower. Square Tower House was the obvious name.

Today, more than 600,000 visitors come to Mesa Verde National Park every year. On the standard tour, they walk through the stabilized ruins of Cliff Palace and Spruce Tree House, and peer from a lookout point down on Square Tower House. The three villages are among the half-dozen cynosures of the park, with Cliff Palace—the best known of all Anasazi sites—one of the most famous ruins in the world.

The finding of Cliff Palace changed Wetherill's life utterly. The eldest of six siblings in a tight-knit Quaker clan from Pennsylvania, Richard struggled to keep the family's Alamo Ranch afloat through years of failed crops and dubious investments. Meanwhile he transformed himself into a self-taught archaeologist. During the next 14 years, with his four brothers, Charlie Mason and a handful of other partners, Wetherill discovered and excavated far more Anasazi sites than any researcher before or since. Their number includes 182 ruins on Mesa Verde alone, as well as dozens in the tortured canyon of Grand Gulch in Utah; the exquisite village of Keet Seel in Arizona; and Pueblo Bonito in New Mexico's Chaco Canyon, the hub of Anasazi civilization in its most complex phase.

One might expect that Wetherill's achievement, which rivals that of

From *Smithsonian* magazine, December 1993, pp. 28-34, 36, 38-39. © 1993 by David Roberts. Reprinted by permission.

Of Wetherill (center, with brothers, c. 1893) his wife
remarked: "his eyes looked a hole right into you."

Heinrich Schliemann at Troy or of
Hiram Bingham at Machu Picchu,
should be hailed as a landmark in
American archaeology. For nearly a
century, however, the reputation of the
rancher-turned-savant has lingered under a cloud of controversy. Schliemann
and Bingham had their own critics, but
the places of both men in the pantheon
of prehistoric discovery are secure.
Wetherill's is not.

An ambivalence toward the Mancos
rancher remains particularly acute regarding his early work at Mesa Verde.
By his own later admission, when he
began digging in the ruins Wetherill
was little more than a pothunter. For
that matter, in 1888 true archaeology
had scarcely been practiced in the
United States, and many a professional
in Wetherill's time excavated as crudely as he.

As a cowboy whose formal education ended in high school, Wetherill
later earned the scorn of a number of
university-trained academics. One of
them was Jesse Nusbaum, himself a

pioneer in Anasazi archaeology as well
as the superintendent of Mesa Verde
National Park from 1921 through 1927.
To the end of his life, Nusbaum dismissed Wetherill's work at Mesa Verde
as "ravaging and looting" and as
"commercial exploitation" of the ruins. He insisted that the Wetherills had
used dynamite to open one ruin at
Mesa Verde. No evidence of such a
practice has ever been produced.
Nusbaum even denied Wetherill credit
for discovering Cliff Palace.

On a visit to Mesa Verde last June,
I found that mixed feelings about
Wetherill persist. As District Inter-
preter Linda Martin told me, "There's
long been a controversy within our
staff over Wetherill. I think what
Wetherill did here a hundred years ago
is what I would have done."

Research archaeologist Jack Smith
was more critical. "I can't condemn
the Wetherill brothers, but I can't
praise them either," he said. "It's hard
not to conclude that their excavating
techniques were pretty brutal. I've seen

three backcountry sites where somebody has used [Anasazi] roof beams as
levers to tear out the back walls of
ruins. At these sites, you find Wetherill's signature scrawled on the cave
walls. Yes, that's only circumstantial
evidence, but I think it's convincing."

At first, as he hauled artifacts out of
the Mesa Verde ruins, Wetherill hoped
to display them in Durango and Denver and sell them to collectors. Gradually, however, he realized that science
would be better served if the intact
collections could find their way into
museums. He began to search for al-
truistic patrons.

One of the first was a young Swedish baron, Gustaf Nordenskiold, who
was traveling across the West. Trained
in geology, Nordenskiold had visited
digs in Italy and was aware of the best
European techniques. Hiring Richard
Wetherill to supervise ambitious excavations at Mesa Verde in 1891, he
taught the rancher to use a trowel
instead of a shovel and stressed the
importance of written and photographic documentation.

Wetherill was an eager student.
Soon he had devised his own field-note
forms, and the records he kept grew
more and more detailed and precise.
As he wrote a later patron, "This
whole subject . . . is in its infancy and
the work we do must stand the most
rigid inspection, and we do not want to
do it in such a manner that anyone in
the future can pick flaws in it."

Eventually, the vast collections of
Anasazi artifacts assembled by
Wetherill would anchor the Southwest
holdings of half a dozen major institutions, including the Field Museum in
Chicago, as well as the American Museum of Natural History and the National Museum of the American
Indian, both in New York City. Nordenskiold's assemblage found its way
to the National Museum of Finland in
Helsinki.

In nearly every case, Wetherill's
field notes were sent to the museums
along with the relics. Over the years,
however, these records were sometimes misinterpreted, ignored or even
misplaced—contributing in a perverse

twist to Wetherill's reputation as a mere pothunter.

Wetherill's passion for the Anasazi soon became an obsession. No longer content to work the ruins of Mesa Verde, he launched far-flung expeditions into the unmapped canyons of Utah, Arizona and New Mexico. These jaunts usually took place during the winter, the only season the brothers could spare from ranch work. The sheer logistics of Wetherill's archaeological toil—up before dawn, working long into the night, camping in snowstorms, digging in frozen ground, packing artifacts by horseback more than a hundred miles back to Mancos—testify to his diligence.

The Alamo Ranch, however, continued to fail. To supplement their income, the Wetherill brothers began guiding visitors through the ruins they had discovered. Among the Wetherill clients in 1895 were the Palmers, a family of traveling musicians from Kansas. Richard fell deeply in love with the 18-year-old harpist and soprano Marietta Palmer. With the family, Wetherill made his first trip to Chaco Canyon, then so remote as to be all but unknown to white explorers. On the way back from their two-month outing, Marietta was the only passenger who dared ride Wetherill's wagon as he forced it through a perilous ford of the swollen San Juan River. On the far bank, both drenched, Richard looked hard at Marietta: "Were you frightened?" "Why sure," she answered, "I was scared to death." "Will you marry me?" he asked.

Abandoning any hope of a "civilized" life back in Kansas, Marietta became Richard's wife, staying at his side through the last 14 eventful years of his life.

INSPIRING TRUST BY SPEAKING THEIR LANGUAGES

Wetherill was a parcel of contradictions. Though he had never gone to college, he read widely and ambitiously. He was miserably insecure about his shortcomings as a scholar, yet his letters reveal a frank, clear

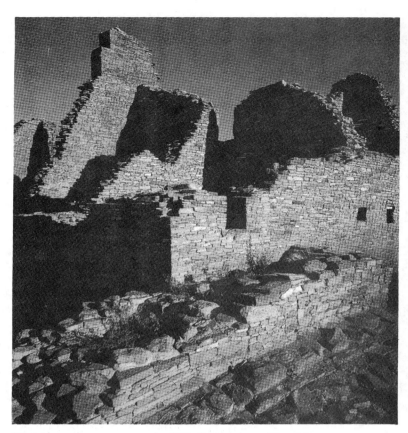

Handsome masonry marks 600-plus rooms of Pueblo Bonito, which Wetherill began excavating in 1896.

prose that many an academic might emulate. A crack shot, he nonetheless, as a Quaker, often refused to carry a rifle even when he rode through hostile Indian country. He had the knack of inspiring trust among the Utes and Navajos, in part because he learned to speak well the languages of both tribes.

In 1902 the family bowed to the inevitable and sold Alamo Ranch. Meanwhile, Richard and Marietta and their infant son had moved to Chaco Canyon, where the rancher built a trading post next to Pueblo Bonito. Masoned with the finest Anasazi stonework ever seen, Pueblo Bonito incorporates astronomical alignments and stands at the center of a mysterious network of far-reaching Anasazi roads.

No archaeologist had ever touched this colossal ruin of some 600 rooms. Here, in 1896, Wetherill had gone to work with a will. He had won the steady patronage of Talbot and Frederick Hyde, millionaire brothers from New York. Incorporated as the Hyde Exploring Expedition, Wetherill dug

190 rooms at Pueblo Bonito over four years and shipped tens of thousands of artifacts to New York, which the Hydes donated to the American Museum of Natural History.

Inevitably, Wetherill's one-man monopoly of what was coming to be recognized as the most important Anasazi site in the Southwest aroused professional attention. A campaign to halt his unsupervised research was launched by Edgar L. Hewett, president of New Mexico Normal University and an archaeologist who had his own eye on Chaco. Decrying Wetherill's work as mere "vandalizing," Hewett persuaded the General Land Office to launch an investigation of the cowboy's doings. The upshot of the prolonged inquiry was dramatic: in 1902 Richard Wetherill was forbidden to dig at Chaco. For the last eight years of his life, the self-taught archaeologist turned not another shovelful of Anasazi soil.

Despite Hewett's antipathy, at Chaco Culture National Historical Park Wetherill's memory is now hon-

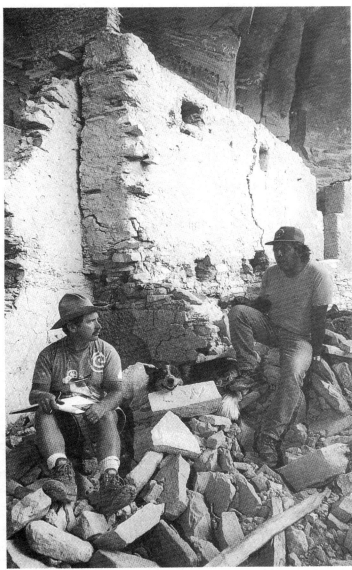

"Reverse archaeologist" Fred Blackburn, guide Tommy May, rest at Sandal House; "CW" was Clate Wetherill.

ored. Says Chief of Interpretation Kim McLean, "As far as archaeology is concerned, Wetherill's work was as good as or better than that of many professionals of his day."

Over the years, the criticisms of Nusbaum, Hewett and others have taken their toll on Richard Wetherill's reputation. Yet the strictures of his detractors are balanced by the praises of some of the Southwest's leading archaeologists. In 1946 John Otis Brew, of Harvard's Peabody Museum, hailed the sum of Wetherill's work as "the most far-reaching single event in Southwestern archaeology." Last spring Jeffrey Dean, of the University of Ari-

zona's Laboratory of Tree-Ring Research in Tucson, told me, "Wetherill was a far better archaeologist than"— Dean then named a well-regarded archaeologist whose career overlapped Wetherill's.

Much of the credit for the rehabilitating of Wetherill's name belongs to a loose band of Westerners—nearly all of them amateurs in archaeology, as Wetherill himself was—who call themselves the Wetherill-Grand Gulch Research Project. Their central figure is 43-year-old Fred Blackburn, a feisty wilderness guide and educator who lives in Cortez, Colorado. In the 1970s, as a Bureau of Land Manage-

ment ranger in Grand Gulch, Utah, Blackburn became preoccupied with retracing the rancher's footsteps across the Southwest.

The cloud over Wetherill's name had much to do with certain museums' negligence in handling his field notes and glass-plate photographs. Without good records of provenance—the stratigraphic context of each artifact in its original site—matchless collections like the ones Wetherill gathered reduce to little more than grab bags of pretty objects.

Blackburn and his colleagues learned, however, that in most cases the notes and photographs still existed. The team realized that it might be possible to relink the artifacts in the museums with their provenances. This sort of "reverse archaeology"—the term is Blackburn's coinage—could hold a vast potential for rejuvenating "dead" collections.

The effort depended crucially on Blackburn's deep knowledge of the obscure topography the cowboy had explored: he could peer at a photograph that Wetherill had made in 1893 and say, "Oh, that's Fishmouth Cave, back of Butler Wash." But the project had a hard time getting a foot in the door at Eastern museums. Curators used to dealing with doctoral candidates looked askance at the uncredentialed pleadings of a band of apparent dilettantes. And, as the team came to recognize, its own proposals were rife with naiveté and imprecision.

From 1986 on, the initially testy back-and-forth between the project and the museums gradually thawed into a good working arrangement. As Anibal Rodriguez, senior technician for anthropology at the American Museum of Natural History, recalls, "They were so ambitious, we finally realized the best thing for us to do was listen, to see what they had to offer."

Last June, Blackburn and another project member, archaeologist Winston Hurst, gave photographer Terrence Moore and me a vivid demonstration of the fruits of reverse archaeology as they guided us on a hike into Whiskers Draw, a minor tributary of Cottonwood Wash in southeastern Utah.

1. ABOUT ARCHAEOLOGY

One hundred years ago this month, Wetherill made perhaps his greatest discovery. Working in an unprepossessing rock shelter he called Cave 7, he dug beneath a scattering of Anasazi relics, the likes of which he had found many a time. Finally, five feet down, he began to uncover something remarkable. The cave was riddled with bottle-shaped pits that had been used as burial cists. Eventually Wetherill unearthed more than 90 skeletons in Cave 7. Some four-fifths of them showed evidence of violent harm, and scattered among the bones were many deadly flint points, including one embedded in a backbone.

The importance of Wetherill's discovery lay not in the skeletons per se, but in the cowboy's acute recognition that these deep-buried remains belonged to a different people from those he had found at Cliff Palace and other sites. Almost at once he put his finger on the crucial distinguishing characteristics. The earlier humans had no pottery but made superb baskets of yucca and willow, some woven so tightly they could hold water; they used the atlatl, or spear-thrower, rather than the bow and arrow; and they had round skulls, rather than the artificially flattened craniums of the later cliff dwellers (now known to have been caused by the use of hard cradleboards in infancy).

Wetherill used the term "Basket People," and the Hyde brothers coined the name "Basketmaker." Today, the distinction between the Basketmaker and the Pueblo phases of Anasazi culture—with the transition taking place around A.D. 700—is one of the cornerstones of Southwest archaeology. By correlating depth with prehistoric age, moreover, Wetherill took another intellectual leap. Six decades later, the great archaeologist Alfred V. Kidder tipped his hat to the Mancos rancher: "[Nels] Nelson and I have often been credited with doing the first stratigraphic work in the Southwest, but Richard, in recognizing the greater antiquity of the Basketmakers than that of the Cliff Dwellers, used the method many years before anyone else in that field."

Archaeologist Winston Hurst makes notes in Cave 7, rediscovered by Wetherill-Grand Gulch Project in 1990.

After Wetherill's death, the location of Cave 7 was forgotten. In Frank McNitt's excellent biography *Richard Wetherill: Anasazi,* published in 1957, one of Wetherill's photographs of the site appeared, with a caption erroneously suggesting it was in Grand Gulch. Hurst, Blackburn and a few other members of the Wetherill Project became determined to find the cave again.

The search took two years. The sleuths had only a few tantalizing clues: a sketch map and description of the site among Wetherill's notes, a pair of photographs, and the heading of the letter in which the cowboy excitedly described his find to his patron back East: "First Valley Cottonwood Creek 30 Miles North Bluff City."

As Hurst and Blackburn took me into Whiskers Draw last June, I could appreciate what must have been the needle-in-a-haystack nature of the search for the ordinary-looking cave. It was a blazing day, with the temperature in the 90s; bullflies stung our arms, while tamarisk thickets lashed our faces as we bushwhacked up the draw. The surrounding country was criss-crossed for miles with mazes of virtually identical side canyons.

A crucial clue lay in the dated signatures Wetherill and his cohorts were wont to scrawl in charcoal or scratch with a bullet cartridge on the cave walls. To later generations, these inscriptions have often seemed offensive graffiti; at Mesa Verde, a number of Wetherill signatures were effaced in the 1950s or '60s. Yet in the 1890s, to leave one's name on an archaeological site was the normal practice, followed by professional excavators and government explorers alike. The deed amounted to no mere braggart "Kilroy was here"; it was an integral part of the documentation of the dig.

As Hurst's team searched the tributaries of Cottonwood Wash, the dates got "warm," clustering within days of December 17, 1893—the date on the letter to Wetherill's patron. But as it turned out, the real Cave 7 was the very last of all the possible rock shelters Hurst and his colleagues looked into. With the photograph from McNitt's book in hand, I stood on the exact spot where Wetherill had exposed the glass plate in 1893. The crumbling Pueblo wall on the left still stood, albeit more ravaged than a century before. In the old picture, Basketmaker skulls litter the floor of the cave. Now I could see the deep depressions in the dirt, a mute memorial to the 90 skeletons Wetherill had extracted.

Before the team relocated Cave 7, Christy Turner of Arizona State University, the leading expert on Anasazi cannibalism (a phenomenon revealed only within the past decade), traveled to the American Museum of Natural History where he examined the very bones and projectile points Wetherill had dug out of the cave nearly a century before. Reintegrating the site and the artifacts, Turner and Hurst demonstrated that Cave 7 had been the scene of a wholesale massacre some 1,500 years ago; the carnage involved stabbing by daggers, shooting with atlatl darts, bludgeoning, scalping, possibly even torture.

Hurst and Turner's work represents a major step in revealing what one might call the dark side of Anasazi culture—its occasional propensity to erupt into internecine violence. As the two archaeologists write in a forthcoming paper, the evidence from Cave 7 "document[s] yet another example of our species' strange capacity for both terrible destructiveness and the creation of beautiful works of art."

As the Wetherill Project's work gathered steam after 1986, some of the leading Anasazi archaeologists, such as Turner, Brigham Young University's

Joel Janetski and Washington State University's William Lipe, began to collaborate with these hardworking amateurs. The project's focus became the Basketmakers. Scholars had done less work on those early Anasazi than on the more accessible Pueblo people succeeding them. The culmination of this effort was a three-day scholarly symposium on the Basketmakers, held in Blanding, Utah, in 1990. With some 500 participants, it was arguably the best-attended Anasazi conference ever. The papers from the symposium have been published in book form by the BLM Utah Cultural Resource Series. In addition, Blackburn and archaeo-astronomer Ray Williamson have written *In Search of the Basketmaker,* a scholarly overview to be published next year by the School of American Research. And in 1995 the Utah Museum of Natural History will mount an exhibition on the Basketmakers featuring the project's work.

The rehabilitation of the Wetherill name has meant much to the brothers' descendants. Last June I met 63-year-old Tom Wetherill, the grandson of Richard's brother Al. A contractor living in Farmington, New Mexico, Tom has inherited the family records. Opening the yellowed pages of the Alamo Ranch guest register, he showed me Nordenskiold's signature from 1891.

A week later, photographer Moore and I were joined by Fred Blackburn and Marietta Davenport on a jaunt into Grand Gulch. Marietta, named for her

great-grandmother, is an archaeologist employed by the U.S. Forest Service. All through college and graduate school she heard her professors cast aspersions on Richard Wetherill. "I wouldn't say anything in class," Marietta recalled. "Afterwards I'd go up to the professor and say, 'Wait a minute, let's talk about this.' I wouldn't let on right away that Richard was my great-grandfather."

Winding our way into Bullet Canyon, a tributary of Grand Gulch, we retraced the stock trail, now faint, that Wetherill had built in 1893 and that Blackburn's team had rediscovered a few years ago. By midafternoon we had reached Jailhouse Ruin, one of the eeriest of all Anasazi sites in Grand Gulch, where huge, baleful "full-moon" pictographs dominate an airy, masoned ledge. It was a glorious, hot afternoon, with canyon wrens singing on the breeze. As we sat on the bedrock sandstone below the ruin, Marietta said quietly, "It's pretty exciting for me to visit a site he dug. It's very powerful."

We camped out, then spent the next day in Sheik's Canyon, another Grand Gulch tributary. By midday we reached Green Mask Spring, a Basketmaker site so profusely decorated with pictographs that in four hours of staring we only began to sort out the enigmatic paintings. Here Wetherill had camped in January 1897.

One evening as dusk approached, Wetherill had dug behind some rocks against the cliff. The burial he uncov-

Anthropomorphic figures painted onto cliff (left) stand guard near where "Princess" was found. Wetherill cut his signature (above), following a 19th-century practice.

ered, working into the night by lantern, would be the most striking find in all his years of Anasazi work. A 66 inch-wide basket covered another; under them lay a turkey-feather blanket decorated with bluebird feathers, and another blanket spangled with canary yellow spots. A final basket covered the perfectly mummified head of a woman. Her body was painted yellow, her face red.

The stunned archaeologist nicknamed his discovery "the Princess." Wetherill had found many a mummy, but never did he excavate one more carefully or pack one more delicately to be carried out of Grand Gulch and back to Durango and the railroad East.

Using Wetherill's field notes and photographs, Blackburn's team had been able to pinpoint the pit at Green Mask Spring from which the Princess had been removed. Now I stood on the spot and pondered a pair of haunting pictographs that had been painted directly above the grave. The androgynous human figures in white, each decorated with a red circle covering its chest, stood solemn and rigid, side by side, almost like some bridal couple. Here was another tantalizing promise spun out of reverse archaeology. Almost nowhere in the world has rock art been convincingly associated with burials. Yet if these pictographs commemorated the woman buried beneath them, then the paintings themselves might tell us more about the Princess— and vice versa.

Two weeks later, Terrence Moore and I went to New York City to view a pair of Wetherill collections. At the American Museum of Natural History, Anibal Rodriguez opened many drawers of Wetherill materials: splendid Chaco black-on-white pots, intricately woven baskets, atlatls, cradleboards and rabbit clubs.

The next day we visited the research branch of the National Museum of the American Indian in The Bronx. Assistant collections manager Mark Clark pulled out a dazzling variety of fine Anasazi artifacts: blankets made of rabbit fur, splendidly woven willow baskets with checkerboard red-and-

Misspelling of his name on tombstone was just the first of many indignities Wetherill's memory has suffered.

black designs, scrapers made from bighorn sheep horns, black lignite beads that had once been strung as a necklace, bowls shaped like pipes.

Barred from digging after 1902, Wetherill stayed on at his Chaco Canyon trading post. No white settlement in the United States lay farther from the beaten path. For Marietta, these were hard years, but Richard was in his element. As he traded regularly with the Chaco Navajos, he got to know these former nomads better than any white man ever had. Realizing the quality of the best Navajo rugs and blankets, Wetherill encouraged the weavers by crossbreeding sheep to produce an animal that bore a better wool.

Trouble struck one day in June 1910. A dispute between Wetherill and several Navajos flared out of control. At sunset, as Wetherill drove cows along the Chaco Canyon wash, a young Navajo man raised his rifle. The first bullet struck Wetherill in the chest; a second, from close range, blew half his face away.

Last June I hiked with Fred Blackburn to Sandal House. Here, a dozen miles down the Mancos River from Alamo Ranch, the Wetherills had dug in their first ruin a few years before the discovery of Cliff Palace. Naming the

site for the scores of yucca sandals they unearthed, they caught the bug of Anasazi exploration.

Sandal House lies only five miles east of thronged Cliff Palace, yet it is in Ute Mountain Ute Tribal Park, can be approached only with a Ute guide and is almost never visited. Blackburn himself had never been there.

Now, sketch pad in hand, he found on the cave's walls the signatures or initials of four of the five Wetherill brothers; no other site had yielded so many. And he discovered his first "Mamie Palmer," Marietta's maiden name, carved in neat capitals that summer when she first got to know the gruff cowboy.

After two hours of inching our way through the jumbled ruin our Ute guide, Tommy May, found a very faint inscription written in pencil on a stone in a kiva wall. Blackburn squatted in the rubble and flashed mirrored light across the evanescent message. After half an hour he had sketched out the memorandum: Wetherill had found a huge Anasazi pot, which he was caching in the ruin and would return to retrieve in four days. Blackburn paused, wiped his sweaty brow with a bandana and said to no one in particular, "This is as close as we're ever going to get to talking to him."

Kentucky Memoir: Digging in the Depression

A noted scholar who got his start during the 1930s recalls how stark times and FDR's New Deal sparked nationwide interest in an emergent American science.

John L. Cotter

John L. Cotter is curator emeritus of American historical archaeology at The University Museum of the University of Pennsylvania.

When the Great Depression of 1929 hit, America staggered. Within three years of the stock market crash, more than 12 million people were out of work—an incredible 24.7 percent of the labor force. Five thousand banks failed; 9 million savings accounts vanished; destitution was rampant.

It was, of course, Roosevelt who forged a bold solution to the country's nightmare. As the thirty-first president of the United States, he embarked on the ambitious undertaking that became known as the New Deal. And from Roosevelt's response to the economic crisis came an unexpected boon: the birth of archaeology as a serious American discipline. This fledgling field was truly a golden beneficiary of Roosevelt's efforts to create jobs for the nation's unemployed. From 1933 through 1941, literally hundreds of archaeological projects were launched under the auspices of one government agency or another—the Civil Works Administration (CWA), the Work Projects Administration (WPA), and a host of others, including the Tennessee Valley Authority.

It was a heady time for the young, emergent American science, whose methods would improve in major ways in the space of a decade, and whose ranks included some of the most colorful personalities that American archaeology has ever seen—scholars of almost messianic intensity like the able Louisianan James Alfred Ford; tough, determined women like New Jersey's Dorothy Cross; the gifted administrator Major William S. Webb of Lexington, Kentucky . . . the list goes on. Dispatched to various sites across the country—many in the south where the weather was mild and excavations could continue throughout the winter months—young archaeologists and graduate-student anthropologists assumed, overnight, tremendous responsibilities and undertook projects involving hundreds of workers. For the first time on this continent north of Mexico, digs were carried out on a scale previously associated only with Egypt, the classical world, and the Near East. Some sites were excavated by crews consisting entirely of women, a fact that remains uncelebrated in archaeological texts.

My own part in this saga was a modest one. A young man of 24 as the Depression deepened, I found myself confronted with a personal setback as well as a national calamity. In my second year on a Harrison Fellowship in anthropology at the University of Pennsylvania, I had—to my chagrin, and with not a little consternation—failed my Ph.D. oral exam, and was looking at mounting financial obligations.

So I gratefully, if a little regretfully, accepted an archaeological summons from William S. Webb to work as a field project supervisor on the Archae-ological Survey of Lexington, Kentucky. I had been recommended by Jesse D. Figgins, former director of the Colorado Museum of Natural History, for whom I had worked at Lindenmeier, a Paleoamerindian site in Colorado, and who had retired to Lexington.

When I stepped off the train at Lexington I entered a hive of laboratory and administrative industry. "Cotter," said Webb, known as the "Major" to us all, "you load up a ton-and-a-half flatbed truck and go start up a mound project in the Green River country of Western Kentucky." Suddenly I found myself in charge of 35 coal miners who would constitute my work force. On a cold winter morning—a Monday, I remember—I drove a '34 Ford truck out to a bleak barren field not far from a town with the curious name of Island, which consisted of a store, a filling station, a church, and a group of miners' houses. There I stood, out beyond Island, looking at a plowed-down mound that was the object of our excavation. My heart sank a notch, but it was time to get going. I set up a transit, staked the mound in five-foot squares, and started explaining the difference between mining coal and delicately exposing archaeological evidence. Little by little we got to work. Not an easy beginning. My men had been brought to the site in a WPA truck. We were all cold and miserable, the crew more than I because many of them suffered from headaches.

"What gives you these headaches?" I asked.

A wizened man in his mid-forties explained, "Well, when somebody picks up a lease on a closed mine and starts up, he don't spend nothin' on ventilation and such, see. He just works up a good shipment, takes the money and skips town. Don't meet the last payroll, neither. That dynamite smoke splits your head!"

The men on the crew had hard lives in any case, lives that their wages from the WPA barely alleviated. I remember one man who came in to a bar one day in Island, ordered a drink, and sat down on a cardboard box while he drank. "Wife's baby," he explained. "Born dead. Going to bury it." Then he got up and left. But they were diligent, reliable workers, intelligent men of considerable dignity. They possessed a sense of humor and responded to field training, and our work progressed well.

My fortunes changed again that first spring in Kentucky, and I was suddenly replaced by another project archaeologist and summoned to Lexington. "Cotter," said Webb, "the WPA wants a state supervisor for the Survey. I want an archaeologist. You go to work Monday." The survey was the largest WPA enterprise in the country, one that employed at the time 11 field supervisors and several hundred workers. The WPA state office wanted someone who was an experienced archaeologist who could also keep up with bureaucratic reports and contacts. In Lexington I worked with two of the most remarkable men among the many who made New Deal archaeology so exciting. The first was Webb—a man of great administrative and archaeological acumen. He had launched Kentucky's original Archaeological Survey together with the University of Kentucky's dean, W. D. Funkhouser: They had begun the first site survey and issued the first of the Archaeological Survey's publications back in the late 1920s. The Major, not formally educated as an archaeologist, was the developer and chairman of the department of physics, where his introductory course was a scientific circus that attracted 98 percent of all the students who graduated from the university. He

had no doctorate in physics, any more than he did in anthropology; but his appetite for knowledge of Kentucky's aborigines was insatiable and prodigious—an appetite acquired as an officer instructor in World War I at the Army's Artillery School of Fire at Fort Sill, Oklahoma. Here Webb had not only developed his organizational and teaching skills, but he had also visited the Cherokee and other reservations to become a close observer of Native American life and traditions. When the potential for a massive statewide Federal relief project appeared on the horizon, Webb was ready for it: he had already developed the Tennessee Valley Authority archaeological investigations on a giant scale with the aid of the Corps of Engineers, enlisting early CWA, WPA, and subsequent Civilian Conservation Corps (CCC) labor. By the time WPA opened up in Kentucky, he had a complete state-wide archaeological survey on paper for approval, funding, and implementation, with the university as sponsor. Wherever sites were located, labor would be there looking for work.

What the Major lacked in analytical archaeology, he compensated for in his selection of capable personnel. His chief of staff, Bill Haag, was a well-trained and indefatigable young archaeologist. Haag set the archaeological tone of the Survey using both his Kentucky background and his entrepreneurial, as well as scholarly, skills to maintain direction of the operation. Meanwhile, Webb published, mostly under his own name, the University of Kentucky Archaeological Survey series, the largest and most complete corpus of archaeological reports ever developed by a WPA project.

Haag also ran the archaeological laboratory, then on the main campus, with the aid of several professional anthropologists. Dozens of workers cleaned and sorted the artifacts and bone material, together with hundreds of well-preserved skeletons of Archaic shell-mound dwellers from the Green River bottoms—the largest such collection in the United States.

My job was to provide liaison among all the field projects under the Sur-

vey's jurisdiction, the museum lab and repository, while laboring over the notes and completing drawings for field men who had gotten behind in their recording, or whose abilities lay more in directing field operations than doing the off-site labor of recording. I also journeyed to Washington to "hand process" the renewal of the whole project through the WPA bureaucracy—a tale worth a long story in itself. I went from office to office, desk to desk, hustling the necessary paperwork from in-box through out-box until it reached the Chief, Vincenzo Petrullo, who had just gotten his doctorate in anthropology—happily at Penn—and keeping in touch with Louisville to supply such progress reports as the WPA required.

My experience was replicated all over the country with sometimes rich and interesting local variations. WPA projects were undertaken in states from Florida to California, from the Carolinas to Michigan. They were, in fact, relatively easy to organize and could get under way quickly: the equipment needed was minimal—lots of shovels and trowels, rudimentary surveying equipment, lots of stakes and strings, a vehicle to move equipment and supplies, and some means of getting the workers to the site. I was by no means the only graduate student who was tempted to leave his studies, train a crew, keep archaeological records, and generally take responsibility for field work. Indeed, many of the men and women who would occupy the front ranks of American archaeology in succeeding generations had their baptism by fire and trowel on New Deal projects: Gordon R. Willey (dean of American archaeology), Arthur Randolph Kelley (one-time chief archaeologist of the National Park Service), George I. Quimby (formerly of the University of Washington), James Alfred Ford, Thomas M. N. Lewis (former professor of anthropology at the University of Tennessee), Albert Spaulding (a foremost analytical archaeologist), Joe Ben Wheat (former professor of anthropology at the University of Colorado), Robert Wauchope (former director of the Middle American Institute of Tulane University).

While states like Kentucky, Georgia, and Florida saw a host of New Deal projects undertaken on a grand scale, smaller-scale operations were producing superior results elsewhere. In New Jersey, for example, the redoubtable Dorothy Cross, who taught at Hunter College in New York City, was putting her indelible stamp on that state's archaeology much as Webb was doing in Kentucky. Cross had just received her doctorate in Oriental Studies and Anthropology at the University of Pennslyvania, under whose auspices she had undertaken a unique analysis of Middle Eastern ceramics and material culture from Tepe Gawra, a Bronze Age site in northern Iraq. Applying her keen analytical insight to New Jersey's prehistory from Paleoamerindian to historic sites, she undertook supervision of the Indian Site Survey, which supervised WPA archaeological projects in the state. From March 1936 until June 1940, she supervised the excavation of 39 sites, including the controversial Abbott Farm site, which had stirred debate in scientific circles since 1872. Cross conclusively demonstrated that the site was a large aboriginal complex with remains that dated from 3000 B.C. through Early, Middle, and Late Woodland complexes through the post-1625 Historic period. A formidable field chief, Cross had a vocabulary that was incisive and pungent. So were her ubiquitous cigarettes, accompanied by her cough. She was tough, but a lady, and deferred only to emphysema.

Another of the key figures of the period was Jean C. (Pinky) Harrington, a pioneer in historical archaeology in this country. Harrington rescued from incipient chaos the first comprehensive effort at interdisciplinary research directed on a grand scale at a major historical site—Jamestown, Virginia. Here, Harrington had the benefit of a work force from the CCC, which, unlike many of the other government-sponsored projects involved in archaeology, housed its crews of young jobless city men in barracks near their workplace. The establishment of Colonial National Historical Park and the acquisition of part of the land of Jamestown Island in 1934 enabled Harrington to undertake meticulous work. Fortunately, his archaeological efforts were implemented by a crew of well-trained young men and keyed to superb field notes and site unit reports.

All these data became part of the Park files—a fortunate fact of history, for the entrance of the United States into World War II terminated scores of such projects across the country as men and women joined the armed forces or took up jobs related to the war effort.

Archaeological talent scattered. For some, the War meant death and irreparable injury; for others, it constituted a fresh opportunity. Charles T. R. Bohannon, for example, a careful archaeologist who was a project supervisor with me in Kentucky and who possessed a reputation as something of a romantic long-rifle—he was a picturesque stickler for obtaining field data, always the hard way—found a permanent career in the Army beginning in the Philippines, where he organized guerrilla harassment of the Japanese invaders, later making such military tactics his specialty. Decorated with a silver star, he retired a colonel and died in Manila. I was swept into the Army like many other young men though, unlike others, I was lucky enough to survive the Normandy invasion and return to the States when the war ended in 1945, rejoining my wife and small daughter as a National Park Service archaeologist in Arizona. In 1953 I took over direction of the work at Jamestown so splendidly begun by Harrington years before. With this stint completed in 1957, I was transferred to Philadelphia as Regional Archaeologist, Northeast Region of the National Park Service. I immediately resumed my work on a Ph.D., which I was granted in 1959. My thesis, published as *Archaeological Excavations at Jamestown, Virginia,* wrapped up Pinky Harrington's and all other reports on the site.

The abrupt entry into the war, together with the complexity and sometimes hasty organization of New Deal archaeology, had an unfortunate effect on the documentation left behind. Donald Cadzow, a Pennsylvania State Archaeologist who used WPA labor to test Tinicum Island, site of the first attempt at a Swedish settlement in this country, felt that he had found the much-sought-for Printzhof, the 1643 Swedish fortified settlement, now Printzhof State Park, on the Delaware River below the Philadelphia airport; but Cadzow, a non-academic with limited archaeological training, left no reports detailing his finds or analyses of the evidence of Printzhof or other colonial frontier forts he investigated; we have only brief notices of the scope of the work done in reports to the Pennsylvania Historical Commission with citations in *Pennsylvania Archaeologist.* A host of sites across the country suffered similar fates, and we have only the sketchiest of records from which to reconstruct the results. Such failures stand in contrast to the successful documentation of the sort Webb and others left behind for the Southeast and Dorothy Cross provided for New Jersey.

Still, the fact remains that modern American archaeology—and its immense public success—grew directly out of the Great Depression. The sheer magnitude of the undertakings sponsored by government agencies provided the field with a massive data base that it had never enjoyed before. In addition, WPA sponsorship of New Deal projects was the forerunner of the massive federal funding of archaeological site identification and conservation, both prehistoric and historic, in the 1960s. This support swelled to $200,000,000 a year in the late 1960s under the rubric Cultural Resources Management Archaeology. Even allowing for inflation, this figure represents at least six times as much support as archaeology got from the government in the 1930s in any single year. Popular interest in archaeology has grown commensurately: practically every American— or so it would seem—has at one time or another wanted to be an archaeologist. Volunteer archaeology has become, in the last decade, a kind of big business; and while the Bush White House did less for the field than previous administrations, the fact still stands: since the dark days of the Depression archaeology has become one of America's great academic success stories.

Thinking Like an Archaeologist

Thinking like an archaeologist can make you a better consumer. It can help you in making decisions about your job choice, marriage partner, or where to take a vacation. It can help you get a job, get the best buy on cereal at the grocery store, and make life and death decisions. It can even cure ingrown toenails. So what is this magic archaeologists are hoarding and why don't they share it with everyone? Well, they try to, but sometimes it seems to get lost somewhere between the pottery shards, the stone tools, and what is going on inside the pith helmet.

The greatest mystery of archaeology is the same thing that solves mysteries. It is called *thinking.* But not just any thinking. It is not thinking in the ordinary, everyday multimedia sense. The popular media gives us information but that information is usually constructed so that we don't have to think. It is spoon-fed to us. We only think we are thinking because we are suddenly filled with novel information that we forget five minutes later. We do not have to think because the conclusions are inherent in the information. How is this done? Well, think. "The President of the United States confirms aliens from outer space are in control of the White House!" Film at eleven! Hyperbole? It gets your attention. You are disbelieving but you still must know for sure. This is not a criticism of the media, just an observation. We are still talking about archaeology, but the media is a major source of the epistemology of the modern world and thus underscores cultural values as well as creating the necessary cultural myths by which all humans must live. The media is as much a response to our demands as we are to its manipulations. We are the media. Our conversations are the media. But in the same manner that modern cultures have moved away from labor-intensive production of goods, we have moved away from labor-intensive language by "glossing" over communication with packages of noncommunicative sounds, e.g., "Like, ya' know what I mean? Like?"

Most of our everyday conversations, if we should have any, are usually characterized by "fuzzy thinking." It is the state in which it seems that brains are made of cotton balls and all our senses are hazy and dulled by the alpha waves of short-cut thinking. Brain-drugged. Of course, the whole world can't be populated by cantankerous scientists and academics challenging every syllable we speak, every action we take, every artifact we discard. But there is a very practical science of thinking, which may be learned and applied to defining, analyzing, and solving problems.

If our minds are trained to be articulate, our mouths and actions will follow suit. Scientific thinking is the real secret of archaeology. If the IRS is knocking on your door, you had better be able to *think.* Scientific thinking involves a very strict set of unchanging rules and regulations by which you test the veracity of your conclusions and decisions. Also, it is best used before sending in your tax return.

But is scientific thinking really worth bothering with? Yes, it is. It may be called scientific thinking or using the scientific method, but it is also known as "being smart." Smart is more than the accumulation of trial-and-error learning, wherein you build up a repertoire of the do's and don'ts of life. And smart is not how many advanced degrees you have hanging on a wall. Smart is the systematic application of scientific thinking to this acquired body of information. This is a major activity of archaeology.

Looking Ahead: Challenge Questions

What is a hypothesis? How is it different from a theory?

Give an example of a general theory.

What is the relationship between thinking and communicating?

What are the four rules of science? Do they ever change?

Give short examples of inductive and deductive logic, using the same information.

What is a new interpretation of some paleolithic cave paintings?

Epistemology: How You Know What You Know

Kenneth L. Feder

KNOWING THINGS

The word *epistemology* means the study of knowledge—how you know what you know. Think about it. How does anybody know anything to be actual, truthful, or real? How do we differentiate the reasonable from the unreasonable, the meaningful from the meaningless—in archaeology or in any other field of knowledge? Everybody knows things, but how do we really know these things?

I know that there is a mountain in a place called Tibet. I know that the mountain is called Everest, and I know that it is the tallest land mountain in the world (there are some a bit taller under the ocean). I even know that it is precisely 29,028 feet high. But I have never measured it; I've never even been to Tibet. Beyond this, I have not measured all of the other mountains in the world to compare them to Everest. Yet I am quite confident that Everest is the world's tallest peak. But how do I know that?

On the subject of mountains, there is a run-down stone monument on the top of Bear Mountain in the northwestern corner of Connecticut. The monument was built toward the end of the nineteenth century and marks the "highest ground" in Connecticut. When the monument was built to memorialize this most lofty and auspicious of peaks—the mountain is all of 2,316 feet high—people knew that it was the highest point in the state and wanted to recognize this fact with the monument.

There is only one problem. In recent times, with more accurate, sophisticated measuring equipment, it has been determined that Bear Mountain is not the highest point in Connecticut. The slope of Frissell Mountain, which actually peaks in Massachusetts, reaches a height of 2,380 feet on the Connecticut side of the border, eclipsing Bear Mountain by about 64 feet.

So, people in the late 1800s and early 1900s "knew" that Bear Mountain was the highest point in Connecticut. Today we *know* that they really did not "know" that, because it really was not true—even though they thought it was and built a monument saying so.

Now, suppose that I read in a newspaper, hear on the radio, or see on television a claim that another mountain has been found that is actually ten (or fifty, or ten thousand) feet higher than Mount Everest. Indeed, recently, new satellite data convinced a few, just for a while, that a peak neighboring Everest was, in actuality, slightly higher. You and I have never been to Tibet. How do we know if these reports are true? What criteria can we use to decide if the information is correct or not? It all comes back to epistemology. How indeed do we know what we think we "know"?

Collecting Information: Seeing Isn't Necessarily Believing

In general, people collect information in two ways:

1. Directly through their own experiences

2. Indirectly through specific information sources like friends, teachers, parents, books, TV, etc.

People tend to think that number 1—obtaining firsthand information, the stuff they see or experience themselves—is always the best way. This is unfortunately a false assumption because most people are poor observers.

For example, the list of animals alleged to have been observed by people that turn out to be figments of their imaginations is staggering. It is fascinating to read Pliny, a first-century thinker, or Topsell, who wrote in the seventeenth century, and see detailed accounts of the nature and habits of dragons, griffins, unicorns, mermaids, and so on (Byrne 1979). People claimed to have seen these animals, gave detailed descriptions, and even drew pictures of them. Many folks read their books and believed them.

Some of the first European explorers of Africa, Asia, and the New World could not decide if some of the native people they encountered were human beings or animals. They sometimes depicted them with hair all over their bodies and even as having tails.

Neither are untrained observers very good at identifying known, living animals. A red or "lesser" panda escaped from the zoo in Rotterdam, Holland, in December 1978. Red pandas are very rare animals and are indigenous to India, not Holland. They are distinctive in appearance and cannot be readily mistaken for any other sort of animal. The zoo informed the press that the panda was missing, hoping the publicity would alert people in the area of the zoo and aid in its return. Just when the newspapers came out with the panda story, it was found, quite dead, along some railroad tracks adjacent to the zoo. Nevertheless, over one hundred sightings of the panda *alive* were reported to the zoo from all over the Netherlands *after* the animal was obviously already dead. These reports did not stop until several days after the newspapers announced the discovery of the dead panda (van Kampen 1979). So much for the absolute reliability of firsthand observation.

Collecting Information: Relying on Others

When we explore the problems of secondhand information, we run into even more complications. Now we are not in place to observe something firsthand; we are forced to rely on the quality of someone else's observations, interpretations, and reports—as with the question of the height of Mount Everest. How do we know what to believe? This is a crucial question that all rational people must ask themselves, whether talking about medicine, religion, archaeology, or anything else. Again, it comes back around to epistemology; how do we know what we think we know, and how do we know what or whom to believe?

Science: Playing by the Rules

There are ways to knowledge that are both dependable and reliable. We might not be able to get to absolute truths about the meaning of existence, but we can figure out quite a bit about our world—about chemistry and biology, psychology and sociology, physics and history, and even prehistory. The techniques we are talking about to get at knowledge that we can feel confident in—knowledge that is reliable, truthful, and factual—are referred to as *science*.

In large part, science is a series of techniques used to maximize the probability that what we think we know really reflects the way things are, were, or will be. Science makes no claim to have all the answers or even to

be right all of the time. On the contrary, during the process of the growth of knowledge and understanding, science is often wrong. The only claim that we do make in science is that if we honestly, consistently, and vigorously pursue knowledge using some basic techniques and principles, the truth will eventually surface and we can truly know things about the nature of the world in which we find ourselves.

The question then is, What exactly is science? If you believe Hollywood, science is a mysterious enterprise wherein old, white-haired, rather eccentric bearded gentlemen labor feverishly in white lab coats, mix assorted chemicals, invent mysterious compounds, and attempt to reanimate dead tissue. So much for Hollywood. Scientists don't have to look like anything in particular. We are just people trying to arrive at some truths about how the world and universe work. While the application of science can be a slow, frustrating, all-consuming enterprise, the basic assumptions we scientists hold are really very simple. Whether we are physicists, biologists, or archaeologists, we all work under four underlying principles. These principles are quite straightforward, but equally quite crucial.

1. There is a real and knowable universe.
2. The universe (which includes stars, planets, animals, and rocks, as well as people, their cultures, and their histories) operates according to certain understandable rules or laws.
3. These laws are immutable—that means they do not, in general, change depending on where you are or "when" you are.
4. These laws can be discerned, studied, and understood by people through careful observation, experimentation, and research.

Let's look at these assumptions one at a time.

There Is a Real and Knowable Universe

In science we have to agree that there is a real universe out there for us to

study—a universe full of stars, animals, human history, and prehistory that exists whether we are happy with that reality or not.

The Universe Operates According to Understandable Laws

In essence, what this means is that there are rules by which the universe works: stars produce heat and light according to the laws of nuclear physics; nothing can go faster than the speed of light; all matter in the universe is attracted to all other matter (the law of gravity).

Even human history is not random but can be seen as following certain patterns of human cultural evolution. For example, the development of complex civilizations in Egypt, China, India/Pakistan, Mesopotamia, Mexico, and Peru was not based on random processes (Lamberg-Karlovsky and Sabloff 1979; Haas 1982). Their evolution seems to reflect similar general patterns. This is not to say that all of these civilizations were identical, any more than we would say that all stars are identical. On the contrary, they existed in different physical and cultural environments, and so we should expect that they be different. However, in each case the rise to civilization was preceded by the development of an agricultural economy. In each case, civilization was also preceded by some degree of overall population increase as well as increased population density in some areas (in other words, the development of cities). Again, in each case we find monumental works (pyramids, temples), evidence of long-distance trade, and the development of mathematics, astronomy, and methods of record keeping (usually, but not always, in the form of writing). The cultures in which civilization developed, though some were unrelated and independent, shared these factors because of the nonrandom patterns of cultural evolution.

The point is that everything operates according to rules. In science we believe that, by understanding these rules or laws, we can understand stars, organisms, and even ourselves.

THE LAWS ARE IMMUTABLE

That the laws do not change under ordinary conditions is a crucial concept in science. A law that works here, works there. A law that worked in the past will work today and will work in the future.

For example, if I go to the top of the Leaning Tower of Pisa today and simultaneously drop two balls of unequal mass, they will fall at the same rate and reach the ground at the same time, just as they did when Galileo performed a similar experiment in the seventeenth century. If I do it today, they will. Tomorrow, the same. If I perform the same experiment countless times, the same thing will occur because the laws of the universe (in this case, the law of gravity) do not change through time. They also do not change depending on where you are. Go anywhere on the earth and perform the same experiment—you will get the same results (try not to hit any pedestrians or you will see some other "laws" in operation). This experiment was even performed by U.S. astronauts on the moon. A hammer and a feather were dropped from the same height, and they hit the surface at precisely the same instant (the only reason this will not work on earth is because the feather is caught by the air and the hammer, obviously, is not). We have no reason to believe that the results would be different anywhere, or "anywhen" else.

If this assumption of science, that the laws do not change through time, were false, many of the so-called historical sciences, including prehistoric archaeology, could not exist.

For example, a major principle in the field of historical geology is that of *uniformitarianism*. It can be summarized in the phrase, "the present is the key to the past." Historical geologists are interested in knowing how the various landforms we see today came into being. They recognize that they cannot go back in time to see how the Grand Canyon was formed. However, since the laws of geology that governed the development of the Grand Canyon have not changed through time, and

since these laws are still in operation, they do not need to. Historical geologists can study the formation of geological features today and apply what they learn to the past. The same laws they can directly study operating in the present were operating in the past when geological features that interested them first formed.

The present that we can observe is indeed the "key" to the past that we cannot. This is true because the laws or rules that govern the universe are constant—those that operate today operated in the past. This is why science does not limit itself to the present, but makes inferences about the past and even predictions about the future (just listen to the weather report for an example of this). We can do so because we can study modern, ongoing phenomena that work under the same laws that existed in the past and will exist in the future.

This is where science and theology are often forced to part company and respectfully disagree. Remember, science depends on the constancy of the laws that we can discern. On the other hand, advocates of many religions, though they might believe that there are laws that govern things (and which, according to them, were established by a Creator), usually (but not always) believe that these laws can be changed at any time by their God. In other words, if God does not want the apple to fall to the ground, but instead, to hover, violating the law of gravity, that is precisely what will happen. As a more concrete example, scientists know that the heat and light given off by a fire results from the transformation of mass (of the wood) to energy. Physical laws control this process. A theologian, however, might agree with this ordinarily, but feel that if God wants to create a fire that does not consume any mass (like the "burning bush" of the Old Testament), then this is exactly what will occur. Most scientists simply do not accept this assertion. The rules are the rules. They do not change, even though we might sometimes wish that they would.

The Laws Can Be Understood

This may be the single most important principle in science. The universe is knowable. It may be complicated, and it may take years and years to understand even apparently simple phenomena. However, little by little, bit by bit, we expand our knowledge. Through careful observation and objective research and experimentation, we can indeed know things.

So, our assumptions are simple enough. We accept the existence of a reality independent of our own minds, and we accept that this reality works according to a series of unchanging laws or rules. We also claim that we can recognize and understand these laws or at least recognize the patterns that result from these universal rules. The question remains then: how do we do science—how do we explore the nature of the universe, whether our interest is planets, stars, atoms, or human prehistory?

THE WORKINGS OF SCIENCE

We can know things by employing the rules of logic and rational thought. Scientists—archaeologists or otherwise—usually work through a combination of the logical processes known as *induction* and *deduction*. The dictionary definition of induction is "arguing from specifics to generalities," while deduction is defined as the reverse, arguing from generalities to specifics.

What is essential to good science is objective, unbiased observations—of planets, molecules, rock formations, archaeological sites, and so on. Often, on the basis of these specific observations, we induce explanations called *hypotheses* for how these things work.

For example, we may study the planets Mercury, Venus, Earth, and Mars (each one presents specific bits of information). We then induce general rules about how we think these inner planets in our solar system were formed. Or, we might study a whole series of different kinds of molecules and then induce general rules about how all molecules interact chemically. We may study different rock formations and make general conclusions about their origin. We can study a number of specific prehistoric sites and make generalizations about how cultures evolved.

Notice that we cannot directly observe planets forming, the rules of molecular interaction, rocks being made, or prehistoric cultures evolving. Instead, we are inducing general conclusions and principles concerning our data that seem to follow logically from what we have been able to observe.

This process of induction, though crucial to science, is not enough. We need to go beyond our induced hypotheses by testing them. If our induced hypotheses are indeed valid—that is, if they really represent the actual rules according to which some aspect of the universe (planets, molecules, rocks, ancient societies) works—they should be able to hold up under the rigors of scientific hypothesis testing.

Observation and suggestion of hypotheses, therefore, are only the first steps in a scientific investigation. In science we always need to go beyond observation and hypothesizing. We need to set up a series of "if . . . then" statements; "if" our hypothesis is true "then" the following deduced "facts" will also be true. Our results are not always precise and clear-cut, especially in a science like archaeology, but this much should be clear—scientists are not just out there collecting a bunch of interesting facts. Facts are always collected within the context of trying to explain something or in trying to test a hypothesis.

As an example of this logical process, consider the health effects of smoking. How can scientists be sure that smoking is bad for you? After all, it's pretty rare that someone takes a puff on a cigarette and immediately drops dead. The certainty comes from a combination of induction and deduction. Observers have noticed for about three hundred years that people who smoked seemed to be more likely than people who did not to get certain diseases. As long ago as the seventeenth century, people noticed that habitual pipe smokers were subject to tumor growths on their lips and in their

mouths. From such observations we can reasonably, though tentatively, induce a hypothesis of the unhealthfulness of smoking, but we still need to test such a hypothesis. We need to set up "if . . . then" statements. If, in fact, smoking is a hazard to your health (the hypothesis we have induced based on our observations), then we should be able to deduce some predictions that must also be true. Sure enough, when we test specific, deduced predictions like

1. Smokers will have a higher incidence than nonsmokers of lung cancer
2. Smokers will have a higher incidence of emphysema
3. Smokers will take more sick days from work
4. Smokers will get more upper respiratory infections
5. Smokers will have diminished lung capacity
6. Smokers will have a shorter life expectancy

we see that our original, induced hypothesis—cigarette smoking is hazardous to your health—is upheld.

That was easy, but also obvious. How about an example with more mystery to it, one in which scientists acting in the way of detectives had to solve a puzzle in order to save lives? Carl Hempel (1966), a philosopher of science, provided the following example in his book *The Philosophy of Natural Science.*

THE CASE OF CHILDBED FEVER

In the 1840s things were not going well at the Vienna General Hospital, particularly in Ward 1 of the Maternity Division. In War 1 more than one in ten of the women brought in to give birth died soon after of a terrible disease called "childbed fever." This was a high death rate even for the 1840s. In one year 11.4 percent of the women who gave birth in Ward 1 died of this disease. It was a horrible situation and truly mystifying when you consider the fact that in Ward 2, another maternity

division in the *same* hospital at the *same* time, only about one in fifty of the women (2 percent) died from this disease.

Plenty of people had tried their hand at inducing some possible explanations or hypotheses to explain these facts. It was suggested that more women were dying in Ward 1 due to "atmospheric disturbances," or perhaps it was "cosmic forces." However, no one had really sat down and considered the deductive implications of the various hypotheses—those things that would necessarily have been true if the proposed, induced explanation were in fact true. No one, that is, until a Hungarian doctor, Ignaz Semmelweis, attacked the problem in 1848.

Semmelweis made some observations in the maternity wards at the hospital. He noted some differences between Wards 1 and 2 and induced a series of possible explanations for the drastic difference in the mortality rates. Semmelweis suggested:

1. Ward 1 tended to be more crowded than Ward 2. The overcrowding in Ward 1 was the cause of the higher mortality rate there.
2. Women in Ward 1 were from a lower socioeconomic class and tended to give birth lying on their backs, while in Ward 2 the predominate position was on the side. Birth position was the cause of the higher mortality rate.
3. There was a psychological factor involved; the hospital priest had to walk through Ward 1 to administer the last rites to dying patients in other wards. This sight so upset some women already weakened by the ordeal of childbirth that it contributed to their deaths.
4. There were more student doctors in Ward 1. Students were rougher than experienced physicians in their treatment of the women, unintentionally harming them and contributing to their deaths.

These induced hypotheses all sounded good. Each marked a genuine difference between Wards 1 and 2 that might have caused the difference in the death rate. Semmelweis was doing what most scientists do in such a situation; he was relaying on creativity and imagination in seeking out an explanation.

Creativity and imagination are just as important to science as good observation. But being creative and imaginative was not enough. It did not help the women who were still dying at an alarming rate. Semmelweis had to go beyond producing possible explanations; he had to test each one of them. So, he deduced the necessary implications of each:

1. If hypothesis 1 were correct, then cutting down the crowding in Ward 1 should cut down the mortality rate. Semmelweis tried precisely that. The result: no change. So the first hypothesis was rejected. It had failed the scientific test; it simply could not be correct.
2. Semmelweis went on to test hypothesis 2 by changing the birth positions of the women in Ward 1 to match those of the women in Ward 2. Again, there was no change, and another hypothesis was rejected.
3. Next, to test hypothesis 3, Semmelweis rerouted the priest. Again, women in Ward 1 continued to die of childbed fever at about five times the rate of those in Ward 2.
4. Finally, to test hypothesis 4 Semmelweis made a special effort to get the student doctors to be more gentle in their birth assistance to the women in Ward 1. The result was the same; 10 or 11 percent of the women in Ward 1 died compared to about 2 percent in Ward 2.

Then, as so often happens in science, Semmelweis had a stroke of luck. A doctor friend of his died, and the way he died provided Semmelweis with another possible explanation for the problem in Ward 1. Though Semmelweis's friend was not a woman who had recently given birth, he did have precisely the same symptoms as did the women who were dying of childbed fever. Most importantly, this doctor had died of a disease just like childbed fever soon after accidentally cutting himself during an autopsy.

Viruses and bacteria were unknown in the 1840s. Surgical instruments were not sterilized, no special effort was made to clean the hands, and doctors did not wear gloves during operations and autopsies. Semmelweis had another hypothesis; perhaps the greater number of medical students in Ward 1 was at the root of the mystery, but not because of their inexperience. Instead, these students, as part of their training, were much more likely than experienced doctors to be performing autopsies. Supposing that there was something bad in dead bodies and this something had entered Semmelweis's friend's system through his wound—could the same bad "stuff" (Semmelweis called it "cadaveric material") get onto the hands of the student doctors, who then might, without washing, go on to help a woman give birth? Then, if this "cadaveric material" were transmitted into the woman's body during the birth of her baby, this material might lead to her death. It was a simple enough hypothesis to test. Semmelweis simply had the student doctors carefully wash their hands after performing autopsies. The women stopped dying in Ward 1. Semmelweis had solved the mystery.

SCIENCE AND NONSCIENCE: THE ESSENTIAL DIFFERENCES

Through objective observation and analysis, a scientist, whether a physicist, chemist, biologist, psychologist, or archaeologist, sees things that need explaining. Through creativity and imagination, the scientist suggests possible hypotheses to explain these "mysteries." The scientist then sets up a rigorous method through experimentation or subsequent research to deductively test the validity of a given hypothesis. If the implications of a hypothesis are shown not to be true, the hypothesis must be rejected and then it's back to the drawing board. If the implications are found to be true, we can uphold or support our hypothesis.

A number of other points should be made here. The first is that in order for a hypothesis, whether it turns out to be upheld or not, to be scientific in the first place, it must be testable. In other words, there must be clear, deduced implications that can be drawn from the hypothesis and then tested. Remember the hypotheses of "cosmic influences" and "atmospheric disturbances"? How can you test these? What are the necessary implications that can be deduced from the hypothesis, "More women died in Ward 1 due to atmospheric disturbances"? There really aren't any, and therefore such a hypothesis is not scientific—it cannot be tested. Remember, in the methodology of science, we ordinarily need to:

1. Observe
2. Induce general hypotheses or possible explanations for what we have observed.
3. Deduce specific things that must also be true if our hypothesis is true
4. Test the hypothesis by checking out the deduced implications

If there are no specific implications of a hypothesis that can then be analyzed as a test of the validity or usefulness of that hypothesis, then you simply are not doing and cannot do "science."

For example, suppose you observe a person who appears to be able to "guess" the value of a playing card picked from a deck. Next, assume that someone hypothesizes that "psychic" ability is involved. Finally, suppose the claim is made that the "psychic" ability goes away as soon as you try to test it (actually named the "shyness effect" by some researchers of the paranormal). Such a claim is not itself testable and therefore not scientific.

Beyond the issue of testability, another lesson is involved in determining whether an approach to a problem is scientific. Semmelweis induced four different hypotheses to explain the difference in mortality rates between Wards 1 and 2. These "competing" explanations are called *multiple working hypotheses*. Notice that Semmelweis did not simply proceed by a process of elimination. He did not, for example, test the first three hypotheses and—after finding them invalid—declare that the fourth was necessarily correct since it was the only one left that he had thought of.

Some people try to work that way. A light is seen in the sky. Someone hypothesizes it was a meteor. We find out that it was not. Someone else hypothesizes that it was a military rocket. Again this turns out to be incorrect. Someone else suggests that it was the Goodyear Blimp, but that turns out to have been somewhere else. Finally, someone suggests that it was the spacecraft of people from another planet. Some will say that this must be correct, since none of the other explanations panned out. This is nonsense. There are plenty of other possible explanations. Eliminating all of the explanations *we* have been able to think of except one (which, perhaps, has no testable implications) in no way allows us to uphold that final hypothesis. . . .

It's like seeing a card trick. You are mystified by it. You have a few possible explanations: the magician did it with mirrors, there was a helper in the audience, the cards were marked. But when you approach the magician and ask which it was, he assures you that none of your hypotheses is correct. Do you then decide that what you saw was an example of genuine, supernatural magic? Of course not! Simply because you or I cannot come up with the right explanation does not mean that the trick has a supernatural explanation. We simply admit that we do not have the expertise to suggest a more reasonable hypothesis.

Finally, there is another rule to hypothesis making and testing. It is called *Occam's Razor* or *Occam's Rule*. In essence it says that when a number of hypotheses are proposed through induction to explain a given set of observations, the simplest hypothesis is probably the best.

Take this actual example. During the eighteenth and nineteenth centuries, huge, buried, fossilized bones were found throughout North America and Europe. One hypothesis, the simplest,

was that the bones were the remains of animals that no longer existed. This hypothesis simply relied on the assumption that bones do not come into existence by themselves, but always serve as the skeletons of animals. Therefore, when you find bones, there must have been animals who used those bones. However, another hypothesis was suggested: the bones were deposited by the Devil to fool us into thinking that such animals existed (Howard 1975). This hypothesis demanded many more assumptions about the universe than did the first: there is a Devil, that Devil is interested in human affairs, he wants to fool us, he has the ability to make bones of animals that never existed, and he has the ability to hide them under the ground and inside solid rock. That is quite a number of unproven (and largely untestable) claims to swallow. Thus, Occam's Razor says the simpler hypothesis, that these great bones are evidence of the existence of animals that no longer exist—in other words, dinosaurs—is better. The other one simply raises more questions than it answers.

THE ART OF SCIENCE

Don't get the impression that science is a mechanical enterprise. Science is at least partially an art. It is much more than just observing the results of experiments.

It takes great creativity to recognize a "mystery" in the first place. In the apocryphal story, countless apples had fallen from countless trees and undoubtedly conked the noggins of multitudes of stunned individuals who never thought much about it. It took a fabulously creative individual, Isaac Newton, to even recognize that herein lay a mystery. Why did the apple fall? No one had ever articulated the possibility that the apple could have hovered in midair. It could have moved off in any of the cardinal directions. It could have gone straight up and out of sight. But it did not. It fell to the ground as it always had, in all places, and as it always would. It took great imagination to recognize that in this simple observation (and in a bump on the

head) rested the eloquence of a fundamental law of the universe.

Further, it takes great skill and imagination to invent a hypothesis in this attempt to understand why things seem to work the way they do. Remember, Ward 1 at the Vienna General Hospital did not have written over its doors, OVERCROWDED WARD or WARD WITH STUDENT DOCTORS WHO DON'T WASH THEIR HANDS AFTER AUTOPSIES. It took imagination first to recognize that there were differences between the wards and, quite importantly, that some of the differences might logically be at the root of the mystery. After all, there were in all likelihood many, many differences between the wards: their compass orientations, the names of the nurses, the precise alignment of the windows, the astrological signs of the doctors who worked in the wards, and so on. If a scientist were to attempt to test all of these differences as hypothetical causes of a mystery, nothing would ever be solved. Occam's Razor must be applied. We need to focus our intellectual energies on those possible explanations that require few other assumptions. Only after all of these have been eliminated, can we legitimately consider others. As summarized by that great fictional detective, Sherlock Holmes:

> It is of the highest importance in the art of detection to be able to recognize, out of a number of facts, which are incidental and which are vital. Otherwise, your energy and attention must be dissipated instead of being concentrated.

Semmelweis concentrated his attention on first four, then a fifth possible explanation. Like all good scientists he had to use some amount of what we can call "intuition" to sort out the potentially vital from the probably incidental. Even in the initial sorting we may be wrong. Overcrowding seemed a very plausible explanation to Semmelweis, but it was wrong nonetheless.

Finally, it takes skill and inventiveness to suggest ways for testing the hypothesis in question. We must, out of our own heads, be able to invent the "then" part of our "if . . . then" statements. We need to be able to suggest those things that must be true if our hypothesis is to be supported. There really is an art to that. Anyone can claim there was a Lost Continent of Atlantis, but often it takes a truly inventive mind to suggest precisely what archaeologists must find if the hypothesis of its existence were indeed to be valid.

Semmelweis tested his hypotheses and solved the mystery of childbed fever by changing conditions in Ward 1 to see if the death rate would change. In essence, the testing of each hypothesis was an experiment. In archaeology, the testing of hypotheses often must be done in a different manner. There is a branch of archaeology called, appropriately enough, "experimental archaeology" that involves the experimental replication and utilization of prehistoric artifacts in an attempt to figure out how they were made and used. In general, however, archaeology is largely not an experimental science. Archaeologists more often need to create "models" of some aspect of cultural adaptation and change. These models are simplified, manipulable versions of cultural phenomena.

For example, James Mosimann and Paul Martin (1975) created a computer program that simulated or modeled the first human migration into America some 12,000 years ago. By varying the size of the initial human population and their rate of growth and expansion, as well as the size of the big-game animal herds in the New World, Mosimann and Martin were able to test their hypothesis that these human settlers caused the extinction of many species of game animals. The implications of their mathematical modeling can be tested against actual archaeological and paleontological data.

Ultimately, whether a science is experimentally based or not makes little logical difference in the testing of hypotheses. Instead of predicting what the results of a given experiment must be if our induced hypothesis is useful or valid, we predict what new data we must be able to find if a given hypothesis is correct.

For instance, we may hypothesize that long-distance trade is a key ele-

ment in the development of civilization based upon our analysis of the ancient Maya. We deduce that if this is correct—if this is, in fact, a general rule of cultural evolution—we must find large quantities of trade items in other parts of the world where civilization also developed. We might further deduce that these items should be found in contexts that denote their value and importance to the society (for example, in the burials of leaders). We must then determine the validity of our predictions and, indirectly, our hypothesis by going out and conducting more research. We need to excavate sites belonging to other ancient civilizations and see if they followed the same pattern as seen for the Maya relative to the importance of trade.

Testing a hypothesis certainly is not easy. Sometimes errors in testing can lead to incorrectly validating or rejecting a hypothesis. Some of you may have already caught a potential problem in Semmelweis's application of the scientific method. Remember hypothesis 4? It was initially suggested that the student doctors were at the root of the higher death rate in Ward 1, because they were not as gentle in assisting in birthing as were the more experienced doctors. This hypothesis was not borne out by testing. Retraining the students had no effect on the mortality rate in Ward 1. But suppose that Semmelweis had tested this hypothesis instead by removing the students altogether prior to their retraining. From what we now know, the death rate would have indeed declined, and Semmelweis would have concluded incorrectly that the hypothesis was correct. We can assume that once the retrained students were returned to the ward (gentler, perhaps, but with their hands still dirty) the death rate would have jumped up again since the students were indeed at the heart of the matter, but not because of their presumed rough handling of the maternity patients.

This should point out that our testing of hypotheses takes a great deal of thought and that we can be wrong. We must remember: we have a hypothesis, we have the deduced implications, and

we have the test. We can make errors at any place within this process—the hypothesis may be incorrect, the implications may be wrong, or the way we test them may be incorrect. Certainty in science is a scarce commodity. There are always new hypotheses, alternative explanations, and more deductive implications to test. Nothing is ever finished, nothing is set in concrete, nothing is ever defined or raised to the level of religious truth.

Beyond this, it must be admitted that scientists are, after all, ordinary human beings. They are not isolated from the cultures and times in which they live. They share many of the same prejudices and biases of other members of their societies. Scientists learn from mentors at universities and often inherit their perspectives. It often is quite difficult to go against the scientific grain, to question accumulated wisdom, and to suggest a new approach or perspective.

For example, when German meteorologist Alfred Wegener hypothesized in 1912 that the present configuration of the continents resulted from the breakup of a single inclusive landmass and that the separate continents had "drifted" into their current positions (a process called *continental drift*), most rejected the suggestion outright. Yet today, Wegener's general perspective is accepted and incorporated into the general theory of *plate tectonics*.

Philosopher of science Thomas Kuhn (1970) has suggested that the growth of scientific knowledge is not neatly linear, with knowledge simply building on knowledge. He maintains that science remains relatively static for periods and that most thinkers work under the same set of assumptions—the same *paradigm*. New ideas or perspectives, like those of Wegener or Einstein, that challenge the existing orthodoxy, are usually initially rejected. Only once scientists get over the shock of the new ideas and start testing the new frameworks suggested by these new paradigms are great jumps in knowledge made.

That is why in science we propose, test, tentatively accept, but never prove a hypothesis. We keep only those hypotheses that cannot be disproved. As long as an hypothesis holds up under the scrutiny of additional testing through experiment and/or is not contradicted by new data, we accept it as the best explanation so far. Some hypotheses sound good, pass the rigors of initial testing, but are later shown to be inadequate or invalid. Others—for example, the hypothesis of biological evolution—have held up so well (all new data either were or could have been deduced from it) that they will probably always be upheld. We usually call these very well supported hypotheses *theories*. However, it is in the nature of science that no matter how well an explanation of some aspect of reality has held up, we must always be prepared to consider new tests and better explanations.

We are interested in knowledge and explanations of the universe that work. As long as these explanations work, we keep them. As soon as they cease being effective because new data and tests show them to be incomplete or misguided, we discard them and seek new ones. In one sense, Semmelweis was wrong after all, though his explanation worked at the time—he did save lives through its application. We now know that there is nothing inherently bad in "cadaveric material." Dead bodies are not the cause of childbed fever. Today we realize that it is a bacteria that can grow in the flesh of a dead body that can get on a doctor's hands, infect a pregnant woman, and cause her death. Semmelweis worked in a time before the existence of such things was known. Science in this way always grows, expands, and evolves.

SCIENCE AND ARCHAEOLOGY

The study of the human past is a science and relies on the same general logical processes that all sciences do. Unfortunately, perhaps as a result of its popularity, the data of archaeology have often been used by people to attempt to prove some idea or claim. Too often, these attempts have been bereft of science.

Archaeology has attracted frauds and fakes. Myths about the human past have been created and popularized. Misunderstandings of how archaeologists go about their tasks and what we have discovered about the human story have too often been promulgated. As I stated . . . my purpose is to describe the misuse of archaeology and the nonscientific application of the data from this field. . . .

The Mysterious Fall
of the Nacirema

Neil B. Thompson

Many archeologists consider themselves to be cultural anthropologists because their ultimate aim is to make interpretations about cultural systems. They use artifacts to infer the nature of both the social organization and cultural orientation of a people. The following article draws such inferences from the few artifacts left by the Nacirema. Neil Thompson attempts to explain why these people suddenly vanished from the face of the earth. His study suggests that a cultural drive to change the land, water, and air may have caused their demise.

The revival of concern in the recently extinct culture of the Nacirema is, to say the least, most interesting, and perhaps reflects an increasing state of concern for our own society. (Aspects of the Nacirema culture were first described by Horace Miner in "Body Ritual Among the Nacirema," American Anthropologist (1956) 58:503–507.) The use of a multidisciplined approach in deciphering this puzzling culture is gratifying, for it is only by bringing all our methodological techniques to bear on the fragments of evidence in our possession that we will be able to rationally study and understand the history of this apparently vigorous but short-lived culture.

Through exploratory digs by our archeological expeditions, we are able to say with some confidence that the Nacirema were the dominant group in the complex of North American cultures. Although the Nacirema left a large number of documents, our linguists have been unable to decipher any more than a few scattered fragments of the Nacirema language. Eventually, with the complete translation of these documents, we will undoubtedly learn a great deal about the reasons for the sudden disappearance of what, from the physical evidence, must have been an explosive and expansive culture. For the present however, we must rely upon the physical evidence we have uncovered and analyzed in order to draw any conclusions concerning its extinction.

When we examine the area occupied by these people in a single overview, it is immediately apparent that the Nacirema considered it of primary importance to completely remake the environment of the lands they occupied. On studying the fringes of their territory, particularly their penetration of the Cree cultural area to the north, one is struck by the energy that they expended on this task. Trees, if in large enough numbers and size to influence the appearance of the landscape, were removed. In treeless regions, hills were leveled and large holes were dug and partially filled with water. In a few areas the Nacirema imported structural steel with which they erected tall, sculpturesque towers. Some of these towers were arranged in series, making long lines that extended beyond the horizon, and were linked by several cables running through the air. Others, particularly in the northern fringe area, were erected in no discernible geometric pattern and were connected by hollow pipes laid on the surface of the earth.

When one views areas normally considered to be within their cultural suzerainty, one sees evidence of similar activity. Most trees were removed. In some areas, however, trees were replanted or areas were allowed to reforest themselves without assistance. Apparently, the fetish against trees went by fits and starts, for the Nacirema would sometimes move into a reforested area and again remove the trees.

Most of the land, however, was kept clear of trees and was sowed each year with a limited variety of plants. Esthetic considerations must have led to the cultivation of plants poisonous to human life because, while the products of the cropland were sometimes used as food, few were consumed without first being subjected to long periods of complicated processing. Purifying chemicals, which radically changed the appearance and the specific weights of the seeds or fibers, were added. These purification rituals were seldom performed in the living quarters, but rather in a series of large temple-like buildings devoted to this purpose. A vast hierarchy of priests dressed in white (a symbol of purity) devoted their lives to this liturgy. Members of another group, the powerful ssenisub community . . . constantly examined the efforts of the first group and, if they approved, would affix to the finished product one of several stamps, such as "ADSU" or "Doog Gni-peekesouh." Still a third group, the repeekkoobs, accepted and recorded on permanent memorial rolls the gifts of the general population to their priestly order.

On a more limited territorial basis, the Nacirema spent great time and energy constructing narrow ribbons, called steerts, across the landscape. Some steerts were arranged and connected in patterns, and in regions with a great concentration of people, the patterns, when viewed from the air, increased in size and became more elaborate. Other ribbons did not follow any particular pattern but aimlessly pushed from one population center to another. In general, their primary function seems to have been to geometricize the landscape into units that could be manipulated by a few men. The steerts also served as environmental dividers; persons of a lower caste lived within the boundaries of defined areas while those of the upper caste were free to live where they chose. Exploratory digs have shown that the quality of life in the different areas varied from very luxurious to poverty stricken. The various areas were generically referred to as ottehgs.

The task of completely altering the appearance of the environment to fit the Nacirema's ideology was given such high priority that the ssenisub community completely controlled the amassing of resources, manpower, and intelligence for this purpose. This group, whose rank bordered on that of a non-regimented priestly caste, lived in areas that were often guarded by electronic systems. There is no evidence to suggest that any restraints—moral, sociological, or engineering—were placed on their self-determined enterprises.

For a period of about 300 solar cycles (a determination made on the basis of carbon-dating studies), the Nacirema devoted a major part of their effort to the special environmental problem of changing the appearance of air and water. Until the last 50 solar cycles of the culture's existence, they seemed to have had only indifferent success. But during the short period

before the fall of the culture, they mastered their art magnificently. They changed the color of the waters from the cool end of the spectrum (blues and greens) toward the warm end (reds and browns).

The air was subjected to a similar alteration: it was changed from an azure shade to a uniform gray-yellow. This alteration of water and air was effected by building enormous plants in strategic locations. These are usually found by our archeologists in or near large population centers, although, as success rewarded the Nacirema's efforts, they seem to have built smaller plants in outlying areas where environmental changes had not yet been effected. These plants constantly produced a variety of reagents, each appropriate to its locale, which were then pumped into the rivers and lakes or released into the atmosphere in the form of hot gases. The problem of disposing of the many by-products of this process was solved by distributing them among the general population, which retained them as venerated or decorative objects in their living quarters for a short time, then discarded them in the huge middens that were established near every population center.

In regions where colder temperatures apparently prevented the reagents from changing the color of the water sufficiently, the Nacirema, near the end of their cultural explosion, built special plants that economically raised the water temperature to an acceptable level for the desired chemical reaction.

The idea of a man-made environment was so pervasive that in some areas, notably in the provinces called Ainrofilac and Anaisiuol, the Nacirema even tried to alter the appearance of the ocean currents. In these regions they erected steel sculptures in the sea itself and through them released a black and slick substance, which stained the waters and the beaches. This experiment, however, was relatively unsuccessful since the stains were not permanent and the Nacirema apparently never mastered a technique for constantly supplying the reagent.

Early research has disclosed the importance of ritualistic observance

among the Nacirema. In support of these observations, we should note the presence of the quasi-religious Elibomotua Cult, which sought to create an intense sense of individual involvement in the community effort to completely control the environment. This pervasive cult was devoted to the creation of an artistic symbol for a man-made environmental system.

The high esteem of the cult is demonstrated by the fact that near every population center, when not disturbed by the accumulation of debris, archeologists have found large and orderly collections of the Elibomotua Cult symbol. The vast number of these collections has given us the opportunity to reconstruct with considerable confidence the principal ideas of the cult. The newest symbols seem to have nearly approached the ultimate of the Nacirema's cultural ideal. Their colors, material, and size suggest an enclosed mobile device that corresponds to no color or shape found in nature, although some authorities suggest that, at some early time in the development, the egg may have been the model. The device was provided with its own climate control system as well as a system that screened out many of the shorter rays of the light spectrum.

The object was designed to eliminate most sounds from the outside and to fill the interior with a hypnotic humming sound when the machine was in operation. This noise could be altered in pitch and intensity by the manipulation, through simple mechanical controls, of an ingenious mechanism located outside the operator's compartment. This mechanism also produced a gaseous substance that, in a small area, could change the appearance of the air in a manner similar to the permanent plant installations.

In the early stages of the symbol's development, this was probably only a ritualistic performance since the production plant was small and was fueled by a small tank. This function, however, may have been the primary reason for the cult's symbol: to provide each family with its own device for altering the environment by giving it a private microuniverse with a system of producing the much desired air-changing reagent.

The complete machined piece was somewhat fragile. Our tests of the suspension system indicate that it was virtually immobile on unimproved terrain; by all of our physical evidence, its movement was restricted to the surfaced streets that the Nacirema had built to geometricize the landscape.

We are relatively certain that a specially endowed and highly skilled group of educators was employed to keep the importance of these enclosed mobile devices constantly in the public eye. Working in an as yet unlocated area that they referred to as Euneva Nosidam, these specialists printed periodical matter and transmitted electronic-impulse images to boxlike apparatus in all homes.

While some of the information was aimed at describing the appearance and performance characteristics of the various kinds of machines, the greatest portion of the material was seemingly aimed at something other than these factors. A distinguished group of linguists, social psychologists, and theologians, who presented the principal symposium at our most recent anthropological conference, offered the hypothesis that the elibomotua symbols, also known as racs, replaced the processes of natural selection in the courtship and mating rituals of the Nacirema. Through unconscious suggestion, which derived from Euneva Nosidam's "mcnahulesque" materials, the female was uncontrollably driven to select her mate by the kind of elibomotua he occupied. The males of the culture were persuaded to believe that any handicap to masculine dominance could be overcome by selecting the proper cult symbol. In this way, the future of the race, as represented by Nacirema culture, was determined by unnatural man-made techniques.

The symposium was careful to point out that we have not yet uncovered any hard evidence to show whether or not this cultural trait actually had any effect on the race or its population growth. We have found, however, one strange sculpture from the Pop Loohcs depicting a male and female mating in

an elibomotua's rear compartment, indicating a direct relationship. The hypothesis has the virtue of corresponding to the standard anthropological interpretations of the Nacirema culture—that it was ritual ridden and devoted to the goal of man's control of the environment.

Further evidence of the Nacirema's devotion to the Elibomotua Cult has been discovered in surviving scraps of gnivom serutcip. Some of these suggest that one of the most important quasi-religious ceremonies was performed by large groups who gathered at open-air shrines built in imitation of a planetary ellipse and called a keartecar. There, with intensely emotional reactions, these crowds watched a ritual in which powerful gnicar racs performed their idealized concept of the correct behavior of the planets in the universe. Apparently, their deep-seated need for a controlled environment was thus emotionally achieved.

The racs did not hold a steady position in the planetarium. but changed their relationship to the other racs rather frequently. Occasionally a special ritual, designed to emphasize man's power over his universe, was enacted. On these unannounced occasions one or more of the planet symbols was destroyed by crashing two of them together or by throwing one against a wall. The emotional pitch of the worshipers rose to its highest level at this moment. Then on command of the high priest of the ceremony, all the gnicar racs were slowed to a funereal speed and carefully held in their relative positions. After an appropriate memorial period honoring man's symbolic control of the universe, the machines were given the signal to resume their erratic speeds and permitted to make unnatural position changes.

We can only speculate on the significance of this ritual, but it seems reasonable to conclude that it served as an educational device, constantly imprinting in the individual the society's most important values.

Many of the findings of archeological explorations suggest that these symbols of universal power took up a large portion of the time and energy of

the Nacirema society. Evidence indicates that a sizable portion of the work force and enormous amounts of space must have been devoted to the manufacture, distribution, and ceremonial care of the devices. Some of the biggest production units of the economy were assigned this function; extensive design laboratories were given over to the manipulation of styles and appearances, and assembly lines turned out the pieces in serial fashion. They were given a variety of names, although all of those made in the same time period looked remarkably alike.

Every family assumed the responsibility for one of the machined pieces and venerated it for a period of two to four solar cycles. Some families who lived in areas where a high quality of life was maintained took from two to four pieces into their care. During the time a family held a piece, they ritually cleansed it, housed it from the elements, and took it to special shrines where priests gave it a variety of injections.

The Nacirema spent much of their time inside their elibomotuas moving about on the steerts. Pictures show that almost everyone engaged, once in the morning and once in the evening, in what must have been an important mass ritual, which we have been unable to decipher with any surety. During these periods of the day, people of both sexes and all ages, except the very young and the very old, left their quarters to move about on the steerts in their racs. Films of these periods of the day show scenes analogous to the dance one can occasionally see in a swarm of honeybees. In large population centers this "dance of the racs" lasted for two or three hours. Some students have suggested that since the swarm dances took place at about the time the earth completed one-half an axial rotation, it may have been a liturgical denial of the natural processes of the universe.

Inasmuch as we are reasonably certain that after the rite most of the adults and all of the children left the racs and were confined inside man-made structures variously called loohcs, eciffos, tnalps, or emohs and, when released, went immediately to their racs and engaged in the next swarming, the suggestion may be apropos. The ardent involvement of the whole population from ages six through sixty five indicates that it was one of the strongest mores of the culture, perhaps approaching an instinctual behavior pattern.

It should also be mentioned that, when inside their racs, people were not restricted to their ottehgs, but were free to go anywhere they chose so long as they remained on the steerts. Apparently, when they were confined inside a rac, the Nacirema attained a state of equality, which eliminated the danger of any caste contamination.

These, then, to the best of our present state of knowledge, were the principal familial uses of the Elibomotua Cult symbols. After a family had cared for a piece long enough to burnish it with a certain patina, it was routinely replaced by another, and the used rac was assigned to a gallery keeper, who placed it on permanent display in an outdoor gallery, sometimes surrounded by trees or a fence, but usually not concealed in any way. During their free time, many persons, especially those from the ottehgs of the lesser sorts, came to study the various symbols on display and sometimes carried away small parts to be used for an unknown purpose.

There seems to be little doubt that the Cult of the Elibomotua was so fervently embraced by the general population, and that the daily rituals of the rac's care and use were so faithfully performed, that the minute quantities of reagent thus distributed may have had a decisive effect on the chemical characteristics of the air. The elibomotua, therefore, may have contributed in a major way toward the prized objective of a totally man-made environment.

In summary, our evaluation of both the Nacirema's man-made environmental alterations and the artifacts found in their territories lead us to advance the hypothesis that they may have been responsible for their own extinction. The Nacirema culture may have been so successful in achieving its objectives that the inherited physiological mechanisms of its people were unable to cope with its manufactured environment.

Rhinos and Lions and Bears (Oh, My!)

An archeologist explores the newly discovered Chauvet Cave

Jean Clottes

Jean Clottes is scientific adviser for prehistoric rock art studies at the French Ministry of Culture and chairman of the International Committee for Rock Art. An archeologist by training, Clottes served for twenty-one years as director of prehistoric antiquities for the Midi-Pyrénées region, where he studied and helped to conserve the painted caves. His current research involves the application of new laboratory techniques for analyzing ancient art: he is also interested in other archeological evidence that may throw light on the artists' motivations, technology, and culture.

On Thursday, December 29, 1994, I was at my home in Foix, France, preparing for a New Year's celebration. My three children, their spouses, and my seven grandchildren (ranging in age from six months to ten years) were arriving that day and the next for a crowded family week-end. At noon the phone rang. Jean-Pierre Daugas, the regional conservator in charge of archeology for the Rhône-Alpes region, was calling to tell me that there had been a major discovery in the Ardèche Valley in southeast France. A few days before, on Christmas, three men had discovered a big cave with hundreds of paintings and engravings representing lions, rhinos, bears, horses, bison, and

even a leopard and a hyena. By chance, they had felt a draft through stone rubble that blocked a small hole at the foot of a cliff in the valley. After moving the stones, they managed to wriggle through a narrow passage into a hitherto unknown painted cave and believed they were the first humans to enter it in 20,000 years.

Leopards and hyenas were unknown in Paleolithic cave art, and lions, rhinos, and bears were rare. Situated near the town of Vallon-Pont d'Arc, the cave is in a very touristy area where more than a million visitors, including many cave explorers, roam every summer. Could this be a hoax? Daugas insisted it was not. One of the discoverers, Jean-Marie Chauvet, was well known to him, as he was employed by the Ministry of Culture as a guard at the painted caves in the Ardèche region. He was trustworthy and so were his two companions, Eliette Deschamps and Christian Hillaire, who had discovered several minor painted or engraved caves in the Ardèche and Gard areas during the past ten years. I said I would go the following week. But Daugas pressed me, saying, "This looks extremely important and I really wish you could come right away." Reluctantly, I decided to disappoint my family and go check out the cave. The same afternoon I packed my cave overalls, miner's lamp, helmet, camera, and flashlight and drove to Vallon-Pont d'Arc, about 250 miles away.

The next morning, Daugas, along with one of his colleagues and the three cave explorers, met me at the hotel and we set off for the cave. I felt duty bound to tell them that I would have to question everything because my first concern was to ascertain whether such a spectacular discovery could be a fake. They just laughed and said they were not worried.

It was a bleak winter day, and heavy fog shrouded the normally beautiful countryside. We climbed briskly through thick woods to the foot of a cliff. After following along its base for a while and passing several small caves, we reached an unpromising cavity, several feet wide, which my guides said was our entry point. We scrambled down the sloping hole for about thirty feet to a heap of loose rocks that covered a much narrower opening. It was here that the discoverers had first noticed the air current rising. When they first came upon this much deeper hole, they had to spend an entire day removing rocks that had been blocking it. Before leaving the site, however, they had stacked enough rocks over the entrance to hide it again. Now they removed this small pile and crawled into the cave. Then it was my turn. The seven-foot passage was so narrow that I had to strip down to my overalls before attempting to go through. After a difficult ten minutes, getting stuck repeatedly and creeping forward only while exhaling, I emerged on the other side, where

I descended a thirty-foot hanging ladder they had left there. At the bottom I found myself inside a vast chamber.

Obviously, the Paleolithic artists had not used the access we had been through, which opened into the ceiling of the cave. Hours later, we found the cave's original entrance some hundreds of feet on the other side of the chamber. It had long been blocked by a huge pile of rocky debris, perhaps soon after the cave had been visited by humans. This blocked entrance will remain as it is, so as not to change the climatic conditions inside the cavern.

In creating one of the bears, the prehistoric artist had utilized the natural relief of the wall as a three-dimensional shoulder for the animal.

My first impression of the cave was that it was vast, pristine, and beautiful. Stalactites and stalagmites sparkled everywhere under our lights. The ground seemed untrodden, and on the other side of the chamber I could distinguish a first panel of red dots. We went over to it, and I examined it closely. The dots were large (two and a half to three inches in diameter) and numerous, resembling those in the cave of Pech-Merle in Quercy. The ancient paint had long ago penetrated into the wall, and a thin veil of calcite covered a few dots. They were undoubtedly authentic. We followed Jean-Marie Chauvet closely, stepping where he told us in order not to destroy any traces or even dirty the ground. He carefully unrolled long slips of black plastic in front of us, choosing a path where the ground was solid rock or covered with thick calcite, and skirting the soft places where prints might be preserved.

In the first chambers, most of the art consisted of red figures. Next to a few hand stencils and red dots, we saw only one black horse, half-hidden under an old layer of calcite. In a smaller gallery, the outlined head of a red deer was followed by three cave bear images and one of a horse. In creating one of the bears, the prehistoric artist had utilized the natural relief of the wall as a three-dimensional shoulder for the animal. Elsewhere, three rhinos followed one another in a long frieze. As is always the case in Paleolithic painted caves, there were many geometric signs: several panels of dots, similar to the one we had first seen; a semicircle of much smaller dots; and a few cryptic drawings. Two of these strange geometrics resembled birds or bats, while others were reminiscent of insects with multiple legs.

The recognizable creatures painted in red included several rhinos, bears, and lions, at least one ibex, four mammoths, one bovid, and two other animals close to each other. One was indisputably a leopard, recognizable by its spots and its tail, which was devoid of the tuft all lions possess. The other one was bigger. At first, I identified it as a bear, but I was bothered by its spindly legs, its shortened hindquarters, and the spots on the front part of the body. I then let myself be persuaded that it might indeed be a hyena, as Chauvet had said in the first place. If it really was a hyena, it would be the first depiction of that animal in Paleolithic art, just as the leopard is the first known example of its kind. However, I am far from certain what it is; it still could be a bear.

After a low passage full of stalactites, we reached other chambers. In one of them, the ground had collapsed, and a deep crater about thirty feet wide had opened up. Above it, an owl, two mammoths, and a horse had been engraved on an overhang at a time when it was easy to reach. Now the engravings stood about fifteen feet above the bottom of the crater. This was further evidence that no forger could have been at work on the walls.

Farther on, we came to several extensive panels crowded with numerous black figures. These paintings were truly astonishing: on the whole they were well preserved and distinct. Most of the animals were recognizable as to species and sometimes even as to sex or behavior. Contrary to what can be seen in most painted caves, these animal depictions seem to be grouped into compositions. For example, one of the main panels appears to be organized on both sides of a small recess, inside of which a horse, a mammoth, and a rhino have been painted. On the right, there is another, young-looking mammoth, several rhinos, and some bison followed by a group of fourteen lions with their heads stretching in the direction of other animals. Behind the lions is a solitary rhino. On the other side of the recess is a spectacular series of at least thirteen or fourteen rhinos, some superimposed on the others; most are facing left while two face right. Then there are four big lions all on the alert and looking to the right. In the middle of the group, one sees a reindeer and at least two series of red spots of various sizes—the smaller ones in a line; the bigger ones in a sort of semicircle.

Could this really be a composition rather than the placing of unrelated animals on the same walls? Already I thought of what would have to be done to try and find an answer to this question. Analyses of paint constituents might reveal whether all the animals had been done at the same time, with the same paint. All the images would have to be traced carefully and the techniques used by the artists investigated. We could not go up to that panel because the ground in front of it was untrodden and fragile, so we stayed about thirty feet back and examined it from a distance.

We could, however, get close to another one, equally complex and beautiful. There, on one wall, animals of different species had also been represented in black, and some of the images had been superimposed on others. Detailed chemical analysis would in time tell us which animals had been done first or last and enable us to establish the different phases in the composition. A first examination showed, for instance, that some small rhinos had been partly covered by four big aurochs, while another rhino was on top of one of the aurochs and four horses' heads were on top of this rhino. Two other male rhinos seemed to be fighting; such a scene is unique in Paleolithic rock art.

While I was gazing at the panel, trying to distinguish the succession of the images and, in particular, looking closely at the splendid heads of the four horses, I was suddenly overcome with emotion. I felt a deep and clear certainty that here was the work of one of the great masters, a Leonardo da Vinci of the Solutrean revealed to us for the first time. It was both humbling and exhilarating. Humbling because of the admiration one could not help but feel for the artist, forever unknown, whose works had spanned the millennia, and because the discovery underlined the immensity of our ignorance. If after more than a century of research such original and important paintings could still come to light, how many had been destroyed or were still unknown in the depths of concealed caves? On the other hand, I was thoroughly exhilarated to be there, one of the fortunate few to first behold such a masterpiece.

After a whole day spent in the cave it was possible to make a preliminary assessment. The authenticity of the paintings and engravings is beyond question. The cave is a major discovery because of the number of animals represented on its walls, their esthetic quality, and their originality. Of course, years of study lie ahead. For now, nothing can be said as to the precise dates for the works of art, the activities of prehistoric people in the cave, the meaning of the paintings, or the choice of panels. That will come later. But the indisputable authenticity makes the Chauvet Cave, as the discoverers want to call it, one of the great archeological finds of the century.

I saw more than 150 animal images that day, and I probably missed many more, as it was impossible to walk to the other side of some chambers in which the ground was littered with cave bear bones and where undisturbed prints could be seen on the surface. Across one of those chambers, we could just make out the outlines of

more images, unrecognizable from a distance. Most probably, when the cave is explored in detail, there will be 200 to 300 animal figures and possibly even more. In comparison, among French caves considered among the most important in Paleolithic cave art, 145 animal paintings or engravings have been found in the Cosquer Cave near Marseille (*see* "Neptune's Ice Age Gallery," *Natural History,* April 1993) and 110 in Niaux, in the Ariège.

Most of the animals in the Chauvet Cave are rhinos, lions, and bears, which is very surprising. Generally, those most often represented at the time were horses, bison, aurochs, mammoths, deer, and ibexes. Images of these animals are also present in the cave, but the emphasis on predatory animals that were probably not hunted testifies to a regional difference in the Ardèche culture during that time.

Exact dates for the paintings are still a matter of conjecture. However, some details point to a pre-Magdalenian period—the Solutrean, about 18,000 to 21,000 years ago, which is already represented in the Ardèche caves but is rare elsewhere. The panels of big dots and at least one deer are similar to the ones in Pech-Merle, a cave where stenciled red hands have also been painted and which is generally attributed to the Solutrean. Several bison are pictured with their horns facing front, while their bodies are shown in profile and their heads in three-quarters view. The style reminded me of a similar bison in the recently discovered Cosquer Cave, which is half-submerged in a seacliff on the Mediterranean and has been radiocarbondated to about 18,500 years ago. Three animals that appear to be Irish elk—an extinct deer with giant antlers—have been painted in the Chauvet Cave. Those animals appear very rarely in Paleolithic art but happen to be present in several caves dated to the Solutrean or even earlier times, such as Cougnac and Pech-Merle in the Lot region, just south of the Massif Central, and again in the Cosquer Cave. If the Chauvet Cave is indeed Solutrean, which we shall know after radiocarbon analyses and archeological studies have

been done, it will be the most important sanctuary ever discovered for that culture. In any case, the Ardèche, and more generally the southeast of France, is no longer a minor area for rock art. It now ranks among the best, along with the Pèrigord, the Pyrenees, and Cantabria.

Finally, the Chauvet Cave stands out because it has been so well preserved. The discoverers were extremely careful to walk where they would cause no damage. In places, the remains of fires can still be seen. Elsewhere, the ancient soil is covered with bear and human prints. Cave bear bones litter the whole cave. It will be necessary to determine whether the bears hibernated in the cave thousands of years before humans came or were present at the same time. An in-depth study of all traces should also tell us whether children went there with the adults and possibly what sorts of activities went on. In one chamber, for example, a cave bear skull has been placed on top of a big block of stone in a very dramatic way. What could this mean? Have any other bear bones been moved? And why? Did the bears go back into the cave after humans had decorated the walls? Many such questions are unanswered for the time being.

Strict precautions must be taken against vandalism of the primary evidence, and some restrictions placed on research. After preservation, scientific study will be the second priority.

In the months and years to come, much research will be carried out in the cave. However, our first priority will have to be its preservation. A discovery such as this is exceptional from many points of view, and exceptional care is therefore in order. We have often regretted that the excavation of such caves as Lascaux and Altamira destroyed their archeological context, either through carelessness or to answer some questions of the time. In future years, our successors will have different theories and models, and they will use different techniques. Nothing should be done to destroy the primary evidence. Strict precautions must be taken against vandalism, and some restrictions placed on research. After preservation, scientific study will be our second priority. Research will take years to complete and must be nondestructive. Our third priority is to respond to the enormous public demand for films, CD-ROMs, and replicas of the images. These will become possible in time, but there is no hurry. After all, what are a few years to wait for a cave that has waited for us for fifteen or twenty millennia!

Problem-oriented Archaeology

What are the goals of archaeology? What kinds of things motivate well-educated people to go out and dig square holes in the ground and sift through their diggings like it were flour for a cake? How do they know where to dig? What are they looking for? What do they do with the things they find? Let's drop in on an archaeology class at Big City University.

"Good afternoon, class, I'm Dr. Penny Pittmeyer. Welcome to Introductory Archaeology. Excuse me, young man. Yes, you in the back with the pith helmet. I don't think you'll need to bring that shovel to class this semester. We aren't going to be doing any digging."

A noise like a bowling bowl rolling down the alley calling "Whaaaaat!" as it thudded into the gutter sounded as eyes bugged out, bodies contorted, foreheads receded, and mouths formed dark, damp caves at this pronouncement.

"That's right, no digging. You are here to learn about archaeology."

"But archaeology *is* digging. What are we going to do in the classroom all semester!" protested a tall, blond woman wearing a safari suit with a Marshalltown trowel tucked firmly into her belt.

Dr. Pittmeyer calmly surveyed the class and quietly repeated, "You are here to learn about archaeology." In a husky but compelling voice she went on. "Archaeology is not digging, nor is it about Egyptian pyramids, or lost civilizations, or ancient astronauts. It's a science. First you have to learn the basics of that science. Digging is just a technique. Digging comes later. Digging comes after you know *why* you are going to dig."

"No Egyptian pyramids," a hollow, sad whisper floated through the silent classroom.

"You can have your pyramids later. Take a class in Egyptian archaeology, fine. If you want ancient civilizations, take a course in world prehistory. But this class is the prerequisite to all those other classes. I hate to be the one to tell you this, people, but there ain't no Indiana Jones!" Dr. Pittmeyer said this with a slightly lopsided smile. A veiled look in her light eyes sent an "uh-oh" to the frontal lobes of all of the students so that they knew at a gut level that the lady had something to teach them.

Dr. Pittmeyer half sat on the old desk at the front of the classroom, leaning one elbow on the podium to her right, and picked up a tall, red, opaque glass and took a long drink from it. Behind her large, black glasses her eyes watered noticeably. She wiped away an invisible mustache from her upper lip and settled onto the desk holding the red glass in her left hand, letting it sway slightly as she unhurriedly looked over the students. Her right eyebrow rose unconsciously and made a few of the more imaginative students think she looked like Scarlet O'Hara in glasses. The quiet lengthened into a place where the students filling out the bright orange drop cards stopped writing, conscious of the now loud silence in the room.

"O.K! Let's go!" Dr. Pittmeyer said with a snap in her voice as if the class were going to run a relay. The startled students went straight-backed in unison.

"Archaeology is a science, ladies and gentlemen. It's part of the larger science of anthropology. The goals of both are to understand and predict human behavior. Let's look at an area or subfield of archaeology we may designate as 'problem-oriented archaeology.' Humans evolved in Africa, Asia, and Europe or what we refer to as the Old World."

Dr. Pittmeyer had clicked on an overhead projector and was writing rapidly with a harshly bright purple pen in a hieroglyphic scrawl. She had a microphone dangling from her neck that was plugged into a speaker that was then plugged back into the same cart where the overhead projector was, which in turn was then plugged into an old cracked wall socket.

"In the New World, in the Americas, from Alaska down to the tip of Tierra del Fuego, people didn't live here until about 13,000 years ago. Whereas in the Old World people have been living there for a 100,000 years or more. People in the sense of *Homo sapiens*."

"So what took them so long to get here?" a perplexed female voice asked.

"The continents were not always connected. But let's leave the geology until later. Let me point out that your question contains a very telling assumption. You said what took them so long to get *here*. The question is moot because these early peoples were not trying to get *here*. We're talking about the Paleolithic. People were migratory. They hunted and collected their food every day. Some of them followed the migrations of big game animals. So it is a nonquestion. Let me explain, please.

"In archaeology, you have to ask the right questions before you can get any useful answers. That is why archaeologists dig. Not to make discoveries, but to answer questions. Now here's what I want you to do. Go home and try to think yourself back into the Paleolithic. It's 100,000 years ago and mostly you hang out with your family and other close relatives. You get your food and shelter and you have a lot of free time. Everyone cooperates. The point is that wherever you are, you are *there.* There is no place to try to get to. There is no notion of private property or ownership of land. Nobody needs to conquer anybody. There are no cities, no freeways, no clocks, no rush. Think about it. It's a concept of time without measurements or urgencies."

"But they must have been pretty stupid back that long ago!" the woman with the Marshalltown trowel protested.

"Please think about that assumption! No, these were people just like you and me. If they were here today, *they* probably could program their VCRs. These were people with many skills and accomplishments. But they also had the wisdom to be *there.* That is, they lived every day in the present. There's a lot to be learned from our prehistoric ancestors. But tomorrow's another day."

As the students left the classroom, Dr. Penny Pittmeyer finished her soda and allowed her eyes to glaze over as the bright orange drop cards fluttered to the floor.

Looking Ahead: Challenge Questions

How long ago did modern humans migrate to the New World? How do we know this?

What is the importance of the Clovis point as a time marker?

What does the archaeological record tell us about the Bible as history? Give some examples.

What does DNA tell us about the Dead Sea Scrolls? How is this done?

How can myths be explained by archaeology? Give an example.

What new evidence suggests a greater cultural complexity for preagricultural hunters and gatherers?

When did humans first start expressing themselves through art?

What can mortuary analysis tell us about ancient economies? What can it tell us about ancient religions? Give examples.

Coming to America

When did humans arrive here? Was it the long-accepted date of 11,200 years ago, or 10,000 years earlier? A remarkably detailed site in Chile may finally give us the answer.

David J. Meltzer

David J. Meltzer is an archeologist at Southern Methodist University in Dallas, a frequent contributor to New Scientist, *and the author of* Search for the First Americans.

The Southern High Plains were dusted with snow, and from 30,000 feet they appeared to be a vast marble slab. Since the flight from San Francisco to Dallas wasn't full, I slipped back and forth across the aisle, peering out the windows, hoping to spot a landmark. There aren't many on this flat, featureless terrain. I was looking, in vain, for a sign that we were passing over Clovis, New Mexico, home of the archeological site that's given its name to the people who first set foot in America. That is supposed to have been about 11,200 years ago.

I'd been thinking about Clovis since we took off from San Francisco that morning last December, mostly because I'd heard so much about it the day before, at the American Anthropological Association's annual meeting. There molecular biologists who use human DNA as a "clock" to date population migrations gave a message to us hands-in-the-dirt archeologists: the Clovis-based arrival date is wrong. Very wrong.

The messenger was molecular anthropologist Tad Schurr, representing the Emory University laboratory of geneticist Douglas Wallace. Schurr and Wallace had examined the mitochondrial DNA of various Native American peoples. This DNA exists in little organelles—mitochondria—outside a cell's nucleus, and you inherit it solely from your mother. Because it doesn't get mixed up with DNA from your father, any changes in the molecule as it moves from generation to generation are a result only of random mutations. These, it turns out, happen at the conveniently steady rate of 2 to 4 percent per million years. That makes mitochondrial DNA a genetic clock.

Schurr and Wallace found that the Native Americans belong to four distinct lineages. The Emory researchers then counted the mitochondrial DNA mutations in each lineage, figured out how much time was needed for them to occur, and deduced when these lineages were last together—that is, when they first diverged from a common maternal ancestor. That ancestor was someone who walked across the land bridge that once connected Siberia with Alaska, and the genetic clock started ticking when her descendants then spread across the New World. According to the biologists, that ancestor took her stroll long before Clovis time. "Upwards of 21,000 to 42,000 years ago," Schurr told us, without batting an eye.

That's hearsay testimony, of course: genes cannot be directly dated. Still, the news caused something of a buzz, and not just because modern genetics was failing to uphold a cherished tenet of old-fashioned archeology. What got people talking was that Schurr's date

provided support, from an unexpected quarter, for one of the most talked-about archeological finds of the last decade. From 1978 to 1985, researchers working in southern Chile excavated a site they claim was occupied earlier than Clovis times—some 2,000 years earlier, in fact. Ever since the news began spreading, that site, called Monte Verde, has received a lot of attention from archeologists seeking traces of a pre-Clovis human presence in the Americas. Schurr's date fits beautifully with the Monte Verde evidence, and together they may revolutionize our views on the peopling of the Americas.

That won't come as much of a surprise to those of us who were at another meeting, three years earlier, on the Orono campus of the University of Maine. A couple hundred archeologists had assembled to wrangle over the origin and antiquity of the first Americans. We were there for three long days and three very long nights, and by the last afternoon session I was—all of us were, I suppose—tired, hungry for dinner, and ready to go home. The *New York Times* reporter had already left: no more news fit to print.

And then Tom Dillehay of the University of Kentucky, the final speaker, began to tell us about Monte Verde.

Ten minutes into the talk, the fellow sitting next to me whistled softly in astonishment, then asked aloud of no one in particular, "What planet is this stuff from?" I was wondering that my-

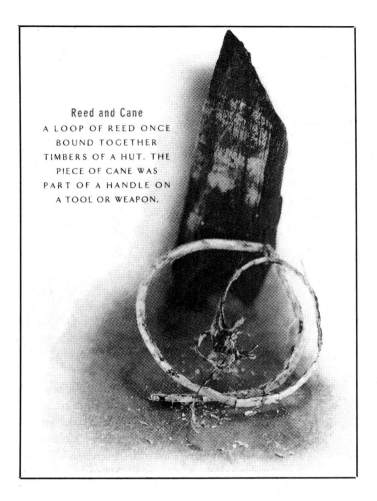

Reed and Cane
A LOOP OF REED ONCE BOUND TOGETHER TIMBERS OF A HUT. THE PIECE OF CANE WAS PART OF A HANDLE ON A TOOL OR WEAPON.

self. The evidence from Monte Verde was unlike anything most of us—who early in our careers learned to be thankful just for stone tools and scraps of bone—had ever encountered before in our archeological earth. When Dillehay finished 45 minutes later, the hall erupted in applause. I forgot about dinner.

That day in Maine many of us saw for the first time pictures of the extraordinary archeological treasures of Monte Verde: artifacts of stone and bone, of course, but also of wood and ivory; freshly preserved leftovers from meals of leaves, fruits, nuts, and seeds; the remains of crayfish and paleo-camel; the torn flesh of an extinct mastodon; even the footprint of a child.

Those are hardly the usual contents of an archeological site. They are unheard of for one in the Americas dating to some 13,000 years before the present. The pros in the hall that afternoon

knew exactly what *that* meant: the Clovis-first barrier to the peopling of the Americas, standing strong at 11,200 years, was threatened.

Established in the 1930s with the discovery of the Clovis site, and buttressed with radiocarbon dating in the 1950s, the idea that Clovis people were the first Americans once made perfect sense. As envisioned, they came out of northeast Asia across the Bering land bridge (Beringia) to Alaska, then headed south. Their migration was thought to be timed to the rhythm of glaciers. By 25,000 years ago those vast ice sheets had frozen 5 percent of the oceans' water on land, plunging global sea levels and uncovering the land bridge. But 20,000 years ago the glaciers had grown so much that they blocked the routes south from Alaska. Only around 12,000 years ago, once the glaciers had melted back and the terrain dried and was reforested,

did a passable southern route reopen, roughly along the present border of Alberta and British Columbia.

The first Americans must have headed south soon thereafter, and fast, for by 11,200 years ago groups were camping at a freshwater pond at Clovis, and by 11,000 years ago they had reached Tierra del Fuego, at the southern tip of South America. One can recognize traces of the Clovis people in the fluted stone spear points they left behind—a design first noted at the New Mexico pond. The explosive move to the south corresponded neatly with the extinction of over 150 million mammoths, mastodons, ground sloths, and other giant Ice Age mammals. To some that was no coincidence: these rapacious hunters, encountering big game that had never before peered down the shaft of a spear, would have had easy pickings and been spurred onward by visions of still more prey.

Not a bad model, all things considered, and for six decades it held up well while pretenders came and went. But the Clovis-first model has problems, and one of them is enormous: How and why, did people race from Alaska—where archeologists have found Clovis-like traces in sites about 11,300 years old—down to Tierra del Fuego, *nearly 10,000 miles away,* in scarcely 300 years?

Granted, that's only 33 miles a year, unbearably slow by today's standards; many of us have longer daily commutes. Yet it's a breakneck pace for hunter-gatherers, easily four times faster than the current world record for prehistoric colonization of an empty area, set by ancestral Thule Eskimos. In just a couple of centuries around A.D. 1000, the Thule flashed from Alaska to Greenland. But they had it easy, following a familiar corridor of animals they had lived with for millennia. The corridor had just stretched thousands of miles eastward following a long period of warmer-than-average temperatures.

The first Americans had no such advantage. They were pioneering an infinitely trackless, ever changing, and (to former Siberians) ecologically exotic realm, from high mountains to high plains, and near-polar deserts to tropical forests. They were slowed each time they entered a new habitat and had to find plants, animals, water, stone, and other resources vital to their survival. Sadly, the romantic vision of fast-moving, mammoth-chasing hunters has no archeological reality. They were slowed by obstacles along the way, such as rivers swollen by glacial melt-water, mountains shrouded in ice, and freshly deglaciated barren landscapes. They were also slowed by the demands of keeping contact with kin, finding mates, and raising families. (Ever try to go *anywhere* fast with kids?)

But if the first Americans didn't race through the continent, why do Clovis sites suddenly spring like dragon's teeth from the ground in the centuries around 11,000 years ago? Maybe Schurr and his colleagues have the answer. Assume for the moment that the Americas were peopled 21,000 to 42,000 years ago, and then around 11,200 years ago someone invented the

Clovis point—a handy, versatile tool useful in dozens of applications. How fast might such a good invention travel among groups?

Of course, if Schurr's group is right, then we ought to find lots of pre-Clovis archeological sites. Some pre-Clovis proponents say we already have, pointing to sites throughout the hemisphere that brandish dates of 13,000, 33,000, and even 200,000 years ago.

But these sites have few believers—and for good reason. Of the scores of pre-Clovis archeological finds made in the last 60 years, none so far has withstood the harsh glare of critical scrutiny. Either their ages were inflated, their artifacts proved of natural and not human origin, or they hid some other fatal flaw. Exposing these flaws usually takes less than a decade, and then the site is tossed on the archeological scrap heap. Archeologists have long memories—it's part of the job, after all—and in the face of many

false alarms over the years, they have grown deeply skeptical of any and all pre-Clovis claims. The first site to topple the Clovis barrier will have to have undeniable artifacts in an undisturbed setting accompanied by unimpeachable dates, and it will have to win over the severest pre-Clovis critics: the Jackie Robinson rule, my colleague Mott Davis calls it.

That's why Monte Verde rivets our attention. It may well be archeology's Jackie Robinson.

Monte Verde sits along a small tributary creek of the Rio Maullín, some 30 miles inland from the Pacific Ocean. This is a region shrouded in mist and clouds and a thick, verdant cover of forest and marsh that softens and rounds the landscape. At the site itself the land opens into a grassy plain about the size of a football field, through which shallow Chinchihuapi Creek slowly meanders. The sharp, snow-capped spine of the

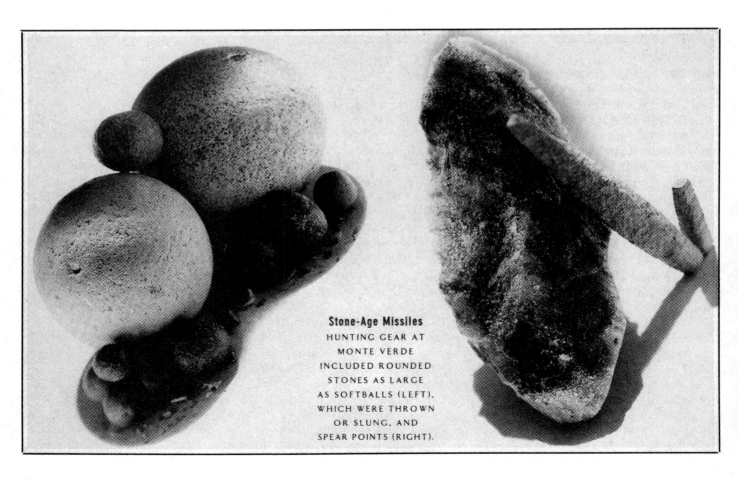

Stone-Age Missiles
HUNTING GEAR AT
MONTE VERDE
INCLUDED ROUNDED
STONES AS LARGE
AS SOFTBALLS (LEFT),
WHICH WERE THROWN
OR SLUNG, AND
SPEAR POINTS (RIGHT).

Andes looms to the east, but only on a clear summer's day can you see the steam and smoke rising from its active volcanoes. And those days are rare enough in this damp and chilly climate.

But it's the damp climate that makes the site special. The archeological debris that Dillehay told us about in Maine rests on a sandy bank, which, soon after the residents departed, was blanketed by water-saturated, grass-matted, oxygen-deprived peat. Beneath this anaerobic quilt the normal decay of organic materials was checked, preserving the site. Monte Verde came to light only in the mid-1970s, when local woodsmen, cutting back the banks of the creek to widen trails for their oxcarts, dislodged some buried wood and mastodon bones from their resting place.

Dillehay's subsequent excavation showed that the bank was littered with the roots, stems, fruits, and nuts of nearly 70 species of plants, and even 3 types of marine algae. That's many more plant species than might be expected in a comparable-size *natural* deposit. We know that because Dillehay's excavators hiked about a mile upstream from Monte Verde to dig where there was no hint of any human presence, just to see what was deposited naturally on surfaces of the same age. Such preemptive shoveling helps muffle critics who argue that the plants could as easily have been left at the site by flood-waters, for instance, as by people.

If nature was responsible for depositing the plants on the site, then nature is awfully hardworking—and more than a little bit devious. More than a third of the plants were imports, brought from their native habitats on the Pacific coast, high in the Andes, or from grasslands and other settings 30 to 250 miles distant. Coincidence or not, 42 of the species found on the sandy bank are still used by contemporary native Mapuche for food, drink, or medicine. Only the usable parts of many of those plants made it to Monte Verde and were found burned in some food pits, on the floors of what once were huts, and in shallow hearths. Even more unusual was the discovery of several plugs of chewed boldo leaves—prehistoric chaw, they'd call that here in Texas—mixed with what appears to be seaweed and a third, as yet unidentified, plant. Boldo leaves are still used today to cure stomach ills and relieve colds and congestion.

The chaw was lying on a wishbone-shaped foundation of sand and gravel, which appeared to be glued together by animal fat. Along the foundation's edges were vertical wood stubs and scraps of animal skin, the remnants of a hide-draped frame hut that once stood there. Fronting the structure was a small cache of salt crystals, plant remains, mastodon bones, a chunk of animal meat (which, based on preliminary DNA analysis, most likely belonged to a mastodon), hearths, and stone tools.

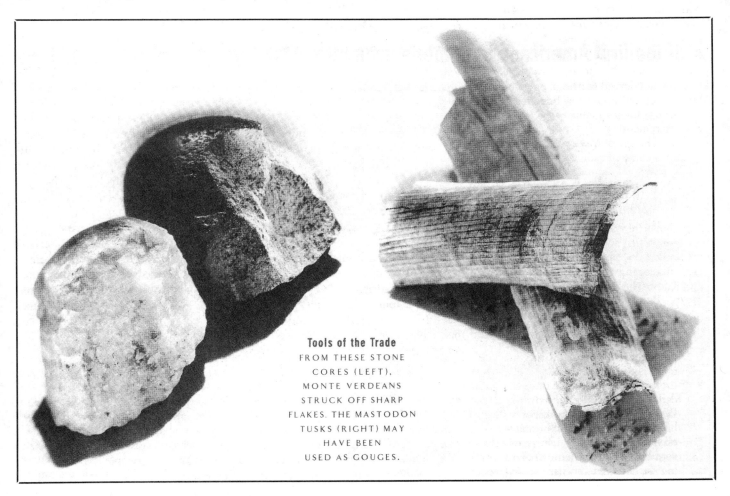

Tools of the Trade
FROM THESE STONE CORES (LEFT), MONTE VERDEANS STRUCK OFF SHARP FLAKES. THE MASTODON TUSKS (RIGHT) MAY HAVE BEEN USED AS GOUGES.

Monte Verde's stone artifact inventory, now 700 pieces strong, includes finely crafted spear points, a slender and polished basalt drill, and cores, choppers, and flakes, several dozen of which are made of rock quarried many miles from the site. One can imagine that with these tools the Monte Verdeans worked, ate, and took cures in the wishbone structure. Most of them, however, lived 40 yards away in a group of 12 rectangular huts, each some 45 feet square. Nine of these huts were arranged in two rows, like row houses, lined by log planks staked together, framed by poles, and draped with a common roof of mastodon hide. Their floors were of sediments high in nitrogen and phosphate—a sure chemical sign of human waste—and littered with ash and grit. The huts surrounded two large communal hearths, two dozen smaller hearths (the child's footprint alongside one of them), and more tools: digging sticks, mastodon-tusk gouges, grinding slabs, knives, spear points, and bola stones (rounded, grooved stones; when sinew is wrapped around the groove, the stone can be whirled and flung). Some of the artifacts were still speckled with the tar that bound them to their wooden or bone handles. In the huts were still more traces of the Monte Verdeans' meals: plant remains, animal remains large and small (mastodon and camel bones, as well as a bird's charred feathers, eggshells, and bone), and even a few human coprolites (the politely scientific word for fossilized excrement).

The age of Monte Verde is anchored by a chain of radiocarbon dates run on artifacts and samples of different materials, including charcoal, wood, bone, and ivory. The dates range in age from 11,790 to 13,565 years ago. Dillehay thinks the oldest one, from charcoal that was sealed and preserved in a clay-lined hole, best represents the age of the site, making it a good 2,000 years older than Clovis times.

But there the skeptics pounce. University of Massachusetts archeologist Dena Dincauze, for example, accuses Dillehay of "uncritical use" of the radiocarbon ages. A better approach, she argues, is to discard the oldest date, then look at the time ranges for each radiocarbon date and use their overlap as the best age for the site. In response, Dillehay suggests dropping the younger dates on bone and ivory (which are more susceptible to contamination) and averaging the dates run on charcoal and wood. Doing so, he says, puts the occupation at around 12,250 years ago, which, as retired archeologist Tom Lynch happily observes, lies "at the very margin of Paleo-Indian time."

Of course, the passage south from Alaska didn't open up for another 250 years, making the trip to Monte Verde an unlikely matter of time travel. But let's assume there's some slop in both dates, and that both the passage and the site appear a little before 12,000 years

---

If the first Americans left Siberia soon after 21,000 years ago, they could have moved south before ice became an obstacle and been at Monte Verde exactly on time.

---

ago, with the passage opening first. Monte Verde is still 6,000 miles farther south than Clovis. To reach the Chilean site on time, these first Americans had to have left Alaska immediately after the passage opened up—giving them maybe 200 or 300 years to make the trip (our record-setting Thule could never have kept up). Leaving Alaska before the glaciers advanced 20,000 years ago, or earlier, seems a little more plausible.

So is Monte Verde just another Paleo-Indian site, albeit slightly older than most? Lynch growls that we cannot be sure, since so few of the artifacts have been illustrated or described in print. Dillehay's first published volume on Monte Verde said next to nothing about the site's artifacts or architecture, saving them for the (yet unpublished) second volume. This was a novel gambit on Dillehay's part to convince his readers, solely on the testimony of the

nonarcheological remains, that Monte Verde was a genuine archeological site. It caused a fair amount of grumbling, but he nearly pulled it off. Lynch, for example, admits the plant remains didn't get to the site by chance—he's just not willing to have them be there as early as Dillehay is.

Ultimately, making the case for Monte Verde—as Dillehay knows—will require more detailed descriptions and photographs of the artifacts. It will require precise maps of the layout of the huts and hearths, showing why these features are demonstrably of human origin. And it will require showing the distribution of the artifacts, organic remains, and dated samples within these features. Jackie Robinson didn't have it easy his first few years in the majors, either.

But will the publication of Dillehay's second volume be all that's needed to reach consensus on this site, and perhaps break the Clovis barrier? I put the question to University of Arizona archeologist Vance Haynes, the dean of the skeptics:

"No."

"But why not?"

"Have you ever visited a site," Haynes asked me, "that looked just the way you thought it would, based on what you'd read of it beforehand?" I had to admit I hadn't (truth is, sometimes I have trouble recognizing sites I've dug from descriptions I've written of them). In archeology, what one reads and what one sees are often very different. Archeology is like that: unlike researchers in the experimental sciences, we cannot replicate a crucial study in our own labs nor fully recreate a site's evidence in words and pictures. Having Haynes visit Monte Verde for a guided tour of the site and an explanation of its history would be the best way for Dillehay to dispose of any lingering doubts the hard-boiled skeptics might have.

"The next book's important," Haynes said, "but one day on the site of Monte Verde would be worth all the words they could write."

Dillehay's response: "Fine. I've been inviting people since 1979 to come to the site. Let's go look at it."

So the wrangling over Monte Verde will last several more years, while we wait for Dillehay and his team of specialists to wrap up volume two, and for Haynes and the other skeptics to hustle funds for the plane tickets to Chile. In the meantime, though, Emory's molecule hunters are doing their part to hasten the end of the Clovis hegemony.

Wallace and his colleagues inaugurated their mitochondrial DNA studies among Native Americans in the mid-1980s, just about the time excavations at Monte Verde were winding down. Almost immediately their results were extraordinarily encouraging. In analyzing mitochondrial DNA from Arizona's native Pima, Wallace's group spotted a mutation that occurs in 1 to 2 percent of Asian people (*Hinc*II morph 6 at bp 13259, in the alphabet-soup idiom of genetics). Among the Pima, however, the mutation's incidence was 20 times higher. That telltale clue does more than affirm the Pima's shared ancestry with Asians. The mutation is so frequent among them that the Pima must have descended from a small number of Asian immigrants, nearly all of whom carried that mutation in their genetic baggage.

Half a dozen years and a couple of hundred more samples later (including mitochondrial DNA samples from Navajo and Apache in North America, Yucatán Maya in Central America and Ticuna in South America), Wallace's team was able to show that all native peoples throughout the Americas share four mitochondrial DNA founding lineages. That's powerful evidence that the very first Americans were few in number. Genetically speaking, they left their Siberian sisters carrying but a fraction of the mitochondrial DNA gene pool.

If Wallace's group is right, the genetic clock started ticking the moment those first Americans left Siberia, at least 21,000 years ago by mitochondrial DNA reckoning. As it happens, the first Siberians appear archeologically

Marching to the New World
MONTE VERDE LIES 30 MILES INLAND FROM THE PACIFIC—AND OVER 9,000 MILES FROM SIBERIA, WHERE ITS SETTLERS CAME FROM.

about then. If they left Siberia soon thereafter, they could have crossed Beringia, moved south before glacial ice became an obstacle, and been at Monte Verde exactly on time (and without having to break any hunter-gatherer speed records).

Of course, Wallace's group may not be right. There are biologists who think the genetic clock was already ticking back in Siberia—long before the future first Americans departed—and some of those naysayers were at the San Francisco meeting to say so. Ryk Ward, of the University of Utah, and Svante Pääbo, of the University of Munich, have also analyzed mitochondrial DNA variation among Native Americans—in their case, the Nuu-Chah-Nulth of Vancouver Island. Of the 63 individuals they studied, they found 28 separate molecular variants. That's an astonishingly high rate of molecular diversity in just one tribe. Measured by the mitochondrial DNA clock, the Nuu-Chah-Nulth's ancestors had to have left Siberia up to 78,000 years ago.

That startling number implies one of two things: either that Americans are

of an antiquity inconceivable to all but the most passionate pre-Clovis crusaders—a humbling prospect for archeologists, because it means people were here for tens of thousands of years before Clovis and we've utterly failed to detect them—or that the Emory group is dead wrong about how the Americas were colonized.

Ward thinks the latter. The genetic diversity evident in the Nuu-Chah-Nulth, he believes, cannot have evolved in America, at least not until archeologists find some evidence of a 70,000-year-old occupation. Therefore, it must have originated in Asia long before the first Americans left Siberia. In other words, the first emigrants were already genetically diverse at departure, and the mitochondrial DNA clock says nothing about when the populations departed for America. "Even if we are able to use molecular data to define the divergence times of a set of lineages," Ward told his Bay Area audience, "we cannot state at what time the representative populations themselves split."

But Wallace's group isn't giving an inch. "We're looking at the genetic tree very differently," Schurr says. For the Emory researchers, the separate branches on which Asians and Native Americans perch are so genetically distinct that there must have been a branching event somewhere near Siberia. But for Ward, the twigs on the American branch are too numerous for the branching to have happened only here.

Are we back where we started? Not entirely—the archeology is proceeding apace. Dillehay expects to complete the second volume on Monte Verde next year, and he, Haynes, and others are planning to visit the site together. If the skeptics leave converted, then the biologists will have a reason to pick one molecular-clock scenario over another. And the rest of us will have a much clearer picture of the hardy pioneers who long ago slipped across the unmarked border between Siberia and Alaska and found a truly new world.

The Politics of First-Century Judea: Searching for Jesus

Neil Asher Silberman

Neil Asher Silberman, a Contributing Editor to ARCHAEOLOGY, *is the author of* The Hidden Scrolls: Christianity, Judaism, and the War for the Dead Sea Scrolls *(Putnam 1994).*

"The heavens and the earth will obey His Messiah . . . he will release the captives, make the blind see, and raise up the downtrodden . . . he will heal the sick, resurrect the dead, and announce glad tidings to the poor."

—from Dead Sea Scroll text 4Q521, "The Messianic Apocalypse"

In the ancient cities and towns of Galilee and Judea where Jesus of Nazareth lived his life, preached to his followers, and was crucified by the Romans, a new generation of archaeologists and historians is radically altering our understanding of early Christianity. Excavations are yielding evidence of major economic and cultural changes that swept the region during the early Roman period. No less important for a re-examination of the historical roots of Christianity are the many Dead Sea Scroll documents released within the past three years that, in combination with evolving New Testament studies, offer surprising insights into the cultural context and possible motivations of Jesus and his early followers.

Several studies of the life of Jesus—based in part on recent archaeological findings—have attracted national publicity and have sparked theological debate. The best known of the new Jesus scholars is John Dominic Crossan of De Paul University, whose books *The Historical Jesus: The Life of a Mediterranean Jewish Peasant* (1991) and *Jesus: A Revolutionary Biography* (1994) have expressed the main themes of the new research. Combining archaeological data on first-century Judea with recent anthropological studies of rural-urban tensions within Spanish, Greek, Cypriote, and North African village cultures, Crossan argues persuasively that the original teachings of Jesus were deeply affected by similar social stresses intensified by oppressive Roman rule. Richard Horsley of the University of Massachusetts, in his books *Sociology and The Jesus Movement* (1990) and *Jesus and the Spiral of Violence* (1993), goes even further in casting Jesus and his followers as radical political activists. Horsley, Crossan, and other prominent New Testament scholars depict the original Jesus movement as a popular response to economic and political oppression whose timeless message shines through the later layers of miracle stories, Christological imagery, and outright hostility to Judaism that were gradually woven into the New Testament texts.

The archaeological and historical re-examination of the birth of Christianity are part of a larger intellectual movement. Over the last century, scholars working in the Near East and

the eastern Mediterranean have achieved striking successes in using material culture to provide alternative cultural and economic explanations for some of the Western world's most cherished myths. Underlying the epics of Homer, for instance, we can now see the outlines of Minoan, Mycenaean, and Dark Age Greek civilizations; in place of Egyptian legends and sacred stories we now have archaeological evidence of the gradual unification of Egypt and the rise of pharaonic power; in the shifting Early Iron Age settlement patterns of the land of Israel we now understand the Israelite conquest of Canaan as a dramatic demographic shift, not a concerted military campaign. Now early Christianity may be understood more fully from an archaeological and historical perspective, in the context of first-century Judean and Galilean society.

The Dead Sea Scrolls are among the most intriguing sources of evidence for a new understanding of early Christianity. Unlike the New Testament, which has undergone centuries of ecclesiastical editing, this huge cache of Hebrew and Aramaic texts, found in caves near the Dead Sea in the 1940s and 1950s, is the only contemporary manuscript evidence of religious thought from first-century Judea that is available to us. Consisting of some 800 separate documents—among them oracles, commentaries, legal codes, scripture, and speculations about the imminent arrival of a messiah—the scrolls offer an unparalleled opportunity for scholars to examine the beliefs of at least one group of Jesus' contemporaries.

Palaeographic dating of the Qumran texts in the 1950s suggested that the latest among them were copied, if not composed, in the first century A.D. A 1991 carbon 14 examination of selected Qumran texts showed they ranged in date from the second century B.C. to the first century A.D., validating the possibility that at least some of the texts for which there are no earlier copies may be original first-century compositions.

The excavations conducted in the 1950s at Khirbet Qumran, the site closest to the caves in which the scrolls were found, revealed the extensive remains of a communal settlement that was identified by the excavator, Father Roland De Vaux of the Ecole Biblique et Archéologique in Jerusalem, as the wilderness retreat of the ancient Jewish sect of Essenes, probably established sometime around 125 B.C. Ancient descriptions of the Essenes stressed their piety, asceticism, and practice of baptism, which naturally aroused scholarly interest in their possible connection to John the Baptist, whose wilderness haunts along the banks of the Jordan River were within hiking distance of Qumran. Yet the interpretation of the site as an Essene monastery cut off from Judean society is now coming under serious attack. In a reevaluation of the pottery, glass, and architectural finds recovered in the original excavations, Jean-Baptiste Humbert, also of the Ecole Biblique et Archéologique, and Robert and Pauline Donceel-Voûte of the University of Louvain have concluded that the site, at least initially, bears no distinctive "monastic" characteristics. They believe that it was originally established as an agricultural center for the cultivation and processing of the famous dates and balsam oil of the Jordan Valley. Brief excavations at the site in late 1993 by the Israel Antiquities Authority (IAA) indicate that the site was founded as a fortress and trade depot in the late second or early first century B.C. by one of the Hasmonean kings.

The results of the recent IAA excavations and a reanalysis of DeVaux's

First-Century Judea

– – – Boundary of Herod's kingdom

MAP BY BETTE DUKE

0 — 20
Miles

original finds suggest that the use of the Qumran site as a communal, religious settlement may have begun at the end of the first century B.C. or early first century A.D. That places the intense literary and scribal activity at Qumran in the turbulent decades after the death of Herod in 4 B.C., when Judea was annexed by the Roman Empire, and when widespread political unrest and messianic agitation arose in both Judea and in the northern region of Galilee.

Some of the scroll texts made public in the past few years have called into question the traditional conception of

the Qumran literature as the feverish speculations of an isolated fringe sect. With the recent publication of previously untranslated legal texts, messianic poetry, unique versions of biblical books, and scriptural interpretation, it is now clear that within this vast collection of writings are literary genres and religious traditions that were cherished by large sections of the Judean and Galilean populace. Conspicuous among these traditions was a distinctive brand of Jewish apocalypticism begun at the time of the later prophets, some 500 years earlier, and typified by a belief that the End of Days was approaching, a time when a messiah would arise to lead the righteous of Israel in a Holy War against the forces of Evil.

Scholars like Harmut Stegemann of the University of Göttingen, Devorah Dimant of the University of Haifa, Philip Davies of the University of Sheffield, and Lawrence Schiffman of New York University now suggest that much of the Qumran literature should be considered as expressions of wider trends in Jewish religious literature over centuries, not merely as the work of an isolated sect. According to Shiffman, "It is now becoming increasingly clear that the scrolls are the primary source for the study of Judaism in all its varieties in the last centuries before the Common Era." That new understanding is what makes the scroll's parallels to early Christian messianic terminology, baptismal ritual, and community organization so intriguing. Although few scholars have gone as far as Robert Eisenman of California State University in asserting that the earliest Christians were members of the community that produced the scrolls, and that the Qumran sect's Teacher of Righteousness was none other than Jesus' own brother James the Just, the study of the life of Jesus and earliest Christianity is increasingly being focused on their roots in Jewish apocalypticism and on the larger religio-political movement in first-century Judea whose purpose was to resist the cultural, political, and economic tyranny of Rome.

Although the first-century Jewish belief in the imminent dawning of the messianic age had many variants, particularly in the timing of the advent and even the identity of the messiah, the expectation of God's impending intervention in human history apparently provided a vast cross section of the Judean and Galilean population with a religious rationale for open revolt against Rome in A.D. 66. "The growing power of messianism," writes Uriel Rappaport of the University of Haifa, "which was itself nourished by the state of affairs in Judea, is what eventually tipped the scales in favor of the radicals, against the moderates."

There are some archaeological indications that, particularly in Galilee, the rise of messianic expectations may have been linked to the painful, dislocating effects of economic change. On the northern lakeshore of the Sea of Galilee, just off the main road between Tiberias and the Lebanese border, is the traditional site of Capernaum, "the village Nahum," the small fishing community where, according to the gospels, Jesus began his public ministry sometime around A.D. 28. Excavations conducted here during the past century have laid bare the outlines of the first-century town with its synagogue and blocks of residential structures reaching to the water's edge. At other places along the lakeshore the New Testament sites of Bethsaida and Gergesa have been identified, and in the muck of the receded waterline a well-preserved fishing dory from the early Roman period was recently found. Together with finds from Nazareth and the Galilean city of Sepphoris, these are all pieces of a vast archaeological puzzle in which patterns of ancient Jewish-Roman cultural, political, and economic interaction are beginning to emerge.

Until the last century, the most common images of the sea and rolling hills of Galilee had far more to do with faith than with topographical reality. Gradually, a first-hand knowledge of Galilean geography became an essential part of New Testament history and scholarship. An important first step was taken by the French historian Ernest Renan, who accompanied Napoleon III's invasion force to Lebanon in 1860. After carrying out brief excavations along the Phoenician coast, Renan traveled through the villages of southern Lebanon and Galilee. The result of this expedition was his own *Life of Jesus* (1863). However, Renan's still somewhat romantic impressions of the simple nobility of the modern Muslim and Maronite villagers deeply colored his descriptions of the birth of Christianity. Indeed, romanticized Middle Eastern peasant life remained the main motif of archaeological descriptions up to and including Franciscan scholar Bellarmino Bagatti's 1950s excavations be-

neath the Church of the Annunciation at Nazareth. Bagatti placed great importance on his discovery of first-century A.D. wells, granaries, and olive presses as evidence of Galilean village life. In the early 1980s, with the start of large-scale excavations at Sepphoris, three miles northwest of Nazareth, archaeologists gained a striking new perspective on the kind of society in which Jesus grew up.

Though Sepphoris is not mentioned in the gospels, it plays a prominent part in the first-century Jewish history of Josephus Flavius as a regional administrative and political center, lavishly rebuilt in the Roman style by Herod's son, Antipas, in A.D. 6. Excavations by James Strange of the University of South Florida, Eric and Carol Meyers of Duke University, and Ehud Netzer and Zev Weiss of the Hebrew University have focused scholarly attention on the social and economic effects of the first-century Romanization of Galilee. Though only scattered potsherds and a few fragmentary walls have been discovered from the preceding Iron Age, Persian, and Hellenistic periods, the reign of Antipas as Roman client ruler over Galilee (4 B.C.–A.D. 39) brought with it the construction at Sepphoris of a gleaming marble theater and surrounding public buildings that were not merely architectural innovations, but powerful, pervasive symbols of the new, Roman way of culture, economics, and life.

The results of the excavations at Sepphoris have helped shape Crossan's quest for the cultural matrix of Christianity. In contrast to the idyllic landscapes of Renan, Crossan has created a world in which the looming power of Roman civilization is always present, influencing the political and religious message of Jesus of Nazareth. Utilizing the archaeological evidence from Romanized Sepphoris, Crossan depicts Jesus and the farmers, fishermen, and tradesmen of Galilee who became his followers not as Middle Eastern bumpkins, but as people fully exposed to cosmopolitan Roman civilization and empire—who consciously rejected it. Eric Meyers believes that

Jesus of Nazareth knew and reacted passionately to Roman culture, "growing up along one of the busiest trade routes of ancient Palestine, at the very administrative center of the Roman provincial government."

But what was the nature of the interaction? Though Meyers and Strange suggest a vibrant syncretism of Jewish and Greco-Roman cultures, other scholars like Richard Horsley suggest a tense and often confrontational relationship between the Galilean peasantry and the Roman officials and urban aristocracy. "The economic impact of Antipas' building programs following upon the heavy taxation of Herod," Horsley writes of the economic changes of the period, "would have left many producer-households heavily in debt." And although Herod Antipas—the patron of Sepphoris—is known from the gospels primarily as the tyrant who executed John the Baptist and who refused to become involved in the trial of Jesus, archaeology now suggests he played a far more pervasive role in the story of first-century Galilee. Inheriting the region from his father, with the blessing of the Romans, Antipas ruled it as his private fiefdom; his costly building projects at Sepphoris and his establishment of the lakeside town of Tiberias in A.D. 18 as the region's new capital enabled him to maintain ever tighter administrative control. Increasing taxation and economic centralization would certainly have had an enormous, negative impact on the lives of many Galilean townspeople, farmers, and fishermen.

Archaeologists working at Roman sites in Italy and Britain have observed that the linking of rural areas to the empire—through regional urban centers, Roman civic ceremonies, and the spread of Roman coinage—sparked an intensification of trade, an increase in cash-crop farming over subsistence, and the creation of vast, plantation-like estates. The work of Stephen Dyson near Cosa, Italy, in particular, has demonstrated the close connection between land-tenure patterns and economic and political change. Given Josephus Flavius' repeated reports of rural unrest and banditry in Galilee

through the first century, it is likely that the social and economic changes of the early Roman period were not viewed favorably by everyone.

In light of what we now know about messianic ideology and first-century Romanization in both Judea and Galilee, it would not have been surprising that a nonconformist Galilean preacher would find it necessary to journey southward to confront the Forces of Darkness—Herodian aristocrats, corrupt priests, and Roman oppressors—in the temple city of Jerusalem. It is astounding how little was known about this ancient city until about 25 years ago. Like Galilee, there was always a fairy-tale quality about Jerusalem—a city filled with unforgettable characters and events. Although the topography of the city began to be studied intensively by European and American scholars in the nineteenth century, excavation opportunities were limited by local religious sensibilities to scattered probes in gardens and empty lots. After the 1967 Israeli takeover of the Old City, however, ambitious excavations were begun throughout the Jewish quarter and on the western and southern sides of the Temple Mount. For the first time, extensive areas within the city walls were dug down to the levels of the Early Roman period.

As a result of these excavations, we know today that Jerusalem expanded enormously beginning in the Hasmonean period (ca. 165–37 B.C.). From its original location on a narrow ridge called the City of David, it expanded to encompass a western hill known as the Upper City. During the reign of Herod (37–4 B.C.) the Temple compound was extended and lavishly embellished by the construction of a massive platform, a huge sanctuary, and surrounding colonnades, making it one of the most impressive structures in the entire Roman world. The city's population swelled. By the time of the reign of Herod's grandson Agrippa I (A.D. 40–44), the outer fortification walls of the city encompassed an area that was not exceeded until the expansion of modern Jerusalem in the nineteenth century.

The question of Jerusalem's size and city walls was an important one

for the first modern explorers, who attempted to determine the authentic location of Golgotha, the place of Jesus' crucifixion, and of the nearby tomb in which his body was reportedly laid to rest. For centuries pious Christians venerated a site within the Church of the Holy Sepulchre, built in the fourth century A.D. under the supervision of Emperor Constantine's mother Queen Helena at a spot *within* the walls of Roman Jerusalem, which she reported seeing in a vision. It was only in the nineteenth century that some Protestant scholars voiced their skepticism about the Holy Sepulchre's historical reliability, noting that in light of the strict Jewish purity laws, respected even by the Roman rulers, the authentic place of Jesus' execution and burial must have lain *outside* the city walls. In recent years, archaeological studies of Jerusalem's urban growth in the Early Roman period have indicated that the site of the Church of the Holy Sepulchre was indeed *outside* the city at the estimated time of Jesus' death, around A.D. 29.

The importance of the latest archaeological work in Jerusalem is, however, far more than a refinement of New Testament geography. As in Galilee, it has deepened our understanding of the social world of Jesus and his followers. In the rubble of the medieval Jewish quarter of the Old City, the excavations of Nahman Avigad of the Hebrew University from 1969 to 1982 uncovered the ruins of elegant first-century A.D. villas. An inscribed weight found in one of the largest of the residences identified it as the home of the Kathros family, which was, according to the Talmud, one of the four most powerful priestly clans. The home of the High Priest Joseph Caiaphas, where Jesus was interrogated before being handed over to the Roman authorities for execution, may have been in this neighborhood, known as the "Upper City" in the description of Josephus Flavius. In 1990, an elaborate family tomb was discovered on the southern outskirts of Jerusalem containing an ossuary, a receptacle for bones, bearing the inscription "Joseph son of Caiaphas."

Many modern visitors are seduced by the elegance and material wealth of such homes in the Upper City, seeing them as evidence of a golden age of Judean history. That age was apparently golden for only a few. Historian Martin Goodman, in his book *The Ruling Class of Judea,* has convincingly linked the sudden material wealth of Jerusalem's high priesthood and Herodian aristocracy with the gradual disintegration of Judean society. Benefiting directly and disproportionately from the taxes and tithes flowing into the expanding temple city of Jerusalem, the priesthood and secular aristocracy were getting richer and the poor were becoming poorer, many even disenfranchised. Traditional land-tenure patterns of Judea were changing, and on the basis of a close reading of Josephus Flavius and rabbinic references, Goodman suggests that small family holdings were bought up by the aristocrats and priests, condemning their former owners to lives as tenant farmers or hired laborers.

Political agitation against the Romans and the Judean priesthood and aristocracy was inevitable. And the consequences were enormous, since, as Goodman puts it, the ruling class of Judea was "not capable of controlling the increasing expressions of social discontent, fueled by economic disparities, that afflicted the population over which they tried to rule." *This* seems to be the social context of Jesus' ministry and of the day-to-day lives of his followers. The coming Kingdom of God was no abstract spiritual concept, but a longing for a new order whereby the corrupt and the wicked would finally be punished for their sins, and the poor and the meek would inherit the earth. It was a message that almost certainly resonated among the majority of Judeans and Galileans, preached with passion and conviction by a number of would-be redeemers—Judah the Galilean, Athronges, Simon of Perea, John the Baptist, Jesus, an unnamed "Egyptian prophet," and the zealot leader Menachem, son of Judah, to name only a few mentioned by Josephus Flavius.

Distant echoes of that first-century rage against a corrupt aristocracy can be perceived even in the much later rabbinic literature. The elegance and the wealth uncovered in the excavations of the House of Kathros in Jerusalem's Upper City was apparently paid for by the misfortunes of others. In a lamentation against the corrupt Temple priesthood, a passage in the Talmud reads: "Woe unto me because of the House of Kathros, woe unto me because of their reed pens . . . for they are high priests and their sons are treasurers and their sons-in-law are temple overseers and their servants smite the people with sticks."

Archaeologists often tended to concentrate on the most impressive and elaborate structures of every period, and this has certainly been true of the investigation of first-century Judean and Galilean society. Yet now, with wide-ranging surveys of settlement patterns and increased interest in social and economic history, additional insights may be gained into the social experience of the vast majority of the Judean and Galilean population. In tracing the changes in the size and placement of rural settlements in relation to the cities, and in concentrating on the changing technology of such prosaic installations as workshops, olive presses, and dye vats—not as illustrations of a timeless New Testament age, but as evidence of changing economic structures—archaeology may provide important insights into the material reality that lay behind Qumran-style messianic expectations and the yearning for change and liberation that characterized earliest Christianity.

That yearning, however, could exact a fearful price. Among the most poignant of the archaeological finds uncovered in one of the vast ancient cemeteries that surround Jerusalem, archaeologists excavated a tomb containing an ossuary with the fragmentary remains of a man named Yehohanan. Hundreds of similar family tombs have been discovered dating from the first century B.C. and the first century A.D., typified by the use of ossuaries, in which the bones of the deceased

were gathered up, placed in stone boxes, and labeled with the name of the deceased, apparently in expectation of resurrection in the World to Come. But the bones in this ossuary told a grim story. An iron spike, driven through Yehohanan's ankle bone, was still deeply embedded in a fragment of olive wood—evidence of the grisly method of crucifixion that was meted out to those who, by their criminal or political activities, challenged (or were accused of challenging) the economic and political status quo.

In sandy mounds by the Mediterranean shore, the sprawling ruins of Caesarea, seat of the Roman administration of Judea, have yielded some of the most telling archaeological evidence for understanding the rise of early Christianity. In the 1960s, an Italian expedition uncovered a fragmentary Latin inscription that gained headlines all over the world. Apparently recording a building commissioned by "Pontius Pilatus, Prefect of Judea," it was the first and is still the only archaeological remnant of the fabled Roman governor. But as the excavations of Caesarea have continued, they have offered evidence far more important than relics of identifiable personalities. In charting the construction of the impressive port city, with its harbor facilities, warehouses, and temples, the archaeologists of the American Joint Expedition to Maritime Caesarea and the Haifa University Underwater Expedition have uncovered the docks, wharves, warehouses, and public administrative buildings that facilitated and encouraged an ever-greater Judean economic link to Rome.

In fact, some of the most ambitious archaeological undertakings under way today in Israel are further documenting the extent to which Roman civilization, with its dominating culture and enormous imperial power, swept over and utterly transformed the province of Palaestina ("the Land of the Philistine"), as Judea, Samaria, and Galilee were renamed after the rebellion of A.D. 66–74 was crushed. The progressive assimilation of Palaestina into the Roman world system is amply documented in the new excavations at

Caesarea, and at the impressive Roman-period cities and commercial centers of Banias (Caesarea-Philippi), Beth Shean (Scythopolis), and Beth Guvrin (Eleutheropolis).

Archaeological research has neither proved nor disproved the historical existence of Jesus, John the Baptist, or the Apostles. Yet it *has* provided information on a wide range of early Roman period sites in Judea and Galilee and has documented their changing material culture. This evidence has now become the raw material for a far-reaching historical reassessment of first-century Judean and Galilean life. Archaeology's power lies in its ability to provide material explanations for the twists and turns of history—the economic, social, and cultural transformations that have given rise to history's great achievements and great tragedies. In the coming years New Testament archaeology will continue to deepen our understanding of Christianity in its first-century context—as part of a wider Judean movement of protest against economic dislocation and political and cultural tyranny.

Dead Sea DNA

The Dead Sea Scrolls are considered one of the greatest finds of modern archeology. But nearly 50 years after the first of them were discovered by a young bedouin shepherd, we know just a fraction of what they're all about. After 1,000 years in arid caves, many of the scrolls survive only as fragments. Researchers have labored for decades to piece the fragments together by shape, like a jigsaw puzzle, and by handwriting style. But now there may be a better way. Scott Woodward, a microbiologist from Brigham Young University in Utah, is bringing DNA analysis to the Dead Sea Scrolls.

Woodward and researchers at Hebrew University have shown that DNA can still be extracted from the parchment scrolls—the DNA of the animal whose skin was dried, scraped of hair, and thinned out to make the parchment. "DNA doesn't last forever," says Woodward. "If you throw a goatskin out into your backyard, it's not going to last for 2,000 years. But the scrolls were preserved under extraordinary conditions." The extreme dryness of the caves, he says, helped keep the DNA intact, in part because bacteria or fungi that would otherwise degrade the organic material need moisture to survive.

From the DNA it is fairly easy to determine what species the parchment came from, Woodward says; most of the fragments he's tested so far have been goatskin, although he's found fragments of other animal skins as well. If two fragments are from different species, he explains, they're probably not from the same scroll. If they're from the same individual animal—something that's also not too hard to tell from the DNA—they're certainly from the same scroll and probably from the same section of it.

Woodward thinks fragments that came from closely related animals—animals from the same herd—would also tend to be part of the same scroll, or at least closely related scrolls. But differentiating between herds will be harder than differentiating between species or individual animals. Woodward is trying to do it by comparing DNA from the scrolls with DNA from animal bones found at archeological sites dating from the same period. He's hoping to find characteristic gene sequences that seem to mark animals from particular locations.

If he succeeds, his results may help settle a long-standing debate about the origin of the scrolls. Some scholars believe the scrolls were all written by members of a Jewish fundamentalist sect, the Essenes, who lived near the Dead Sea; others believe the scrolls were a collection of important Jewish works from various places that were hidden together to protect them from the Romans. By identifying a herd, explains Woodward, "we can nail down where they were written."

DNA tests may help scholars reassemble the Dead Sea Scrolls.

Egil's Bones

An Icelandic saga tells of a Viking who had unusual, menacing features, including a skull that could resist blows from an ax. He probably suffered from an ailment called Paget's disease

Jesse L. Byock

Jesse L. Byock is a professor of Old Norse and medieval Scandinavian studies at the University of California, Los Angeles. He has published three books on Iceland and the sagas— Medieval Iceland: Society, Sagas, and Power; Feud in the Icelandic Saga; *and* The Saga of the Volsungs: The Norse Epic of Sigurd the Dragon Slayer. *After studying in Sweden, Iceland and France, he received his Ph.D. from Harvard University. A specialist in North Atlantic and Viking studies, he once herded sheep in the northern fjords of Iceland.*

Egil, the son of Skalla-Grim, is the most memorable Viking to appear in the Old Norse sagas. Born in Iceland in the early 10th century, he participated in Viking raids and adventures throughout Norway, Sweden, Denmark, the east Baltic lands, England, Saxony and northern Germany. Fierce, self-willed and violent, Egil Skalla-Grimsson was also a fine poet and a man with a sense of ethics. He epitomizes the Viking urge to travel into the unknown world seeking action and fortune. From Athelstan, king of the Anglo-Saxons, he receives valuable gifts and pledges of friendship, but from Erik Blood-Axe, the Viking ruler of Norway, he hears death threats. Combining courage and brawn with high intelligence, Egil survives war and treachery to live to an old age of

80. He dies among his kinsmen in Iceland in about 990, apparently from natural causes stemming from longevity.

For all Egil's heroic stature, however, there is something deeply troubling about his character. Despite his prowess and secure social status, his temperament, as well as his physical appearance, causes alarm. He is portrayed as an ugly, irritable, brooding individual. In this respect, Egil resembles his father and his grandfather, men described as physically menacing. The saga clearly distinguishes them as physiologically different from their kinsmen, who are depicted as fair and handsome.

What set Egil apart was more than simply a small, personal peculiarity. Through prose and verse, the saga tells us that Egil became deaf, often lost his balance, went blind, suffered from chronically cold feet, endured headaches and experienced bouts of lethargy. Furthermore, the saga describes unusual disfigurements of his skull and facial features. These symptoms suggest that Egil may have suffered from a syndrome that results from a quickening of normal bone replacement. The disease, first diagnosed by Sir James Paget in 1877, runs in families and is uncannily similar to Egil's affliction.

Is it really important to determine whether Egil suffered from Paget's disease? I pondered this question at the beginning of my research and considered it again when I realized that

the enigma of Egil lies at a nexus of medical science, history, archaeology and literary analysis. The answer is yes: such a determination does matter. An understanding of Egil's affliction is a critical step in assembling the evidence needed to evaluate the historical accuracy of the Icelandic sagas. Do sagas provide accurate information about a Viking period 250 years before they were written? Or are they merely flights of fancy and fabrications by 13th-century authors? Historians, literary scholars, archaeologists and linguists have all had their say, but science has scarcely played a role in the debate. At times the subject has stirred so much passion that one scholar promised to maintain his view until forced by death to lay down his pen. The argument would change drastically if a new source of information could be found.

For me, that new source lies unexpectedly in the field of modern medicine. Rather than attributing conflicting aspects of Egil's personality to artistic hyperbole, I believe the descriptions stem from the progress of Paget's disease. In breaking tradition to arrive at these conclusions, I frequently have recourse to another science—philology, the historical and comparative study of language and its relation to culture.

FAMILY STORIES

The Icelandic sagas constitute one of the largest collections of extant vernacular narratives from medieval times. In 31 major sagas and scores of shorter narratives, these texts recount the travels of the first generations of Norse settlers in Iceland, the major Viking outpost in the North Atlantic. Written in prose and studded with verse, the family sagas are set in the period from 870 to 1030. Unlike myths and fantastic tales, which the Icelanders also produced, the sagas are sober in style. With an often stark realism they detail everyday agrarian and political life and describe adventurous Viking voyages, including those to Greenland and Finland. The crucial question that has remained is whether the sagas are the product of a long oral tradition or the invention of authors after Iceland became literate in the 13th century.

According to *Egil's Saga*, Egil spent his final years with his adopted daughter, Thordis, at the farm of Mosfell, in southwestern Iceland, not far from the present-day capital of Reykjavik. Initially he was buried there in a pagan grave mound. But 10 years later, when Iceland converted to Christianity in 1000, Thordis and her husband, Grim, moved Egil's remains to be interred at a small church built on their farm. About 150 years later a second church was built about 500 meters from the first. Skapti, one of Egil's prominent descendants, exhumed Egil's bones to move them to the new churchyard. The final pages of *Egil's Saga* relate a curious tale about Skapti's findings:

Under the altar some human bones were found, much bigger than ordinary human bones. . . . Skapti Thorarinsson, a priest and man of great intelligence, was there at the time. He picked up Egil's skull and placed it on the fence of the churchyard. The skull was exceptionally large, and its weight was even more remarkable. It was ridged all over on the outside like a scallop shell. Skapti wanted to find out just how thick the skull was, so he picked up a heavy ax, swung it in one hand and struck as hard as he was able with the hammer side of the ax, trying to break the skull. But the skull neither broke nor dented when hit; it simply turned white at the point of impact, and from that result anybody could guess that it could not have been easily cracked by

small fry while still covered by skin and flesh.

This passage has often been used to exemplify the untrustworthiness of the sagas. No matter how realistic the description may seem to be, everyone, so the argument goes, knows that a 150-year-old skull could not possibly have withstood the blow of Skapti's ax.

Modern medical knowledge, however, suggests that we cannot treat this episode as a purely literary device intended to magnify heroic Viking qualities. *Egil's Saga* precisely describes the skull as "ridged all over on the outside like a scallop shell." The precision is striking because the passage marks the only instance in all Old Norse literature that the otherwise well-known words *hörpuskel* (scallop shell) and *báróttr* (ridged, undulated, waved, corrugated, wrinkled) are used to describe human characteristics. A "scalloped" bone surface, unique in descriptions of Viking heroes, closely matches medical portrayals of Paget's disease. Diagnoses repeatedly list irregularities of the outer skull surface, describing its appearance as corrugated and wavy. Such a feature appears in about one in 15 symptomatic cases.

Physicians have also noted the exceptionally resilient, ivorylike hardness of the afflicted bones. Even the whitening of Egil's skull where Skapti's ax struck is a clear indication of Paget's disease. When subjected to a blow, the soft, pumicelike outer material of the enlarged Pagetic skull gives way to a white, hardened, highly resilient core.

A HELM'S-ROCK OF A HEAD

In the saga, Egil himself refers to his head in strange ways. In one poem, written in response to a pardon granted him by his sworn enemy, King Erik Blood-Axe, Egil composed this verse:

I am not opposed,
Though I may be ugly,
To accepting my helm's-rock of a head,
From a ruler.

Paget's disease may have been responsible for Egil's memorable facial appearance, a subject that over the years has engendered a great deal of creative literary interpretation. The saga offers a detailed description of Egil as he sits at a feast in England after battle. He faces King Athelstan, the ruler who he believes owes him compensation for the death of his brother, Thorolf.

Egil sat upright, but his head hung forward. Egil was marked by prominent features. He had a broad forehead and large eyebrows, a nose that was not long but enormously thick, and lips that, seen through his beard, were both wide and long. He had a remarkably broad chin, and this largeness coninued throughout the jawbone. He was thick-necked and broad-shouldered and, more so than other men, hard-looking and fierce when angry. Well built and taller than others, he had thick wolf-gray hair but was early bald. While he sat as was written above, he jerked one eyebrow down to his chin and lifted the other one up into his hairline; Egil was black-eyed with eyebrows joined. He refused to drink, although drink was brought to him, but alternately he jerked his eyebrows up and down.

King Athelstan does not overlook Egil's threatening stance. Acting to defuse the Viking's anger, Athelstan offers Egil a liberal payment in compensation for his brother's death and thus wins his loyalty.

Although literary license may be assumed, it is curious and highly unusual for the physical features of a saga protagonist to be portrayed in so grotesque a manner, unless the writer was reporting a well-known story. Distortion and hardening of the cranium, changes that are characteristic of Paget's, may lead to leontiasis ossea, or cranial hyperostosis. In this condition, the facial bones thicken, giving an individual a lionlike appearance. This pathology, which may occur as early as the first two decades of life, closely fits the descriptions of Egil. As for the bizarre mobility of the eyebrows, it is conceivable that a person as menacing as Egil learned to exploit his facial distortion and was remembered for its outrageous effect.

Corroborating evidence for a Pagetic diagnosis comes from the saga's description of the problems Egil had in his old age. These difficulties—including loss of balance, hearing and sight, chill in the extremities, headaches and the phenomenon described as a hanging, swaying head—are all major symptoms of advanced Paget's disease. According to the saga, the elderly Egil, after moving in with his son-in-law, Grim, at Mosfell, was walking outside one day when he stumbled and fell. Some of the women who saw this laughed:

"You're really finished, now, Egil," they said, "when you fall without being pushed."
"The women didn't laugh so much when we were younger," said Grim. Egil made this verse:

The horse of the necklace sways,
My bald head bangs when I fall;
My piece's soft and clammy
And I can't hear when they call.

Why would people remember this poem about a head that "sways" and other physical difficulties? One reason is that the utterance is a powerful example of Old Norse verse, encasing personal emotion in a complex and colorful word puzzle. In Viking times, verse was viewed as the gift of Odin, and poetic skill was highly respected. Here the lines reflect the aged warrior's still agile ability to turn physical disorders into memorable imagery.

Old Norse poetry was a game of puzzles, which, once the rules are understood, supplies us with critical information. The first line carries the understanding: "I have swayings of the neck." In building this image, the author fashioned a Norse poetic circumlocution called a kenning. Kennings are stylistically similar to certain English metaphors, such as calling a camel a ship of the desert. The saga's kenning, *helsis valr* (the horse of the necklace), means the neck. The word "swayings" is built on the verb *váfa*, "to sway or dangle while hanging." Thus, the line in the verse refers to a neck bent under the weight of a head that wobbles.

A drooping, swaying head is not a standard feature of old age; so, too, the graphic description "swayings of the neck" is by no means a common usage in Old Icelandic poetry. I conducted a computer search and found no other occurrences of this combination, so the poet is clearly describing a condition that is unusual and highly personal.

The saga further narrates that Egil becomes blind and is humiliated in his old age by his lethargy and his craving for warmth—all symptoms of Paget's:

Egil became totally blind. One day in winter when the weather was cold, he went up to the fire to warm himself. . . . "On your feet!" said the woman. "Get back to your place and let us do our work." Egil stood up, walked over to his seat, and made this verse:

I flounder blind by the fireside,
Ask females for mercy,
Bitter the battle
On my brow-plains.

In this verse the Icelandic words for "brow-plains" *(hvarma hnitvellir)* mean the part of the face where the eyes meet or are located. The passage is thus unclear as to whether the words refer to the eyes themselves or to the area of the eyes, including the part behind and around the eye sockets. If the former, the words again mean Egil's blindness. If the latter, the phrase expresses the notion that "I bear pain where the eyes meet," suggesting that Egil has headaches. Possibly, both interpretations were intended.

Egil's headaches and chills are consistent with his other symptoms. Victims of Paget's disease sometimes have headaches caused by the pressure of enlarged vertebrae on the spinal cord. They also show a high incidence of arteriosclerosis and heart damage. Attendant circulatory problems, particularly coldness in hands and feet, develop as the heart is overtaxed and blood is diverted from the extremities in order to support the rapid bone remodeling.

COLD FEET, COLD WOMEN

Another of Egil's laments supplies further information about his chills and cold feet—and of his ability to create clever wordplays.

Two feet I have,
Cold widows.
These frigid crones
Need a flame.

In Icelandic, the words are

Eigum ekkjur
allkaldar tvær,
en pær konur
purfa blossa.

Here the poet is skillfully playing on an understood double entendre. In unraveling the puzzle, the Norse audience would know that the key to the stanza is to find another unmentioned word, one that would provide a bridge of meaning. That unmentioned word is *hoell* (heel). When substituted for the word *ekkja*, meaning "widow," it carries a double connotation; it also means "heel"—that is, "foot." The members of Egil's audience, who enjoyed the intricacies of skaldic verse, would know to replace the words *ekkjur* (widows) and *konur* (women)—both translated here as "crones"—with *hælar*, the plural of *hæll*, meaning both "feet" and "women."

Once the connection with feet is made, the rest is easy. Both nouns are connected with the adjective *allkaldar*, "thoroughly cold." Thus, the passage carries the meanings of "cold feet" and "cold women," both of which sadly afflicted Egil in his later years.

Is there a tradition of Icelandic warrior-poets complaining about women? Yes. But about their cold feet? Hardly. There is, however, a tradition of recording struggles against one's fate, including enfeeblement. In this instance the lines preserve the memory of a man's private battle with an exceptionally harrowing plight. Despite his condition, Egil still had the acuity to compose clever poetry. James Paget's classic formulation puts it this way: "Even when the skull is hugely thickened and all its bones are exceedingly altered in structure, the mind remains unaffected."

Because Egil's symptoms provide a striking picture of Paget's disease, one might ask whether the unearthing of the bones in the mid-12th century might be the source for the poetry. Could a 13th-century poet, having learned about the condition of Egil's bones, have written verses about the hardness of Egil's head using kennings? The answer is, perhaps yes, at least about the bones. Such a poet, however, would not have known the particulars of Paget's disease and could hardly have expounded on the enlarged bones to construct a detailed portrait of a man with cold feet, chills, headaches, a swaying, hanging head, inconsistent bouts of lethargy, and loss of balance, hearing and sight.

The answer is even more persuasive when we remember that the medieval text simply treats Egil's physical problems as the ravages of time. It makes no connection whatsoever between the bones and any kind of disease. In fact, the saga draws the opposite conclusion. Awed by the size and the resiliency of the skull, it points out how useful such a tough head would be for a warrior. The crucial factor is that the poetry, which may be the oldest element in the saga, independently corroborates the specifics about the bone by giving different details.

Could another disease have caused Egil's problems? I considered conditions that produce similar symptoms, such as osteitis fibrosa, acromegaly (gigantism), hyperostosis frontalis interna, fibrous dysplasia, and osteopetrosis. In each instance, however, critical symptoms do not match. By using all the sources available today, we can diagnose Egil as a probable victim of Paget's disease.

PAGET'S IN SCANDINAVIA

I was led to the question of Paget's disease by research intended to explain passages in a medieval saga, but it is now clear to me that the currently accepted statistics about the disease in Iceland, and possibly in all Scandinavia, are certainly inaccurate. Most studies posit an extremely low inci-

HANS HUBER VERLAG

TENTH-CENTURY SKELETON of an Anglo-Saxon male shows the ravages of extensive Paget's disease, such as the curved spine and the thickened and deformed long bones of the limbs.

dence, or an almost nonexistence, of the condition in this region. This situation exists because little attention has been directed to the effective diagnosis of the pathology. For example, an extensive 1982 study to determine the European distribution of Paget's disease used questionnaire replies by

4,755 radiologists. It found the disease more prevalent in Britain than in any other western European country. The study excluded Norway, Iceland, Sweden and Finland on the assumption that incidences there were very low.

Although uncommon, Paget's disease is more prevalent in modern Scandinavia than these conclusions would suggest. Until recently, the disease was thought not to exist in Iceland. During the past 10 years, however, Paget's disease has slowly but increasingly been found in modern Iceland, a fact unpublished except for a 1981 case study reported in a small journal there by Gunnar Sigurdsson of the City Hospital in Reykjavik. In July 1991, I interviewed Sigurdsson, who informed me he was treating 10 patients with Paget's disease. His observations about the symptoms closely match those of Thordur Hardarson of Iceland's National University Hospital, who was also treating patients with Paget's disease.

To the growing evidence of Paget's in Iceland, we can add the high probability that a saga-age Icelander, and perhaps even a medieval family, could have been afflicted. Recognizing these individuals as victims of Paget's disease begins to fill in the picture of the epidemiological history, of the disease in early Scandinavia, providing examples of Paget's at both ends of a 1,000-year period.

Egil's poetry, Skapti's medieval observation and modern medical knowledge together provide a detailed composite of a Pagetic affliction. With this insight, we do not have to discount *Egil's Saga* to explain the misshapen skull and bones unearthed in the 12th century. On the contrary, we can see that the saga may well contain accurate information. Although we surely cannot conclude that all the sagas are historical truths, Egil's bones strongly suggest that some passages may reliably detail the past.

Is there more work to be done? Yes, for Egil's bones are possibly still buried in the old churchyard at Mosfell. We await the opportunity to unearth his remains for the third time in 1,000 years.

Paget's Disease

In 1854 Sir James Paget became surgeon extraordinary to Queen Victoria and, a few years later, surgeon ordinary to the Prince of Wales. Paget's fame rests on his descriptions of several diseases, the most famous of which is osteitis deformans. According to Paget's classic description, this disease of the bones "begins in middle age or later, is very slow in progress, may continue for many years without influence on the general health, and may give no other trouble than those which are due to changes in shape, size, and direction of the diseased bones. . . . The limbs, however misshapen, remain strong and fit to support the trunk."

Paget's disease is bone growth gone awry. Normal human bones continuously renew themselves, rebuilding completely about once every eight years. Paget's quickens the pace of breakdown and reformation, with the result that the layers of new bone are structurally disorganized, misshapen and considerably larger than the original ones. The cause of the condition could be an inherited weakness of the immune system or a virus, or both.

Paget's is an extremely old disease. The first recorded evidence of the ailment is a grossly thickened Egyptian skull dating from about 1000 B.C. It affects slightly more men than women, and it usually occurs after the age of 40.

Increasingly, statistics show that osteitis deformans is not especially rare. British studies estimate that from 3 to 5 percent of all adult males older than 40 in the U.K. have Paget's disease in some form; the frequency may reach 10 percent after age 70. In the U.S. as many as three million people probably have Paget's disease. Of these, up to 25 percent show distressing symptoms. Besides its tendency to run in families, the disease is known to cluster in specific geographical areas, mostly in Europe and particularly in England and France. Even among populations not prone to Paget's, the disease may exist, frequently limited to relatively small areas, such as the town of Avellino in Italy, where a cluster of cases was found within an extended family.

Pagetic symptoms are frequently misunderstood, and even today many cases have been attributed to the effects of advancing age. In the example of the Avellino family, the affliction was recognized only after an emigrant relative had been diagnosed in New York City. Accurate diagnosis relies on x-rays or blood tests. These examinations look for increased levels of alkaline phosphatase, a product of the cells that form bone. Urine tests may show an increased amount of hydroxyproline, another product of bone breakdown. Treatment includes drugs, specifically calcitonin and disphosphonates, which slow or block the rate of bone breakdown and formation.

FURTHER READING

EGIL'S SAGA. Translated by Hermann Pálsson and Paul Edwards. Penguin Books, 1976.

CORRUGATION OF THE SKULL IN PAGET'S DISEASE OF THE BONE, N. K. Chakravorty, S. K. Das and M. S. Kataria in *Post graduate Medical Journal,* Vol. 53, No. 615, pages 40–46; January 1977.

PAGET'S DISEASE OF THE BONE: ASSESSMENT AND MANAGEMENT. R. C. Hamdy. Praeger Scientific, 1981.

MEDIEVAL ICELAND: SOCIETY, SAGAS, AND POWER. Jesse L. Byock. University of California Press, 1988.

PAGET'S DISEASE OF THE BONE: CLINICAL ASSESSMENT, PRESENT AND FUTURE THERAPY. Edited by Frederick R. Singer and Stanley Wallach. Elsevier Science Publishing, 1991.

THE SKULL AND BONES IN EGIL'S SAGA: A VIKING, A GRAVE, AND PAGET'S DISEASE. Jesse L. Byock in *Viator,* Vol. 24, pages 23–50; 1993.

Find Suggests Weaving Preceded Settled Life

Discovery pushes date of earliest cloth back 7,000 years, to 27,000 years ago.

Brenda Fowler

MINNEAPOLIS

Some 27,000 years ago, an innovative group of hunters and gatherers were in the habit of setting up their summer base camps near a river along the Pavlov Hills in what is now the southeastern Czech Republic. They mixed the fine soil with water and molded it into human and animal figurines and fired them, creating the oldest known fired ceramics. They took the two-and-a-half-million-year-old technology of flaking stone tools a step further by grinding them into smoothly polished pendants and rings, the earliest known examples of ground stone technology in Europe.

And now, at a meeting here last week of the Society for American Archeology, scientists announced that this same group, contemporaries of the earliest cave painters of France and northern Spain, has left the oldest evidence of weaving in the world. The site has yielded clay fragments bearing impressions of textiles or basketry, which according to Dr. James M. Adovasio of Mercyhurst College in Erie, Pa., and Dr. Olga Soffer of the University of Illinois at Urbana, push back the known origin of these technologies at least 7,000 years, to 27,000 years ago.

It also validates a suggestion long offered by some archeologists that the origin of textile technology by far predates the Neolithic period of plant and animal domestication to which it had traditionally been assigned. Archeologists tended to believe that people did not weave until they abandoned the migratory hunting and gathering way of life and settled into permanent agricultural villages with domesticated plants and animals, a process that was getting under way in many parts of the world by around 8000 B.C. and is known as the Neolithic. Once they were sedentary, the story went, they could develop such technologies as ceramics and weaving.

"I think this will really blow the socks off the Neolithic people because they always think they've got the first of everything," Dr. Soffer said in an interview. "We have this association of fabric and ceramics and ground stone technology with the Neolithic although we've known about ceramics from these people at Pavlov for a while, but it was written in Czech or German and it didn't make an impact."

Some scholars of the Upper Paleolithic, which in that part of the world stretches from about 40,000 to 12,000 years ago, had predicted that textiles might have been around at that time. "It's not very unexpected but it's very important," said Dr. Anthony Marks, an archeologist at Southern Methodist University in Dallas.

Textile specialists, especially, were encouraged by the discovery.

"It indicates how important textile structures are," said Dr. John Peter Wild, an archeologist at the University of Manchester in England. "You're way ahead of metals. The only technologies you have to compare it with in sheer brilliance of execution are stone implements. This is the organic technology that matches it."

Previously, the earliest known basketry dated to no earlier than around 13,000 years ago and the oldest piece of woven cloth was a 9,000-year-old specimen from Cayonu in southern Turkey. The oldest known twisted fibers, which could have been woven into basketry or textiles, were found in Israel and date to about 19,300 years ago.

Because baskets and textiles are made of organic materials, they perish rapidly once deposited, Dr. Adovasio said in an interview. Not surprisingly, the absence of hard evidence for textiles in the Paleolithic molded the theories on the origins and development of weaving technology.

People invented textiles in the hunter-gatherer stage of development.

The evidence presented last week consists of four small fragments of fired clay bearing negative impressions of a textile or finely twined basket, Dr. Soffer said. Along with hundreds of thousands of other artifacts at the rich site, they were excavated in 1954 by Dr. Bohuslav Klima, a retired Moravian archeologist. In the summer of 1990, Dr. Soffer, sorting through about 3,000 clay fragments in an effort to categorize them stylistically, noticed four pieces, about the size of a quarter, with markings on their concave sides.

She photographed them, with the notation "plant fibers?" and the next year showed them to her colleague, Dr. Adovasio, who, she said, went "absolutely ballistic."

Three radiocarbon dates of ashes at the site ranged from 24,870 to 26,980 years ago, so the pieces could not have come from any other layers deposited later.

Analyzing magnified, high resolution photographs of the fragments, Dr. Adovasio determined that two fragments bore two different weaves and two bore indistinct parallel impressions that might be from warps, the vertical threads of a weave. He could see the alignment of the plant fibrils in the photographs so he knew the fibers were made of plant material, or bast, and not sinew, which can also be woven. Among the plants that could have provided bast were the yew and alder trees or the milkweed and nettle, the researchers said.

The archeologists did not know whether the impressions were made intentionally or accidentally. Many of the fragments were found in ash deposits. Analysis of all four showed that they had been fired at 600 to 800 degrees Fahrenheit, which is consistent with a simple kiln or a bonfire, or even a dwelling burning down, Dr. Soffer said. One possibility is that the woven item was unintentionally pressed into wet clay near a hearth—perhaps by walking on it—and subsequently fired.

Because the fragments are so small and no selvage, or defined edge, is apparent on them, Dr. Adovasio could not determine what they came from. He said the mesh would have been similar to that in a potato sack and might have come from a bag, mat, clothing or a basket. While it would have been possible to make the pieces without some sort of loom, it would

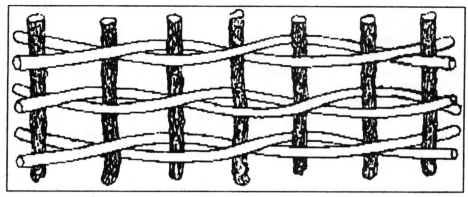

Dr. J. M. Adovasio

One clay impression of early weaving from Pavlov Hills site shows pattern above, called open diagonal twining, S-twist weft. Diagram depicts rigid vertical warp threads; specimen had flexible warps.

have been far easier using one, he said, even if that meant only tying one end of the warp around a tree and the other around one's waist.

"This demonstrates an amazing investment of energy," he said.

Dr. Elizabeth J. W. Barber, a prehistoric textile scholar at Occidental College in Los Angeles, noted that plain, or true weave, involved passing a weft, or horizontal, thread over one warp thread, under the next warp thread, over the next and so on. If a nonflexible stick is woven through the warp like this, then the process can be mechanized halfway. Raising the stick lifts up every other thread of the warp (or whichever warp threads are required for the desired weave) and the weft thread can be speedily pulled through. For the following pass, the position of the separated warp threads must be reversed and that is where a heddle, which individually holds the warp threads of the second group and attaches them to a bar, comes in.

The type of weave in the Pavlov clay fragments is "twining"; though it too can produce a cloth, it cannot be mechanized because the parallel weft threads cross each other. Dr. Barber said twining produced a more stable weave because the weft threads twisted around each other and prevented sliding.

"When you see them switching from twining over to the true weave or plain weave by around 7000 B.C., then they've figured out mechanization," she said. "They've given up stability of weave for speed of production."

Dr. Adovasio noted that twining itself was already a relatively advanced form of weaving technology. He suggested twining might even be as much as 40,000 years old.

"If they're making this, then they're making cordage," said David Hyland, an archeologist at Gannon University in Erie, Pa. Cordage, essentially plant fibers twisted together, includes string and rope.

"And if they can make this, they can make anything in the way of a net, trap or snare," said Dr. Adovasio, who believes that because of the scarcity of evidence, prehistorians had underestimated the importance of woven materials in early peoples' lives. Conversely, he said, because of their relative abundance, stone tools have been overemphasized in archeologists' interpretations of prehistoric economies.

"I don't buy a lot of the gender studies stuff," began Dr. Adovasio.

"But mostly men have done the analysis of Paleolithic sites and they have in their minds the macho hunter of extinct megafauna. Guys who hunt woolly mammoths are not supposed to be making these."

The model of the Paleolithic men going off with spears to hunt while the women stayed home and gathered plants around the camp may be too simple, he said.

"Maybe they killed one mammoth every 10 years and never stopped talking about it," Dr. Soffer said.

At the Pavlov and nearby Dolni Vestonice sites, for example, Dr.

Klima unearthed far more bones of smaller animals than of mammoths. While the former may have been hunted with spears, it is more likely that nets were used to capture small animals like rabbits, the archeologists said.

"This tool,' noted Dr. Hyland, of cloth, "represents a much greater level of success where used for hunting than lithic tools."

Dr. Adovasio, who has been working with textiles for more than 25 years, said he hoped the discovery would inspire archeologists to learn more about how textiles and basketry decayed and to pay more attention to the possibility that textiles or their impressions are preserved on sites.

One mystery is what became of the apparently advanced technologies of these Central European hunters and gatherers after 22,000 years ago, when, as the weather gradually turned colder, the archeological record of their presence in the Pavlov Hills suddenly ceased.

"You've got the huge Scandinavian ice sheet coming down from the north and glaciers coming from the Alps and you get this no-man's land and people get out of there," Dr. Soffer said.

She suspects that some went east and some southest. But except for a few random fired ceramics and bits of net or cord in eastern Europe, the technologies themselves remain silent for the next 7,000 to 10,000 years. When they resurface, the skills the Pavlov people employed so fancifully have been converted to practical purpose. The technique of stone grinding, instead of being used in decorative items alone, is now applied to making hoes and axes. Fired clay turns up not in figurines but in cooking and storage vessels.

"It had never dawned on these people that they could make a pot," Dr. Soffer noted.

Textiles and basketry, too, anchor themselves firmly into the technological landscape.

"It's like who invented the first flying machine? Leonardo da Vinci," Dr. Soffer said. "But Boeing didn't start making them until this century. There has to be a social and economic context for new technology. If you don't have the context, then it won't really go anywhere."

Czech Republic
mammoth-bone huts, personal decorations, fired ceramic figurines

Russia and Ukraine
mammoth-bone huts, decorations

Arctic Ocean

25,000 B.P.
• Malta

20,000 B.P.
to 15,000 B.P.

E U R O P E

• Sungir

• Dolní Věstonice
• Kostenki
Pech-Merle
Lascaux
Altamira
Niaux
Chauvet

40,000 B.P.

A S I A

100,000 B.P.
(Before Present)

70,000 B.P. (?)

France and Spain
cave paintings, engravings, decorations

Pacific Ocean

A F R I C A

Movements of early modern humans

Indian Ocean

40,000 B.P.

Atlantic Ocean

200,000 B.P.

Australia
rock art, decorations

• Kakadu National Park

50,000 B.P. (?)

A U S T R A L I A

• Border Cave

Apollo 11

Southern Africa
rock art, decorative objects

• Bimbowrie Hills

TIME Map by Joe Lertola and Paul J. Pugliese

Ancient Odysseys

As early humans migrated around the globe, image making spread rapidly

Michael D. Lemonick

The human mind can't easily comprehend huge expanses of time. Once the years run into the tens of thousands, our brain lumps them together into an undifferentiated mass. The catchall term prehistoric art works perfectly with this sort of thinking. It sounds like just another episode in art history—modern art, Renaissance art, Byzantine art, prehistoric art.

In reality, the artworks created before history began—prior, say, to about 10,000 B.P. (before the present)—cover a much longer time span than what has come afterward. Southwestern European cave painting, only the most familiar expression of ancient creativity, was done over a period of at least 10,000 years. And when Paleolithic people first crawled into the Chauvet cave to daub the walls with images of rhinos and bears, nearly half of all art history was already over with.

When art first appeared, presumably around 40,000 B.P., it spread quickly. Within a mere 5,000 years—barely the blink of an eye on paleontological time scales—the work of early artists popped up in several corners of the globe. Archaeologists have found more than 10,000 sculpted and engraved objects in hundreds of locations across Europe, southern Africa, northern Asia and Australia. The styles range from realistic to abstract, and the materials include stone, bone, antler, ivory, wood, paint, teeth, claws, shells and clay that have been carved, sculpted and painted to represent animals, plants, geometric forms, landscape features and human beings—virtually every medium and every kind of subject that artists would return to thousands of years later.

This creative explosion is best documented in Europe, largely because that is where most of the excavations have taken place. Early body decoration, for example, was found in the 1950s by

Soviet archaeologists at Sungir, near the Russian city of Vladimir. From graves dating back to 28,000 B.P., they unearthed the remains of a 10-year-old girl, a 12-year-old boy and a 60-year-old man. The three are festooned with beads, more than 14,000 all told. But each is adorned in a different way, evidence that body decoration was used to emphasize gender and age distinctions in social groups. In addition to the beads, the girl has delicate snowflake-like carvings around her head and torso. The boy has no snowflakes but wears a belt made from 240 fox canine teeth. And the man is wearing a single pendant made of stone in the middle of his chest. Another distinction: the beads on the children's bodies are approximately two thirds the size of those the man is wearing.

At about the same time that the three were being buried—give or take a few millenniums—a new sort of artifact begins to appear in the prehistorical

Art through the Prehistoric Ages

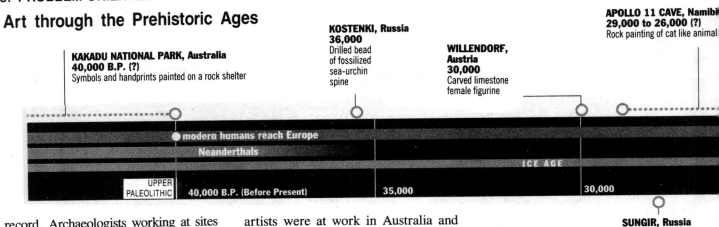

KAKADU NATIONAL PARK, Australia
40,000 B.P. (?)
Symbols and handprints painted on a rock shelter

KOSTENKI, Russia
36,000
Drilled bead of fossilized sea-urchin spine

WILLENDORF, Austria
30,000
Carved limestone female figurine

APOLLO 11 CAVE, Namib
29,000 to 26,000 (?)
Rock painting of cat like animal

modern humans reach Europe

Neanderthals

ICE AGE

UPPER PALEOLITHIC 40,000 B.P. (Before Present)   35,000   30,000

SUNGIR, Russia
28,000
Ivory animal pendant with traces of paint

record. Archaeologists working at sites all across Europe and well into Russia have found dozens of so-called Venus figurines: miniature sculptures of big-breasted, broad-hipped women. The statuettes, which may have been used in fertility rites or even religious ceremonies, suggest a worshipful attitude toward fertility and reproduction.

By 22,000 B.P., archaeologists have found, the first evidence of the cave paintings that appeal so strongly to modern eyes begins to appear. The paintings, some of them realistic portraits of animals, others depicting half-human, half-animal figures or abstract symbols, soon became the dominant form of prehistoric European art. They remained important until 10,000 B.P., when, along with the glaciers of the last Ice Age, they seem to have melted away from human consciousness.

Those are the broad outlines, at least, of early art history. The details are much messier: it's not as though one phase gave way smoothly to another. Beadwork and statuette carving didn't stop just because cave painting began—and the presence of caves didn't automatically inspire people to cover them with images. Says Jean Clottes, one of France's pre-eminent authorities on prehistoric art: "There are a lot of caves in Yugoslavia, for example, but no paintings in them." Moreover, there is enormous regional variation in what sorts of art were produced at what times.

The story is even less straightforward in other parts of the world. Not only have extensive explorations been less common outside Europe, but also what's been found has proved difficult to date. Nonetheless, it is clear that

artists were at work in Australia and southern Africa, at least, at roughly the same time as their European cousins.

The Australian continent abounds in Aboriginal rock art, both paintings and engravings. Much of it lies in a 1,500-mile-long, boomerang-shaped area across the country's north coast. Archaeologist Darrell Lewis of the Australian National University estimates that there are at least 10,000 rock-art sites on the Arnhem Land plateau alone, in the Northern Territory. "Each of these sites," he says, "can have several hundred paintings." But unlike early inhabitants of Europe, who frequently decorated caves over a short period and then abandoned them, the Australian Aborigines would return over and over to the same sites—a practice that still goes on today. Unraveling the history of a single site can thus be extremely complicated.

How old is Australia's art? Some archaeologists insist that certain paintings of human hands and life-size crocodiles and kangaroos were done 50,000 years ago, but these experts may be overconfident of their dating techniques. Another controversial assertion is the claim by anthropologist Alan Thorne of the Australian National University that a small piece of red ochre (a kind of clay), dated to 50,000 B.P., was worn down on one side like a piece of chalk by humans. "Whether it was ground to paint a shelter or a person or part of a wall, I don't think anyone would disagree that it is evidence of art," says Thorne. Even if Australia's art is not as ancient as Thorne thinks, there is strong evidence that at least two rock carvings found in the Bimbowrie Hills are more than

40,000 years old, and that scores of others in the area fall between 30,000 and 20,000 B.P.

Southern Africa's artistic record is much sparser. Scientists have unearthed a pendant made from a seashell that may be more than 40,000 years old, carved bones and beads made from ostrich eggshells that probably date from around 27,000 B.P., and paintings on slabs of rock in a Namibian cave that may be nearly as old. But like Australia's Aborigines, southern Africa's indigenous people carried on their rock-art tradition into modern times, confusing anthropologists' tasks considerably.

And in the rest of the world . . . nothing. Not in the Middle East, not in Southeast Asia, not in China or Japan or Korea, and not in North Africa before 15,000 B.P. at the very earliest—although there is ample evidence of an ancient human presence in all these areas. This may mean the people there weren't interested in art, or it may simply be that they painted or carved on wood or animal skins, which have long since rotted away.

Nobody can do more than speculate about the answer. That uncertainty, along with the spottiness of the archaeological record—even in an intensively studied area like southern France—makes it hard to know whether art, once invented, was a universal practice. Probably not, argues archaeologist Olga Soffer, of the University of Illinois at Urbana-Champaign: "Art is

OLNI VESTONICE, Czech Republic
26,000
Engraved mammoth tusk

GRIMALDI,
Italy
23,000
Serpentine pendant
depicting a pregnant woman

LASCAUX, France
18,000 to 17,000
Portion of the Hall of the Bulls

ALTAMIRA, Spain
12,000
Cave painting of a bison

modern humans reach Siberia/Arctic regions

farming begins in Mesopotamia

POST GLACIAL PERIOD

MESOLITHIC PERIOD

25,000   20,000   15,000   10,000

TIME Graphic by Steve Hart

CHAUVET, France
20,000
Painting of a giant deer

MEZHIRICH, Ukraine
18,000 to 15,000
Intricately patterned mammoth-bone hut

ROCHER DE LA PEINE, France
12,000
Necklace of shells and animal teeth

VDEEVO,
ussia
5,000
ory figurine
a woman

a social phenomenon that appears and disappears and, in some places, may not arise at all." But many anthropologists counter that the term art is usually defined too narrowly. What paleolithic humans really invented, they say, is symbolic representation, and by that definition art may well appear in every culture—though it might not be easy for us to recognize.

It's also difficult to say whether art originated in a specific part of the world. By the time of humanity's great artistic awakening, Homo sapiens had probably already traveled from its African homeland through most of Europe and Asia. The urge to make art could have arisen in any of these places and spread throughout the world, or it could have happened in many areas independently.

There are problems with either scenario, however. "The pattern is puzzling," observes anthropologist Randall White. "One of the most common forms of body adornment in Western Europe during this early period is canine teeth from carnivores, drilled with holes and worn as dangling ornamentation. And damned if in Australia, some 35,000 to 40,000 years ago this isn't exactly what they're doing too." It might seem like an unremarkable coincidence—after all, carnivores must have loomed large in every culture. But an-

thropologists have learned that such coincidences are actually quite rare. If art did spread around the world, it moved with astonishing speed (on a paleontological time scale, that is), and, says White, "it's a long way from southern France to Australia."

One possible explanation: art was percolating along for tens of thousands of years before most of the known examples show up. Perhaps the original Homo sapiens populations in Africa invented art and carried it to other regions. The reasons nothing much has been found dating before 40,000 B.P., goes the argument, are that scientists haven't looked hard enough and most of the evidence has perished. As appealing as it may seem though, this art-is-older-than-we-think theory has attracted little support; the demarcation line at 40,000 B.P. is just too sharp.

New discoveries like the one at the Chauvet cave, and more intensive study of existing sites, are constantly giving archaeologists more information to work with. Also, dating techniques are becoming more refined. It used to be that scientists needed to test a large sample of paint to pinpoint its age. And, says anthropologist Margaret Conkey, "no one was willing to scrape a bison's rump off the wall." Now it takes only a tiny sample. French prehistory expert Arlette Leroi-Gourhan

estimates dates by using pollen particles preserved on cave floors.

The results of all these studies, while always enlightening, don't necessarily simplify things for scientists. A new analysis of the Cosquer cave on the French Riviera, for example, has shown that painted handprints on the walls date to 27,000 B.P., while images of horses and other animals came some 9,000 years later. Rather than being decorated in a single, prolonged burst of creativity, the cavern was painted over scores of centuries, quite possibly by artists who had no connection of any kind with one another, unlike Aborigines, whose culture has direct links to the distant past.

Prehistoric art was created over so long a period by so many different humans in so many parts of the world, and presumably for so many different reasons, that it may never fit into a tidy catalog. These ancient masterpieces are telling us that our prehistoric forebears had modes of expression more varied than we once imagined—and also that we'll never truly understand just how rich their lives must have been.

—Reported by David Bjerklie and Andrea Dorfman/New York, Tim Blair/Melbourne, Peter Hawthorne/Cape Town and Thomas Sancton/Paris

Thailand's Good Mound

*Twenty generations of burials provide an intimate portrait of
a Stone Age village*

Charles Higham and
Rachanie Thosarat

About 650 feet wide and 40 feet high, Khok Phanom Di, "the good mound," stands out on the flat flood plain of Thailand's Bang Pakong River. Unoccupied in living memory except for a Buddhist temple, the site passed as a natural hill until a bulldozer, cutting a new path to the top, revealed a deep sequence of archeological deposits. These contained abundant remains of shellfish adapted to coastal mud flats, although nowadays the sea lies fourteen miles to the west. Damrongkiadt Noksakul, a staff member of the local teachers' college, excavated a small test square, which we visited in 1981. Peering into the inky gloom, we saw layer upon layer of hearths, ash, and discarded shellfish remains stretching down twenty-eight feet. This preliminary excavation had yielded eleven human burials, numerous pottery shards, abundant remains of rice, and shells from species of mollusks and crustaceans adapted to life in an estuary and along the seashore.

The site intrigued us because little was known of prehistoric settlements in Thailand so close to the sea. Most archeological work on early groups had been done along small tributary streams in the interior. Yet the wealth of resources on the coast or along major rivers probably played an important role in the spread of rice cultivation and in making mainland Southeast Asia the home of some of the world's great early civilizations. The best known of these civilizations had as its court center Angkor (in present-day Cambodia), a site that represented heaven in stone and incorporated vast temple mausoleums for its deified lords.

Toward the end of 1984, we returned to Khok Phanom Di with an archeological team to excavate a square measuring one hundred square meters, or about 1,075 square feet. We had no illusions about the ease of our undertaking, which eventually involved the removal of 28,000 cubic feet of prehistoric material. We chose this single large square, however, in hopes of discovering the spatial arrangement of ancient life—perhaps house plans, the layout of a cemetery, or distinct areas for different activities. Our research was designed to find out about the way of life of the occupants and how their environment may have changed over the generations.

We erected a steel roof to shelter the square from rain and sun and arranged for electrical wiring. Water was piped in to allow us to clean the finds before sorting and packing them. Jill Thompson, a member of the team, set up a large metal tank to float plant remains out of the archeological deposits. Brian Vincent processed much of the pottery as it was recovered, and Bernard Maloney was on hand to analyze the remains of pollen, a key to understanding the changing environment in the vicinity of the site. After seven months of digging, we reached a com-

pacted, sandy layer at a depth of about twenty-one feet. At last, we were able to stand on the river flood plain that was first occupied in antiquity. The Thai workers who were helping us—and who had shown as much interest in our discoveries as we did—were equally relieved to reach bottom.

In our square—still only a fraction of the total mound—we encountered part of a cemetery. We also observed that nearer the edge of the mound, the road-cut exposed layers of debris where prehistoric pots had been fired. The remains of houses probably lay elsewhere. In the earliest layers of the excavated material, we found extensive spreads of ash and much charcoal, along with pottery shards and blunted, well-used stone adz heads. Some of the pottery shards were encrusted with marine barnacles; judging from the species of ostracods and foraminifers, the earliest inhabitants established their settlement on a sheltered estuary of a major river near its entrance to the open sea. Dating of the charcoal showed that these early deposits were about 4,000 years old.

To determine the environment prior to the site's occupation, Bernard Maloney removed a series of cores from the natural sediments that surround the site (the base of the site itself was too hard for our equipment to penetrate). Beneath the present day rice fields he found about eighteen feet of stiff, blue clay that had been laid down under a shallow sea. The clay contained microscopic fragments of charcoal and the

The inhabitants of ancient Khok Phanom Di, map below, exploited many resources, including rice, which was originally cultivated in China's Yangtze Valley.

we have found tell us that they set nets in the estuary for the many species of passing fish. They also took their boats out to coastal waters to fish by line, using barbed fishhooks made of bone, and cultivated rice in the freshwater swamps behind the coastal mangrove belt. These ideal conditions favored permanent settlement, and during the ensuing years, from 4,000 until 3,500 years ago, twenty-one feet of cultural debris built up.

The inhabitants of Khok Phanom Di were in a good position to trade up-river with people inhabiting the interior and along the coast with other maritime settlements. A sedentary way of life means that trading partners know where to find one another. It permits the accumulation of weighty personal possessions and makes the construction of buildings worthwhile. And not least, it opens up the possibility of an expanding population. Where mobility is the rule, births need to be widely spaced, or there will be too many young children to carry. Permanence removes this constraint, and women can reduce the interval between pregnancies. The need to feed more mouths within such sedentary communities may help explain the rapid spread of agriculture that took place in many different parts of the world beginning 12,000 years ago.

Long-term occupation also allows for the maintenance of a cemetery as a resting place for dead ancestors. Such was the custom at Khok Phanom Di, where we found about twenty generations of burials (assuming an average interval of twenty-five years between generations). In preliterate times, the continuing presence of the ancestors may have helped signify the ownership of local land and resources.

Covered in red ocher and wrapped in shrouds fashioned from beaten bark cloth or sheets of asbestos fiber, the dead were interred face-up with their heads to the east. The oldest level of burials in the excavated part of the cemetery included only six interments, and they were very simple. Only one contained a durable grave offering—a necklace of twelve shell beads. Thereafter, burials accumulated steadily, and

remains of pollen. By dating samples of the charcoal taken at different levels in the cores, he was able to estimate that the clay was deposited between 8,000 and 4,000 years ago. And by identifying and counting the pollen grains in samples taken at intervals throughout the deposit, Maloney was also able to get a picture of the vegetation.

Mangrove pollen dominated, reinforcing other evidence that the area was near the seashore. At times, however, the quantity of charcoal rose spectacularly and the pollen of grasses and some plants that flourish in rice fields today became more prominent. Such episodes occurred sporadically beginning 7,800 years ago. Several explanations are possible: natural forest fires, burn-offs by local hunters and gatherers, and the clearing of land by rice cultivators. Possibly, people frequented the area long before they settled at Khok Phanom Di itself about 4,000 years ago. A modern fish pond dug into the marine clay near the site

revealed a deep layer of ash and pottery that may belong to this earlier time (we didn't venture to date this material, since it was not covered by our research permit).

Toward the top of the sediment cores, Maloney found evidence for a major episode of burning and the proliferation of grass pollen. This stratum was dated to the early period when Khok Phanom Di was occupied and surely reflects the activities of its inhabitants. They probably were cutting the coastal forests for fuel, including that needed to fire clay vessels, which they shaped from the rich local source of clay. They may also have been burning off dry-season plant growth in order to make way for their rice.

Because their estuary provided a wide range of renewable food resources, the inhabitants of Khok Phanom Di were probably rarely, if ever, short of food. At low tide they collected the abundant shellfish that lived on the mud flats. The clay net weights the accompanying grave goods became more elaborate, until the cemetery was abandoned.

The cemetery was arranged in a grid of at least six separate clusters. With time, new burials were placed over preceding ones, continuing the same pattern of clusters. We noted many post holes, the residue of building foundations. Their distribution is irregular, but some alignments hint that each of the grave clusters was housed within a wooden structure, forming, in effect, a collective tomb. Doubtless the wood decayed with time, and the structures had to be refurbished or replaced.

The space between the burials contained the remains of much activity. We found middens (refuse heaps), circular pits containing the remains of unopened—and therefore uneaten—shellfish, and thin layers of ash. Very likely burial was an occasion for funerary ritual, including grave-side feasting and, perhaps, the placing of food in pits to provision the ancestors. At inland sites of comparable age, archeologists find bones from the legs of cattle or pigs, with no sign of cut marks from butchering. The animals were probably slaughtered for a mortuary feast and a limb placed with the dead. These practices seem to have disappeared with the introduction of Buddhism and cremation.

When one of our Thai colleagues, Praphid Choosiri, examined the human remains, she sometimes found rare or unusual bone structures thought to be genetically determined. Two examples of these, with the technical names *metopic suture* and *os inca,* concern the presence of extra sutures between bones in the skull. She noted that successive interments in the grave clusters sometimes exhibit the same rare characteristic, suggesting that each of the burial areas was devoted to a particular lineage. Based on this assumption, we set out to reconstruct prehistoric family trees and consider their ups and downs.

We found that two lineages were especially stable, in that they continued for the full complement of generations for the life of the cemetery. For

one reason or another, however, some lineages failed to maintain themselves. In general, we observed that infant mortality was high for the first eight or so generations, so perhaps these families died out. An alternative explanation is that, as the number of inhabitants grew, the leaders of some lineages left with their relatives to found new settlements elsewhere.

In studying the two stable lineages, we found that the quantity of grave goods varied considerably between burials: some had nothing, while others were very rich. They included lustrously burnished and decorated pots, iridescent shell beads, translucent shell disks, and stone adz heads. Small clay anvils used in making pots were found only with the remains of women, children, and infants. (Such an anvil would have been held inside the vessel as it was shaped with a wooden paddle.) On the other hand, twelve-inch-wide plaques fashioned from sea turtle carapaces, apparently worn as chest ornaments, were found only with the skeletons of men. Both men and women were interred with the stones used to burnish pottery vessels until they shone.

Neither of the two stable lineages appeared consistently wealthier than the other. Fortunes rose or fell after a generation or two, or at most three. This suggests that esteem and status—assuming these translated into mortuary wealth—had to be attained through personal achievement. They were not inherited by right, except to the extent that when infants died, wealthy parents were able to endow them with rare and beautiful grave goods. (Interestingly, infants less than a month or two old were not accorded such attention; perhaps they were still too young to be regarded as official members of society.)

Evidence of important changes at Khok Phanom Di emerged after the actual excavation, as our team of specialists completed their analyses of various kinds of data. Up to the ninth or tenth generation, the inhabitants of the village continued to exploit both the river and seacoast. Men had strong muscular development in their upper

bodies, and men and women apparently had somewhat different diets—women had more caries and tooth loss, while men kept their teeth longer and therefore showed more tooth wear. People were interred with beautifully decorated pots, and many wore shell jewelry. Infant mortality was high.

Then, about the tenth generation, something happened to the maritime connection. Marine and coastal shellfish gave way to species from freshwater or backwater mangrove stands. Mangrove wood became less common in the charcoal. From this time on, men appeared less muscular. Shell jewelry practically disappeared, and even pottery vessels became less common and lacked ornate decoration. Men and women shared a new diet pattern, probably including fewer shellfish. And infant mortality rates dropped.

We think these changes were a reaction to a swift alteration in the environment, probably a major flood followed by a shift in the river channel away from Khok Phanom Di. A gradual deposition of sediment also left the site farther from the sea. Men, whose previous strength probably reflected habitual paddling of boats, now embarked on fewer coastal voyages. The local source of high-quality shell for ornaments also suffered as the sediments killed off preferred species. And the change in habitat or diet may have reduced the danger of certain diseases, improving infant survival.

After three or four generations of relative poverty, yet another pattern emerged. We encountered a very large grave belonging to one of the two main clusters. It contained the remains of a woman in her mid-thirties. Her body was covered with a pile of clay cylinders, which may represent clay destined for conversion into pots, and the broken pieces of five ornately decorated vessels. Her personal jewelry included 120,000 shell beads, two shell disks, a headdress, and on her left wrist, a bangle made of an exotic shell. In life this woman must have been dazzling in her finery. Beside her right ankle lay a shell containing two burnishing pebbles next to a clay anvil. We think that she must have been an outstanding potter. She had well-developed wrist muscles, consistent with preparing and molding clay.

Beside her was a matching grave containing the remains of a fifteen-month-old infant. Again, we encountered a pile of clay cylinders, the body festooned with 12,000 shell beads, a bangle placed over the left wrist, beautiful pots, and a miniature clay anvil beside the right ankle.

Despite the opulence of these two burials, the succeeding generation in what we believe was the same lineage displayed very little wealth. In contrast, the other main lineage now attained greater status within the community. We found the remains of two women and a nine-year-old child buried beneath the two-foot-high raised floor of a rectangular mortuary building. Both women were buried with clay anvils, and one was buried with 11,000 shell beads. The child was accompanied by a thick shell disk and at least 18,000 beads.

Our interpretation is that the community adapted to its now more inland habitat by expanding its ceramic industry, already established owing to the settlement's rich resources and favorable location. This craft, apparently the province of women, might have provided a valuable commodity for trade. Perhaps more than ever, a potter's skill became a source of individual prestige and a route to wealth. Jewelry came to include new styles of heavy bracelets and disks made of tridacna and trochus shell. These species of mollusks are adapted to a clean, coralline habitat and so must have been obtained by exchange from some distance away.

As before, while individuals might attain the prestige evident in a rich burial, they do not seem to have been able to convert this into inherited status and rank. Rather, one family might be successful in one generation, only to be followed by less able or less fortunate descendants in the next. This might have reflected success or failure in craftsmanship and in exchange dealings with other communities, depending on individual skill or charisma. Only when a mortuary tradition in a single community can be followed over so many generations can we gain such an intimate glimpse into its operating principles. No similar site exists elsewhere in Southeast Asia, and very few in the rest of the prehistoric world.

Any community that relies on female potters for making vessels for mortuary ritual and exchange would be reluctant to lose them to other communities through marriage. We believe that the custom at Khok Phanom Di, at least for this later period, was for women to remain at their place of birth. In such a "matrilocal" community, failure to produce a female heir would have spelled the end of the lineage. This may explain the attention given to the details of child or infant burials, some of whom, presumably the young girls, were interred with clay anvils.

We also noted that proportionately fewer men were buried in the cemetery during the later phase, although at least one was well provided with grave goods. A possibility is that men were now using sailing craft to engage in long-distance trade, taking pots and returning with shells. The present-day seafaring people of southern Thailand have a tradition of such voyaging, which is usually the work of men. When they die at sea, their bodies are interred in caves remote from their home base.

Despite its renewed prosperity, Khok Phanom Di was eventually abandoned, about 3,500 years ago. Perhaps the inhabitants chose to move closer to the coast. While we cannot say what happened to them, we have subsequently excavated another cemetery about eight miles to the south, at Nong Nor. This cemetery was in use from about 500 to 800 years after Khok Phanom Di was abandoned. In some ways it shows a similar mortuary ritual, with the bodies oriented with the head to the east and clusters containing men, women, and children (but there is no buildup of successive graves that would enable us to trace individual family groups through time). At Nong Nor, the men were buried with the potter's anvils and usually had the richest grave goods. The artifacts include ornaments cast in bronze and tin as well as jewelry of serpentine, talc, carnelian, and jade, indicating wider trade contacts.

Khok Phanom Di is one in a series of sites that mark the origins and expansion of rice-growing agriculturists in the hot, densely forested lands of Southeast Asia. The spread of agriculturists can be reconstructed by identifying similarities between many languages spoken in southern China and Southeast Asia today and by tracing them back to a common origin. According to this linguistic and associated radiocarbon evidence, there was a transition to rice farming in the Yangtze Valley of China about 8,500 years ago. The ancestors of the Vietnamese and Khmer, as well as the Munda speakers of eastern India, apparently moved down the major rivers, bringing their farming economy along with them.

Recent evidence suggests that the first farmers reached Thailand about 4,500 years ago. Occupied between 4,000 and 3,500 years ago, Khok Phanom Di has provided us with the clearest available evidence for their way of life. At the time the site was abandoned, Southeast Asia was entering the Bronze Age, as copper and tin began to be cast separately or alloyed to create ornaments, weapons, and tools. The later site of Nong Nor already includes some of these artifacts.

In terms of social organization, however, little changed in Southeast Asia until about 2,500 years ago, when the smelting of iron ores was discovered or introduced. Regional leaders began to control metal-working specialists, who cast a new range of luxury bronzes, including drinking vessels and drums. Over the next 500 years, Southeast Asia joined ever widening trade networks, and powerful regional chiefdoms arose as the rivalry and competition over luxury goods grew. The later chiefs forged the first states in Southeast Asia, a heritage that culminated 1,000 years ago in the founding of the great holy city of Angkor.

Experimental Archaeology

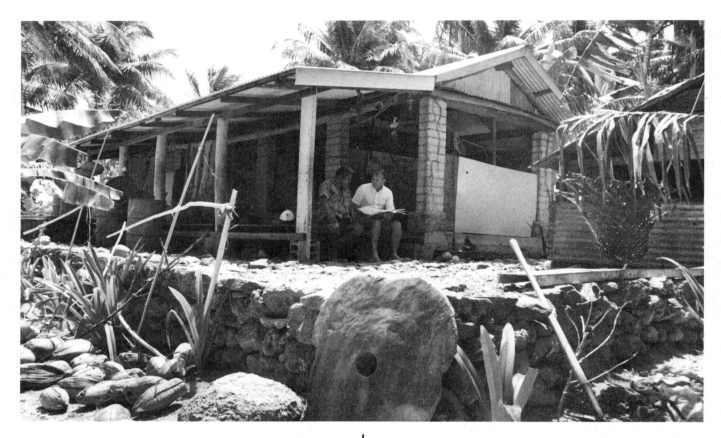

Some archaeologists would like to see experimental archaeology become a major subfield of the science of archaeology. Until recently, most archaeologists have viewed this approach as a supplementary technique to enhance archaeological data.

The criteria of experimental archaeology in the strictest sense are that an experiment must be set up in the present which will in some way reenact or recreate a past archaeological process. The idea underlying experimental archaeology is similar to the principle of *uniformitarianism* that Charles Lyell presented in the nineteenth century in order to interpret geological phenomena.

This principle is based on two ideas. One is that geological processes that occur in the present also occurred in the past. This would include such things as earthquakes, water erosion, mountain building, continental drift, volcanic activity, and so forth. The second idea is that the rate at which geological processes modified the crust of the Earth is uniform (the same) in the present as it is was in the past. For example, consider the Grand Canyon in the United States. This great wonder of geology was formed by water erosion. The canyon's depth consists of about one mile of sedimentary rock layers leveled down by the pressure of ages of water literally cutting into the rock. It is this same process that continues to erode rock at Niagara Falls. The processes that modify the Earth's crust are universal.

In the case of Niagara Falls, for many years observers have been monitoring the rate at which the rock recedes each year due to water erosion. In this manner they have been able to establish a *uniform* rate of erosion. This does not mean that the rate of erosion at Niagara Falls is exactly the same every year. It means that given X amount of water pressure, a rock density of Y will erode at the rate of Z inches per year. Usually the sum total of the different rates of erosion over a period of years will be averaged, so that a statement such as "the average rate of erosion per year at Niagara Falls is four and one half inches of rock" may be made.

Experimental archaeology is based on the same general principles. Usually, archaeologically derived processes involve shorter time spans and can be stated with greater accuracy. However, archaeological processes also involve the eccentricities of human behavior and must be treated with considerable caution.

One variable in archaeology in which experimental archaeology may be used is with respect to questions about the state of preservation of archaeological materials. In archaeology there are many absolute dating methods which give good approximations of how old a thing is. One of the most frequently used is the radio-carbon dating method. However, people have a tendency to unconsciously assume that the more recent an artifact is, the better its state of preservation will be. And likewise, that the older an artifact is, the more deteriorated it will be.

The state of preservation of archaeological materials is dependent upon many variables, most particularly the original material of the artifact and the conditions of the medium (site) in which it is preserved. A nineteenth-century adobe mission in the Mojave desert in California may be so weathered as to be unrecognizable. This is because the extreme temperatures, from very hot to very cold, typical of a low desert climate tend to rapidly destroy any kind of matter. On the other hand, consistently wet or consistently dry conditions will tend to preserve organic matter in a relatively pristine state for long periods of time. The preservation of human remains is therefore very good in bogs (such as in Denmark), which are consistently damp, or in the coastal deserts of Peru where the conditions are consistently dry over the millennia.

But archaeologists need not wait for such discoveries to be made. They may set up their own experiments in terms of preservation. Both material (artifacts) and medium (soil) may be infinitely varied and repeatedly tested and fine-tuned under laboratory conditions. Not only does this generate a set of relationships that may be used as a basis in any archaeological situation, it also acts as a cross-check on other dating methods. For example, radiocarbon dates can be seriously skewed by unusual chemical conditions in the artifact, the soil, or by inadvertent contamination in the process of excavation or laboratory analysis. These dates may be salvaged by using experimentally generated data to correct for such contamination, or it may be shown that the samples are not correctable.

Experimental archaeology may also elucidate cultural historical reconstruction and questions of human behavior. In this unit William Rathje's famous "Garbage Project" is examined. Modern garbology presents archaeologists with an opportunity to practice a kind of "sociology of garbage." What people say they do, eat, or practice is often quite different from what their garbage tells of their actual behavior. Furthermore, these deviations seem to vary in predictable patterns based on chosen variables such as income level, occupation, family unit, and so forth.

This study of modern garbology has also reinforced what archaeologists already know, that is, the recognition that written history or the information received from living informants is sometimes heavily biased in certain directions. These biases may be discerned through archaeological excavation. In fact, all anthropologists have to be somewhat wary of both the written and spoken word. Often the fish wasn't as long as the tale. A healthy dose of skepticism is always part of the recipe for scientific thinking.

Looking Ahead: Challenge Questions

Why do archaeologists study modern garbage? Does any other discipline do this?

Have you ever looked at your own garbage after a week? What might it tell you?

How can seemingly impossible feats be accomplished by ancient peoples? Give an example.

Cultural anthropologists use "participant observation." Could an archaeologist do this?

If you want to know how something was done, what is the best way to find out? Give an example.

Why do people give lip service to values they no longer practice? Give an example and discuss it.

What kinds of practical things can modern peoples learn from ancient peoples?

Yes, Wonderful Things

William Rathje and Cullen Murphy

On a crisp October morning not long ago the sun ascended above the Atlantic Ocean and turned its gaze on a team of young researchers as they swarmed over what may be the largest archaeological site in the world. The mound they occupied covers three thousand acres and in places rises more than 155 feet above a low-lying island. Its mass, estimated at 100 million tons, and its volume, estimated at 2.9 billion cubic feet, make it one of the largest manmade structures in North America. And it is known to be a treasure trove—a Pompeii, a Tikal, a Valley of the Kings—of artifacts from the most advanced civilization the planet has ever seen. Overhead sea gulls cackled and cawed, alighting now and then to peck at an artifact or skeptically observe an archaeologist at work. The surrounding landscape still supported quail and duck, but far more noticeable were the dusty, rumbling wagons and tractors of the New York City Department of Sanitation.

The site was the Fresh Kills landfill, on Staten Island, in New York City, a repository of garbage that, when shut down, in the year 2005, will have reached a height of 505 feet above sea level, making it the highest geographic feature along a fifteen-hundred-mile stretch of the Atlantic seaboard running north from Florida all the way to Maine. One sometimes hears that Fresh Kills will have to be closed when it reaches 505 feet so as not to interfere with the approach of aircraft to Newark Airport, in New Jersey, which lies just across the waterway called Arthur Kill. In reality, though, the 505-foot elevation is the result of a series of calculations designed to maximize the landfill's size while avoiding the creation of grades so steep that roads built upon the landfill can't safely be used.

Fresh Kills was originally a vast marshland, a tidal swamp. Robert Moses's plan for the area, in 1948, was to dump enough garbage there to fill the marshland up—a process that would take, according to one estimate, until 1968—and then to develop the site, building houses, attracting light industry, and setting aside open space for recreational use. ("The Fresh Kills landfill project," a 1951 report to Mayor Vincent R. Impelliteri observed, "cannot fail to affect constructively a wide area around it. It is at once practical and idealistic.") Something along these lines may yet happen when Fresh Kills is closed. Until then, however, it is the largest active landfill in the world. It is twenty-five times the size of the Great Pyramid of Khufu at Giza, forty times the size of the Temple of the Sun at Teotihuacan. The volume of Fresh Kills is approaching that of the Great Wall of China, and by one estimate will surpass it at some point in the next few years. It is the sheer physical stature of Fresh Kills in the hulking world of landfills that explains why archaeologists were drawn to the place.

To the archaeologists of the University of Arizona's Garbage Project, which is now entering its twentieth year, landfills represent valuable lodes of information that may, when mined and interpreted, produce valuable insights—insights not into the nature of some past society, of course, but into the nature of our own. Garbage is among humanity's most prodigious physical legacies to those who have yet to be born; if we can come to understand our discards, Garbage Project archaeologists argue, then we will better understand the world in which we live. It is this conviction that prompts Garbage Project researchers to look upon the steaming detritus of daily existence with the same quiet excitement displayed by Howard Carter and Lord George Edward Carnarvon at the unpillaged, unopened tomb of Tutankhamun.

"Can you see anything?" Carnarvon asked as Carter thrust a lighted candle through a hole into the gloom of the first antechamber. "Yes," Carter replied. "Wonderful things."

Garbage archaeology can be conducted in several ways. At Fresh Kills the method of excavation involved a mobile derrick and a thirteen-hundred-pound bucket auger, the latter of which would be sunk into various parts of the landfill to retrieve samples of garbage from selected strata. At 6:15 a.m. Buddy Kellett of the company Kellett's Well Boring, Inc., which had assisted with several previous Garbage Project landfill digs, drove one of the company's trucks, with derrick and auger collapsed for travel, straight up the steep slope of one of the landfill mounds. Two-thirds of the way up, the Garbage Project crew directed Kellett to a small patch of level ground. Four hydraulic posts were deployed from the stationary vehicle, extending outward to keep it safely moored. Now the derrick was raised. It supported a long metal rod that in turn housed two other metal rods; the apparatus, when pulled to its full length, like a telescope, was capable of penetrating the landfill to a depth of ninety-seven feet—enough at this particular spot to go clear through its bottom and into the original marsh that Fresh Kills had been (or into what was left of it). At the end of the rods was the auger, a large bucket made of high-tension steel: four feet high, three feet in diameter, and open at the bottom like a cookie cutter, with six graphite-and-steel teeth around the bottom's circumference. The bucket would spin at about thirty revolutions per minute and with such force that virtually nothing could impede its descent. At a Garbage Project excavation in Sunnyvale, California, in 1988, one of the first things the bucket hit in the cover dirt a few feet below the surface of the Sunnyvale Landfill was the skeleton of a car. The bucket's teeth snapped the axle, and drilled on.

The digging at Fresh Kills began. Down the whirring bucket plunged. Moments later it returned with a gasp, laden with garbage that, when released, spewed a thin vapor into the chill autumnal air. The smell was pungent, somewhere between sweet and disagreeable. Kellett's rig operator, David Spillers, did his job with the relaxation that comes of familiarity, seemingly oblivious to the harsh grindings and sharp clanks. The rest of the archaeological crew, wearing cloth aprons and heavy rubber gloves, went about their duties with practiced efficiency and considerable speed. They were veteran members of the Garbage Project's A-Team—its landfill-excavating arm—and had been through it all before.

Again a bucketful of garbage rose out of the ground. As soon as it was dumped Masakazu Tani, at the time a Japanese graduate student in anthropology at the University of Arizona (his Ph.D. thesis, recently completed, involves identifying activity areas in ancient sites on the basis of distributions of litter), plunged a thermometer into the warm mass. "Forty-three degrees centigrade," Tani called out. The temperature (equivalent to 109.4 degrees Fahrenheit) was duly logged. The garbage was then given a brusque preliminary examination to determine its generic source and, if possible, its date of origin. In this case the presence of telltale domestic items, and of legible newspapers, made both tasks easy. Gavin Archer, another anthropologist and a research associate of the Garbage Project, made a notation in the running log that he would keep all day long: "Household, circa 1977." Before the next sample was pulled up Douglas

Wilson, an anthropologist who specializes in household hazardous waste, stepped up to the auger hole and played out a weighted tape measure, eventually calling out, "Thirty-five feet." As a safety precaution, Wilson, like any other crew member working close to the sunken shaft on depth-measure duty, wore a leather harness tethered to a nearby vehicle. The esophagus created by the bucket auger was just large enough to accept a human being, and anyone slipping untethered a story or two into this narrow, oxygen-starved cavity would die of asphyxiation before any rescue could be attempted.

Most of the bucketfuls of garbage received no more attention than did the load labeled "Household, circa 1977." Some basic data were recorded for tracking purposes, and the garbage was left on a quickly accumulating backdirt pile. But as each of what would finally be fourteen wells grew deeper and deeper, at regular intervals (either every five or every ten feet) samples were taken and preserved for full-dress analysis. On those occasions Wilson Hughes, the methodical and serenely ursine co-director and field supervisor of the Garbage Project, and the man responsible for day-to-day logistics at the Fresh Kills dig, would call out to the bucket operator over the noise of the engine: "We'll take the next bucket." Then Hughes and Wilson would race toward the rig in a running crouch, like medics toward a helicopter, a plywood sampling board between them. Running in behind came a team of microbiologists and civil engineers assembled from the University of Oklahoma, the University of Wisconsin, and Procter & Gamble's environmental laboratory. They brought with them a variety of containers and sealing devices to preserve samples in an oxygen-free environment—an environment that would allow colonies of the anaerobic bacteria that cause most of the biodegradation in landfills (to the extent that biodegradation occurs) to survive for later analysis. Behind the biologists and engineers came other Garbage Project personnel with an assortment of wire mesh screens and saw horses.

Within seconds of the bucket's removal from the ground, the operator maneuvered it directly over the sampling board, and released the contents. The pile was attacked first by Phillip Zack, a civil engineering student from the University of Wisconsin, who, as the temperature was being recorded, directed portions of the material into a variety of airtight conveyances. Then other members of the team moved in—the people who would shovel the steaming refuse atop the wire mesh; the people who would sort and bag whatever didn't go through the mesh; the people who would pour into bags or cannisters or jars whatever did go through the mesh; the people who would label everything for the trip either back to Tucson and the Garbage Project's holding bins or to the laboratories of the various microbiologists. (The shortest trip was to the trailer-laboratory that Procter & Gamble scientists had driven from Cincinnati and parked at the edge of the landfill.) The whole sample-collection process, from dumping to sorting to storing, took no more than twelve minutes. During the Fresh Kills dig it was repeated forty-four times at various places and various depths.

As morning edged toward afternoon the bucket auger began to near the limits of its reach in one of the wells. Down through the first thirty-five feet, a depth that in this well would date back to around 1984, the landfill had been relatively dry. Food waste and yard waste—hot dogs, bread, and grass clippings, for, example—were fairly well preserved. Newspapers remained intact and easy to read, their lurid headlines ("Woman Butchered-Ex-Hubby Held") calling to mind a handful of yesterday's tragedies. Beyond thirty-five feet, however, the landfill became increasingly wet, the garbage increasingly unidentifiable. At sixty feet, a stratum in this well containing garbage from the 1940s and 1950s, the bucket grabbed a sample and pulled it toward the surface. The Garbage Project team ran forward with their equipment, positioning themselves underneath. The bucket rose majestically as the operator sat at the controls, shouting something over the noise. As near as anyone can reconstruct it now, he was saying, "You boys might want to back off some, 'cause if this wind hits that bucket. . . ." The operator broke off because the wind did hit that bucket, and the material inside—a gray slime, redolent of putrefaction—thoroughly showered the crew. It would be an exaggeration to suggest that the victims were elated by this development, but their curiosity was certainly piqued, because on only one previous excavation had slime like this turned up in a landfill. What was the stuff made of? How had it come to be? What did its existence mean? The crew members doggedly collected all the usual samples, plus a few extra bottles of slime for special study. Then they cleaned themselves off.

It would be a blessing if it were possible to study garbage in the abstract, to study garbage without having to handle it physically.* But that is not possible. Garbage is not mathematics. To understand garbage you have to touch it, to feel it, to sort it, to smell it. You have to pick through hundreds of tons of it, counting and weighing all the daily newspapers, the telephone books; the soiled diapers, the foam clamshells that once briefly held hamburgers, the lipstick cylinders

*A note on terminology. Several words for the things we throw away—"garbage," "trash," "refuse," "rubbish"—are used synonymously in casual speech but in fact have different meanings. *Trash* refers specifically to discards that are at least theoretically "dry"—newspapers, boxes, cans, and so on. *Garbage* refers technically to "wet" discards—food remains, yard waste, and offal. *Refuse* is an inclusive term for both the wet discards and the dry. *Rubbish* is even more inclusive: It refers to all refuse plus construction and demolition debris. The distinction between wet and dry garbage was important in the days when cities slopped garbage to pigs, and needed to have the wet material separated from the dry; it eventually became irrevelant, but may see a revival if the idea of composting food and yard waste catches on. We will frequently use "garbage" in this book to refer to the totality of human discards because it is the word used most naturally in ordinary speech. The word is etymologically obscure, though it probably derives from Anglo-French, and its earliest associations have to do with working in the kitchen.

coated with grease, the medicine vials still encasing brightly colored pills, the empty bottles of scotch, the half-full cans of paint and muddy turpentine, the forsaken toys, the cigarette butts. You have to sort and weigh and measure the volume of all the organic matter, the discards from thousands of plates: the noodles and the Cheerios and the tortillas; the pieces of pet food that have made their own gravy; the hardened jelly doughnuts, bleeding from their side wounds; the half-eaten bananas, mostly still within their peels, black and incomparably sweet in the embrace of final decay. You have to confront sticky green mountains of yard waste, and slippery brown hills of potato peels, and brittle ossuaries of chicken bones and T-bones. And then, finally, there are the "fines," the vast connecting mixture of tiny bits of paper, metal, glass, plastic, dirt, grit, and former nutrients that suffuses every landfill like a kind of grainy lymph. To understand garbage you need thick gloves and a mask and some booster shots. But the yield in knowledge— about people and their behavior as well as about garbage itself—offsets the grim working conditions.

To an archaeologist, ancient garbage pits or garbage mounds, which can usually be located within a short distance from any ruin, are always among the happiest of finds, for they contain in concentrated form the artifacts and comestibles and remnants of behavior of the people who used them. While every archaeologist dreams of discovering spectacular objects, the bread-and-butter work of archaeology involves the most common and routine kinds of discards. It is not entirely fanciful to define archaeology as the discipline that tries to understand old garbage, and to learn from that garbage something about ancient societies and ancient behaviors. The eminent archaeologist Emil Haury once wrote of the aboriginal garbage heaps of the American Southwest: "Whichever way one views the mounds—as garbage piles to avoid, or as symbols of a way of life—they nevertheless are features more productive of information than any others." When the British archae-

ologist Sir Leonard Woolley, in 1916, first climbed to the top of the ancient city of Carchemish, on the Euphrates River near the modern-day Turkish-Syrian border, he moistened his index finger and held it in the air. Satisfied, he scanned the region due south of the city—that is, downwind—pausing to draw on his map the location of any mounds he saw. A trench dug through the largest of these mounds revealed it to be the garbage dump Woolley was certain it was, and the exposed strata helped establish the chronological sequence for the Carchemish site as a whole. Archaeologists have been picking through ancient garbage ever since archaeology became a profession, more than a century ago, and they will no doubt go on doing so as long as garbage is produced.

Several basic points about garbage need to be emphasized at the outset. First, the creation of garbage is an unequivocal sign of a human presence. From Styrofoam cups along a roadway and urine bags on the moon there is an uninterrupted chain of garbage that reaches back more than two million years to the first "waste flake" knocked off in the knapping of the first stone tool. That the distant past often seems misty and dim is precisely because our earliest ancestors left so little garbage behind. An appreciation of the accomplishments of the first hominids became possible only after they began making stone tools, the debris from the production of which, along with the discarded tools themselves, are now probed for their secrets with electron microscopes and displayed in museums not as garbage but as "artifacts." These artifacts serve as markers—increasingly frequent and informative markers—of how our forebears coped with the evolving physical and social world. Human beings are mere placeholders in time, like zeros in a long number; their garbage seems to have more staying power, and a power to inform across the millennia that complements (and often substitutes for) that of the written word. The profligate habits of our own country and our own time—the sheer volume of the garbage that we create and must dispose of—

will make our society an open book. The question is: Would we ourselves recognize our story when it is told, or will our garbage tell tales about us that we as yet do not suspect?

That brings up a second matter: If our garbage, in the eyes of the future, is destined to hold a key to the past, then surely it already holds a key to the present. This may be an obvious point, but it is one whose implications were not pursued by scholars until relatively recently. Each of us throws away dozens of items every day. All of these items are relics of specific human activities—relics no different in their inherent nature from many of those that traditional archaeologists work with (though they are, to be sure, a bit fresher). Taken as a whole the garbage of the United States, from its 93 million households and 1.5 million retail outlets and from all of its schools, hospitals, government offices, and other public facilities, is a mirror of American society. Of course, the problem with the mirror garbage offers is that, when encountered in a garbage can, dump, or landfill, it is a broken one: our civilization is reflected in billions of fragments that may reveal little in and of themselves. Fitting some of the pieces back together requires painstaking effort—effort that a small number of archaeologists and natural scientists have only just begun to apply.

A third point about garbage is that it is not an assertion but a physical fact—and thus may sometimes serve as a useful corrective. Human beings have over the centuries left many accounts describing their lives and civilizations. Many of these are little more than self-aggrandizing advertisements. The remains of the tombs, temples, and palaces of the elite are filled with personal histories as recorded by admiring relatives and fawning retainers. More such information is carved into obelisks and stelae, gouged into clay tablets, painted or printed on papyrus and paper. Historians are understandably drawn to written evidence of this kind, but garbage has often served as a kind of tattle-tale, setting the record straight.

It had long been known, for example, that French as well as Spanish forts had been erected along the coast of South Carolina during the sixteenth century, and various mounds and depressions have survived into our own time to testify to their whereabouts. Ever since the mid-nineteenth century a site on the tip of Parris Island, South Carolina, has been familiarly known as the site of a French outpost, built in 1562, that is spelled variously in old documents as Charlesfort, Charlesforte, and Charles Forte. In 1925, the Huguenot Society of South Carolina successfully lobbied Congress to erect a monument commemorating the building of Charlesfort. Subsequently, people in nearby Beaufort took up the Charlesfort theme, giving French names to streets, restaurants, and housing developments. Gift shops sold kitschy touristiana with a distinctly Gallic flavor. Those restaurants and gift shops found themselves in an awkward position when, in 1957, as a result of an analysis of discarded matter discovered at Charlesfort, a National Park Service historian, Albert Manucy, suggested that the site was of Spanish origin. Excavations begun in 1979 by the archaeologist Stanley South, which turned up such items as discarded Spanish olive jars and broken majolica pottery from Seville, confirmed Manucy's view: "Charlesfort," South established, was actually Fort San Marcos, a Spanish installation built in 1577 to protect a Spanish town named Santa Elena. (Both the fort and the town had been abandoned after only a few years.)

Garbage, then, represents physical fact, not mythology. It underscores a point that can not be too greatly emphasized: Our private worlds consist essentially of two realities—mental reality, which encompasses beliefs, attitudes, and ideas, and material reality, which is the picture embodied in the physical record. The study of garbage reminds us that it is a rare person in whom mental and material realities completely coincide. Indeed, for the most part, the pair exist in a state of tension, if not open conflict.

Americans have always wondered, sometimes with buoyant playfulness, what their countrymen in the far future will make of Americans "now." In 1952, in a monograph he first circulated privately among colleagues and eventually published in *The Journal of Irreproducible Results,* the eminent anthropologist and linguist Joseph H. Greenberg—the man who would one day sort the roughly one thousand known Native American languages into three broad language families—imagined the unearthing of the so-called "violence texts" during an excavation of the Brooklyn Dodgers' Ebbets Field in the year A.D. 2026; what interpretation, he wondered, would be given to such newspaper reports as Yanks Slaughter Indians" and "Reese made a sacrifice in the infield"? In 1979 the artist and writer David Macaulay published *Motel of the Mysteries,* an archaeological site-report setting forth the conclusions reached by a team of excavators in the year A.D. 4022 who have unearthed a motel dating back to 1985 (the year, Macaulay wrote, in which "an accidental reduction in postal rates on a substance called third- and fourth-class mail literally buried the North Americans under tons of brochures, fliers, and small containers called FREE"). Included in the report are illustrations of an archaeologist modeling a toilet seat, toothbrushes, and a drain stopper (or, as Macaulay describes them, "the Sacred Collar . . . the magnificent 'plasticus' ear ornaments, and the exquisite silver chain and pendant"), all assumed to be items of ritual or personal regalia. In 1982 an exhibit was mounted in New York City called "Splendors of the Sohites"—a vast display of artifacts, including "funerary vessels" (faded, dusky soda bottles) and "hermaphrodite amulets" (discarded pop-top rings), found in the SoHo section of Manhattan and dating from the Archaic Period (A.D. 1950–1961), the Classical Period (1962–1975), and the Decadent Period (1976– c.1980).

Greenberg, Macaulay, and the organizers of the Sohites exhibition all meant to have some fun, but there is an uneasy undercurrent to their work, and it is embodied in the question: What are we to make of ourselves? The Garbage Project, conceived in 1971, and officially established at the University of Arizona in 1973, was an attempt to come up with a new way of providing serious answers. It aimed to apply *real* archaeology to this very question; to see if it would be possible to investigate human behavior "from the back end," as it were. This scholarly endeavor has come to be known as garbology, and practitioners of garbology are known as garbologists. The printed citation (dated 1975) in the *Oxford English Dictionary* for the meaning of "garbology" as used here associates the term with the Garbage Project.

In the years since its founding the Garbage Project's staff members have processed more than 250,000 pounds of garbage, some of it from landfills but most of it fresh out of garbage cans in selected neighborhoods. All of this garbage has been sorted, coded, and catalogued—every piece, from bottles of furniture polish and egg-shaped pantyhose packaging to worn and shredded clothing, crumpled bubble-gum wrappers, and the full range of kitchen waste. A unique database has been built up from these cast-offs, covering virtually every aspect of American life: drinking habits, attitudes toward red meat, trends in the use of convenience foods, the strange ways in which consumers respond to shortages, the use of contraceptives, and hundreds of other matters.*

*A question that always comes up is: What about garbage disposers? Garbage disposers are obviously capable of skewing the data in certain garbage categories, and Garbage Project researchers can employ a variety of techniques to compensate for the bias that garbage disposers introduce. Studies were conducted at the very outset of the Garbage Project to determine the discard differential between households with and without disposers, and one eventual result was a set of correction factors for various kinds of garbage (primarily food), broken down by subtype. As a general rule of thumb, households with disposers end up discarding in their trash about half the amount of food waste and food debris as households without disposers. It should be noted, however, that the fact that disposers have ground up some portion of a household's garbage often has little relevance to the larger issues the Garbage Project is trying to address. It means, for example, not that the Garbage Project's findings about the extent of food waste are invalid, but merely that its estimates are conservative.

The antecedents of the Garbage Project in the world of scholarship and elsewhere are few but various. Some are undeniably dubious. The examination of fresh refuse is, of course, as old as the human species—just watch anyone who happens upon an old campsite, or a neighbor scavenging at a dump for spare parts or furniture. The first systematic study of the components of America's garbage dates to the early 1900s and the work of the civil engineers Rudolph Hering (in New York) and Samuel A. Greeley (in Chicago), who by 1921 had gathered enough information from enough cities to compile *Collection and Disposal of Municipal Refuse,* the first textbook on urban trash management. In academe, not much happened after that for quite some time. Out in the field, however, civil engineers and solid-waste managers did now and again sort and weigh fresh garbage as it stood in transit between its source and destination, but their categories were usually simple: paper, glass, metal. No one sorted garbage into detailed categories relating to particular consumer discard patterns. No one, for example, kept track of phenomena as specific as the number of beer cans thrown away versus the number of beer bottles, or the number of orange-juice cans thrown away versus the number of pounds of freshly squeezed oranges, or the amount of candy thrown away in the week after Halloween versus the amount thrown away in the week after Valentine's Day. And no one ever dug into the final resting places of most of America's garbage: dumps (where garbage is left in the open) and sanitary landfills (where fresh garbage is covered every night with six to eight inches of soil).

Even as America's city managers over the years oversaw—and sometimes desperately attempted to cope with—the disposal of ever-increasing amounts of garbage, the study of garbage itself took several odd detours—one into the world of the military, another into the world of celebrity-watching, and a third into the world of law enforcement.

The military's foray into garbology occurred in 1941, when two enlisted men, Horace Schwerin and Phalen Golden, were forced to discontinue a survey they were conducting among new recruits about which aspects of Army life the recruits most disliked. (Conducting polls of military personnel was, they had learned, against regulations.) Schwerin and Golden had already discovered, however, that the low quality of the food was the most frequently heard complaint, and they resolved to look into this one matter with an investigation that could not be considered a poll. What Schwerin and Golden did was to station observers in mess halls to record the types of food that were most commonly wasted and the volume of waste by type of food. The result, after 2.4 million man-meals had been observed, was a textbook example of how garbage studies can produce not only behavioral insights but also practical benefits. Schwerin and Golden discovered that 20 percent of the food prepared for Army mess halls was eventually thrown away, and that one reason for this was simply excess preparation. Here are some more of their findings, as summarized in a wartime article that appeared in the *The Saturday Evening Post:*

Soldiers ate more if they were allowed to smoke in the mess hall. They ate more if they went promptly to table instead of waiting on line outside—perhaps because the food became cold. They ate more if they fell to on their own initiative instead of by command. They cared little for soups, and 65 percent of the kale and nearly as much of the spinach went into the garbage can. Favorite desserts were cakes and cookies, canned fruit, fruit salad, and gelatin. They ate ice cream in almost any amount that was served to them.

"That, sergeant, is an excellent piece of work," General George C. Marshall, the Army chief of staff, told Horace Schwerin after hearing a report by Schwerin on the research findings. The Army adopted many of Schwerin and Golden's recommendations, and began saving some 2.5 million pounds of food a day. It is perhaps not surprising to learn that until joining the Army Horace Schwerin had been in market research, and, among other things, had helped CBS to perfect a device for measuring audience reaction to radio shows.

The origins of an ephemeral branch of garbage studies focused on celebrities—"peeping-Tom" garbology, one might call it—seem to lie in the work of A. J. Weberman. Weberman was a gonzo journalist and yippie whose interest in the songs of Bob Dylan, and obsession with their interpretation, in 1970 prompted him to begin stealing the garbage from the cans left out in front of Dylan's Greenwich Village brownstone on MacDougal Street. Weberman didn't find much—some soiled Pampers, some old newspapers, some fast-food packaging from a nearby Blimpie Base, a shopping list with the word vanilla spelled "vannilla." He did, however, stumble into a brief but highly publicized career. This self-proclaimed "garbage guerrilla" quickly moved on to Neil Simon's garbage (it included a half-eaten bagel, scraps of lox, the Sunday *Times*), Muhammad Ali's (an empty can of Luck's collard greens, an empty roach bomb), and Abbie Hoffman's (a summons for hitchhiking, an unused can of deodorant, an estimate of the cost for the printing of *Steal This Book,* and the telephone numbers of Jack Anderson and Kate Millet). Weberman revealed many of his findings in an article in *Esquire* in 1971. It was antics such as his that inspired a prior meaning of the term "garbology," one very different from the definition established today.

Weberman's work inspired other garbage guerrillas. In January of 1975, the *Detroit Free Press* Sunday magazine reported on the findings from its raids on the garbage of several city notables, including the mayor, the head of the city council, the leader of a right-wing group, a food columnist, a disk jockey, and a prominent psychiatrist. Nothing much was discovered that might be deemed out of the ordinary, save for some of the contents of the garbage taken from a local Hare Krishna temple: a price tag from an Oleg Cassini garment, for example, and four ticket stubs from the Bel-Aire Drive-In Theater, which at the time was showing *Horrible House on the*

Hill and *The Night God Screamed.* Six months after the *Free Press* exposé, a reporter for the *National Enquirer,* Jay Gourley, drove up to 3018 Dumbarton Avenue, N.W., in Washington, D.C., and threw the five garbage bags in front of Secretary of State Henry A. Kissinger's house into the trunk of his car. Secret Service agents swiftly blocked Gourley's departure, but after a day of questioning allowed him to proceed, the garbage still in the trunk. Among Gourley's finds: a crumpled piece of paper with a dog's teeth marks on it, upon which was written the work schedules of the Secret Service agents assigned to guard the Secretary; empty bottles of Seconal and Maalox; and a shopping list, calling for a case of Jack Daniel's, a case of Ezra Brooks bourbon, and a case of Cabin Still bourbon. Gourley later returned most of the garbage to the Kissingers—minus, he told reporters, "several dozen interesting things."

After the Kissinger episode curiosity about the garbage of celebrities seems to have abated. In 1977 the *National Enquirer* sent a reporter to poke through the garbage of President Jimmy Carter's press secretary, Jody Powell. The reporter found so little of interest that the tabloid decided not to publish a story. In 1980 Secret Service agents apprehended A. J. Weberman as he attempted to abduct former President Richard Nixon's garbage from behind an apartment building in Manhattan. Weberman was released, without the garbage.

The third detour taken by garbage studies involves police work. Over the years, law enforcement agents looking for evidence in criminal cases have also been more-than-occasional students of garbage; the Federal Bureau of Investigation in particular has spent considerable time poring over the household trash of people in whom it maintains a professional interest. ("We take it on a case-by-case basis," an FBI spokesman says.) One of the biggest criminal cases involving garbage began in 1975 and involved Joseph "Joe Bananas" Bonanno, Sr., a resident of Tucson at the time and a man with alleged ties to organized crime that

were believed to date back to the days of Al Capone. For a period of three years officers of the Arizona Drug Control District collected Bonanno's trash just before the regular pickup, replacing it with "fake" Bonanno garbage. (Local garbagemen were not employed in the operation because some of them had received anonymous threats after assisting law enforcement agencies in an earlier venture.) The haul in evidence was beyond anyone's expectations: Bonanno had apparently kept detailed records of his various transactions, mostly in Sicilian. Although Bonanno had torn up each sheet of paper into tiny pieces, forensic specialists with the Drug Control District, like archaeologists reconstructing ceramic bowls from potsherds, managed to reassemble many of the documents and with the help of the FBI got them translated. In 1980 Bonanno was found guilty of having interfered with a federal grand jury investigation into the business operations of his two sons and a nephew. He was eventually sent to jail.

Unlike law-enforcement officers or garbage guerrillas, the archaeologists of the Garbage Project are not interested in the contents of any particular individual's garbage can. Indeed, it is almost always the case that a given person's garbage is at once largely anonymous and unimaginably humdrum. Garbage most usefully comes alive when it can be viewed in the context of broad patterns, for it is mainly in patterns that the links between artifacts and behaviors can be discerned.

The seed from which the Garbage Project grew was an anthropology class conducted at the University of Arizona in 1971 that was designed to teach principles of archaeological methodology. The University of Arizona has long occupied a venerable place in the annals of American archaeology and, not surprisingly, the pursuit of archaeology there to this day is carried on in serious and innovative ways. The class in question was one in which students undertook independent projects aimed precisely at showing links between various kinds of artifacts and various kinds of behavior. For example, one student, Sharon Thomas, decided to look into the relationship between a familiar motor function ("the diffusion pattern of ketchup over hamburgers") and a person's appearance, as manifested in clothing. Thomas took up a position at "seven different hamburger dispensaries" and, as people came in to eat, labeled them "neat" or "sloppy" according to a set of criteria relating to the way they dressed. Then she recorded how each of the fifty-seven patrons she studied—the ones who ordered hamburgers—poured ketchup over their food. She discovered that sloppy people were far more likely than neat people to put ketchup on in blobs, sometimes even stirring it with their fingers. Neat people, in contrast, tended to apply the ketchup in patterns: circles, spirals, and crisscrosses. One person (a young male neatly dressed in a body shirt, flared pants, and patent-leather Oxfords) wrote with ketchup what appeared to be initials.

Two of the student investigations, conducted independently by Frank Ariza and Kelly Allen, led directly to the Garbage Project. Ariza and Allen, wanting to explore the divergence between (or correlation of) mental stereotypes and physical realities, collected garbage from two households in an affluent part of Tucson and compared it to garbage from two households in a poor and, as it happens, Mexican-American part of town. The rich and poor families, each student found, ate about the same amount of steak and hamburger, and drank about the same amount of milk. But the poor families, they learned, bought more expensive child-education items. They also bought more household cleansers. What did such findings mean? Obviously the sample—involving only four households in all—was too small for the results even to be acknowledged as representative, let alone to provide hints as to what lay behind them. However, the general nature of the research effort itself— comparing garbage samples in order to gauge behavior (and, what is more, gauging behavior unobtrusively, thereby avoiding one of the great biases inher-

ent in much social science)—seemed to hold great promise.

A year later, in 1972, university students, under professorial direction, began borrowing samples of household garbage from different areas of Tucson, and sorting it in a lot behind a dormitory. The Garbage Project was under way. In 1973, the Garbage Project entered into an arrangement with the City of Tucson, whereby the Sanitation Division, four days a week, delivered five to eight randomly selected household pickups from designated census tracts to an analysis site that the Division set aside for the Project's sorters at a maintenance yard. (Wilson Hughes, who as mentioned earlier is the Garbage Project's co-director, was one of the first undergraduate garbage sorters.) In 1984 operations were moved to an enclosure where many of the university's dumpsters are parked, across the street from Arizona Stadium.

The excavation of landfills would come much later in the Garbage Project's history, when to its focus on issues of garbage and human behavior it added a focus on issues of garbage management. The advantage in the initial years of sorting fresh garbage over excavating landfills was a basic but important one: In landfills it is often quite difficult and in many cases impossible to get some idea, demographically speaking, of the kind of neighborhood from which any particular piece of garbage has come. The value of landfill studies is therefore limited to advancing our understanding of garbage in the aggregate. With fresh garbage, on the other hand, one can have demographic precision down to the level of a few city blocks, by directing pickups to specific census districts and cross-tabulating the findings with census data.

Needless to say, deciding just which characteristics of the collected garbage to pay attention to posed a conceptual challenge, one that was met by Wilson Hughes, who devised the "protocol" that is used by the Garbage Project to this day. Items found in garbage are sorted into one of 150 specific coded categories that can in turn be clustered into larger categories representing food

(fresh food versus prepared, health food versus junk food), drugs, personal and household sanitation products, amusement-related or educational materials, communications-related materials, pet-related materials, yard-related materials, and hazardous materials. For each item the following information is recorded on a standardized form: the date on which it was collected; the census tract from which it came; the item code (for example, 001, which would be the code for "Beef"); the item's type (for example, "chuck"); its original weight or volume (in this case, derived from the packaging); its cost (also from the packaging); material composition of container; brand (if applicable); and the weight of any discarded food (if applicable). The information garnered over the years from many thousands of such forms, filled out in pursuit of a wide variety of research objectives, constitutes the Garbage Project's database. It has all been computerized and amounts to some two million lines of data drawn from some fifteen thousand household-refuse samples. The aim here has been not only to approach garbage with specific questions to answer or hypotheses to prove but also to amass sufficient quantities of information, in a systematic and open-minded way, so that with the data on hand Garbage Project researchers would be able to answer any future questions or evaluate any future hypotheses that might arise. In 1972 garbage was, after all, still terra incognita, and the first job to be done was akin to that undertaken by the explorers Lewis and Clark.

From the outset the Garbage Project has had to confront the legal and ethical issues its research involves: Was collecting and sorting someone's household garbage an unjustifiable invasion of privacy? This very question has over the years been argued repeatedly in the courts. The Fourth Amendment unequivocally guarantees Americans protection from unreasonable search and seizure. Joseph Bonanno, Sr., tried to invoke the Fourth Amendment to prevent his garbage from being used as evidence. But garbage placed in a garbage can in a public thoroughfare, where it awaits removal by impersonal refuse collectors, and where it may be picked over by scavengers looking for aluminum cans, by curious children or neighbors, and by the refuse collectors themselves (some of whom do a thriving trade in old appliances, large and small), is usually considered by the courts to have been abandoned. Therefore, the examination of the garbage by outside parties cannot be a violation of a constitutional right. In the Bonanno case, U.S. District Court Judge William Ingram ruled that investigating garbage for evidence of a crime may carry a "stench," but was not illegal. In 1988, in *California v. Greenwood,* the U.S. Supreme Court ruled by a margin of six to two that the police were entitled to conduct a warrantless search of a suspected drug dealer's garbage—a search that led to drug paraphenalia, which led in turn to warrants, arrests, and convictions. As Justice Byron White has written, "The police cannot reasonably be expected to avert their eyes from evidence of criminal activity that could have been observed by any member of the public."

Legal issues aside, the Garbage Project has taken pains to ensure that those whose garbage comes under scrutiny remain anonymous. Before obtaining garbage for study, the Project provides guarantees to communities and their garbage collectors that nothing of a personal nature will be examined and that no names or addresses or other personal information will be recorded. The Project also stipulates that all of the garbage collected (except aluminum cans, which are recycled) will be returned to the community for normal disposal.

As noted, the Garbage Project has now been sorting and evaluating garbage, with scientific rigor, for two decades. The Project has proved durable because its findings have supplied a fresh perspective on what we know—and what we think we know—about certain aspects of our lives. Medical researchers, for example, have long made it their business to question people about their eating habits in order to uncover relationships between patterns of diet and patterns of disease. These researchers have also long suspected that people—honest, well-meaning people—may often be providing information about quantities and types and even brands of food and drink consumed that is not entirely accurate. People can't readily say whether they trimmed 3.3 ounces or 5.4 ounces of fat off the last steak they ate, and they probably don't remember whether they had four, five, or seven beers in the previous week, or two eggs or three. The average person just isn't paying attention. Are there certain patterns in the way in which people wrongly "self-report" their dietary habits? Yes, there are, and Garbage Project studies have identified many of them.

Garbage archaeologists also know how much edible food is thrown away; what percentage of newspapers, cans, bottles, and other items aren't recycled; how loyal we are to brand-name products and which have earned the greatest loyalty; and how much household hazardous waste is carted off to landfills and incinerators. From several truckloads of garbage and a few pieces of ancillary data—most importantly, the length of time over which the garbage was collected—the Garbage Project staff can reconstruct the community from which it came with a degree of accuracy that the Census Bureau might in some neighborhoods be unable to match.

Garbage also exposes the routine perversity of human ways. Garbage archaeologists have learned, for example, that the volume of garbage that Americans produce expands to fill the number of receptacles that are available to put it in. They have learned that we waste more of what is in short supply than of what is plentiful; that attempts by individuals to restrict consumption of certain foodstuffs are often counterbalanced by extra and inadvertent consumption of those same foodstuffs in hidden form; and that while a person's memory of what he has eaten and drunk in a given week is inevitably wide of the mark, his guess as to what a family member or even

neighbor has eaten and drunk usually turns out to be more perceptive.

Some of the Garbage Project's research has prompted unusual forays into arcane aspects of popular culture. Consider the matter of those "amulets" worn by the Sohites—that is, the once-familiar detachable pop-top pull tab. Pull tabs first became important to the Garbage Project during a study of household recycling practices, conducted on behalf of the federal Environmental Protection Agency during the mid-1970s. The question arose: If a bag of household garbage contained no aluminum cans, did that mean that the household didn't dispose of any cans or that it had recycled its cans? Finding a way to answer that question was essential if a neighborhood's recycling rate was to be accurately determined. Pull tabs turned out to hold the key. A quick study revealed that most people did not drop pull tabs into the cans from which they had been wrenched; rather, the vast majority of people threw the tabs into the trash. If empty cans were stored separately for recycling, the pull tabs still went out to the curb with the rest of the garbage. A garbage sample that contained several pull tabs but no aluminum cans was a good bet to have come from a household that recycled.

All this counting of pull tabs prompted a surprising discovery one day by a student: Pull tabs were not all alike. Their configuration and even color depended on what kind of beverage they were associated with and where the beverage had been canned. Armed with this knowledge, Garbage Project researchers constructed an elaborate typology of pull tabs, enabling investigators to tease out data about beverage consumption—say, beer versus soda, Michelob versus Schlitz—even from samples of garbage that contained not a single can. Detachable pull tabs are no longer widely used in beverage cans, but the pull-tab typology remains useful even now. Among other things, in the absence of such evidence of chronology as a newspaper's dateline, pull tabs can reliably help to fix the dates of strata in a landfill. In archaeological parlance objects like these that have been widely diffused over a short period of time, and then abruptly disappear, are known as horizon markers.

The unique "punch-top" on Coors beer cans, for example, was used only between March of 1974 and June of 1977. (It was abandoned because some customers complained that they cut their thumbs pushing the holes open.) In landfills around the country, wherever Coors beer cans were discarded, punch-top cans not only identify strata associated with a narrow band of dates but also separate two epochs one from another. One might think of punch-tops playfully as the garbage equivalent of the famous iridium layer found in sediment toward the end of the Cretaceous Era, marking the moment (proponents of the theory believe) when a giant meteor crashed into the planet Earth, exterminating the dinosaurs.

All told, the Garbage Project has conducted nine full-scale excavations of municipal landfills in the United States and two smaller excavations associated with special projects. In the fall of 1991 it also excavated four sites in Canada, the data from which remains largely unanalyzed (and is not reflected in this book). The logistics of the landfill excavations are complex, and they have been overseen in all cases by Wilson Hughes. What is involved? Permission must be obtained from a raft of local officials and union leaders; indemnification notices must be provided to assure local authorities that the Garbage Project carries suffi-

cient insurance against injury; local universities must be scoured for a supply of students to supplement the Garbage Project team; in many cases construction permits, of all things, must be obtained in advance of digging. There is also the whole matter of transportation, not only of personnel but also of large amounts of equipment. And there is the matter of personal accommodation and equipment storage. The time available for excavation is always limited, sometimes extremely so; the research program must be compressed to fit it, and the staff must be "tasked" accordingly. When the excavation has been completed the samples need to be packed and shipped—frequently on ice—back to headquarters or to specialized laboratories. All archaeologists will tell you that field work is mostly laborious, not glamorous; a landfill excavation is archaeology of the laborious kind.

For all the difficulties they present, the Garbage Project's landfill digs have acquired an increasing timeliness and relevance as concerns about solid-waste disposal have grown. Even as the Garbage Project has trained considerable attention on garbage as an analytical tool it has also taken up the problem of garbage itself—garbage as a problem, garbage as symbolized by *Mobro 4000,* the so-called "garbage barge," which sailed from Islip, Long Island, on March 22, 1987, and spent the next fifty-five days plying the seas in search of a place to deposit its 3,168

tons of cargo. Strange though it may seem, although more than 70 percent of America's household and commercial garbage ends up in landfills, very little reliable data existed until recently as to a landfill's contents and biological dynamics. Much of the conventional wisdom about garbage disposal consists of assertions that turn out, upon investigation, to be simplistic or misleading: among them, the assertion that, as trash, plastic, foam, and fast-food packaging are causes for great concern, that biodegradable items are always more desirable than nonbiodegradable ones, that on a per capita basis the nation's households are generating a lot more garbage than they used to, and that we're physically running out of places to put landfills.

This is not to say that garbage isn't a problem in need of serious attention. It is. But if they are to succeed, plans of action must be based on garbage realities. The most critical part of the garbage problem in America is that our notions about the creation and disposal of garbage are often riddled with myth. There are few other subjects of public significance on which popular and official opinion is so consistently misinformed. . . .

Gaps—large gaps—remain in our knowledge of garbage, and of how human behavior relates to it, and of how best to deal with it. But a lighted candle has at least been seized and thrust inside the antechamber.

Moving the Moai

Transporting the megaliths of Easter Island: How did they do it?

Jo Anne Van Tilburg

Jo Anne Van Tilburg is a research associate of the Institute of Archaeology, UCLA, and has directed the Moai Documentation Project on Easter Island since 1982.

Easter Island's stone statues—sacred objects, emblems of status, and the dominant symbol of a complex ideology—have astounded and perplexed nearly all who have seen or read about them. Pioneering British ethnographer Katherine Scoresby Routledge was the first to investigate the meaning and function of the sculptures, known as *moai*. She and her husband William mounted the 1914–15 Mana Expedition to Easter Island, or Rapa Nui, and mapped Rano Raraku quarry, the volcanic crater where 95 percent of the statues were carved. They discovered and traced the unpaved roads that led from Rano Raraku to ceremonial platforms called *ahu*. Scattered along these roads were 45 statues, presumably abandoned "in transport."

In 1982 I joined the Instituto de Estudios, Universidad de Chile, in its archaeological survey of the island. During the past 12 years my Chilean colleagues and I have located, measured, photographed, drawn, and mapped 883 moai. This number includes visible quarry statues, those on ahu sites, many hidden in caves or partially buried, statues taken from the island to foreign museums, and 47 recorded as "in transport." In mapping Rano Raraku, the Chilean team located 397 of the total number of statues. With 80 percent of the island surveyed, it is possible that another 35–50 moai will be found.

Our goal was to produce a comprehensive description of moai form, style, context, and distribution. In the process we collected a massive amount of data about the political and ideological contexts of the statues. This information holds answers to many questions, not the least of which is how the moai were moved.

To answer this question, I first researched contemporary observations of large stone transport in many parts of the world. In Indonesia, huge gravestones weighing many tons are still hauled on sledges by as many as 150 men, women, and children pulling on attached ropes. In northeastern India, stones of two tons or more were moved over narrow trails as late as the 1940s. Other sources of information are the ethnographically documented cases of stone transport in Madagascar, Tonga, Micronesia, and the Marquesas Islands, and experimental archaeology projects at La Venta in Mexico, at the Giza Plateau in Egypt, and at Stonehenge and elsewhere in Great Britain. In virtually all cases, the stones were moved in a horizontal or occasionally, lateral position on a sledge over rollers.

Next, I studied how eight Rapa Nui statues were collected by foreign museums. In 1886 U.S. Navy Paymaster William J. Thomson and the crew of the USS *Mohican* removed one that is now in the Smithsonian Institution. Islanders and draft animals hauled it two and one-half miles from an inland ahu to Anakena Bay, from which the *Mohican* sailed. The British Museum's statue, called Hoa Hakananai'a ("stolen or hidden friend"), was removed in 1868 from a stone house then dragged by Rapa Nui people and crew members of HMS *Topaze,* without benefit of a sled. A missionary on the island noted the "precautions" taken to avoid damaging the statue as it was dragged face down, "tracing with its nose, a long furrow on the ground." In 1935 a statue was taken to the Musée d'Art et d'Histoire in Brussels from a site near the village of Hanga Roa. It was wrapped in a cargo net, then placed in a prone position on a wooden sledge, hauled to a nearby bay, and loaded on the Belgian training ship *Mercator.* Alfred Métraux, an ethnographer who witnessed the event, took the opportunity to ask questions about prehistoric transport methods. He found that the Rapa Nui were "unable to explain the methods used by their ancestors for transporting the stone images." In 1955 scientists of Thor Heyerdahl's Norwegian Archaeological Expedition attached a 13-foot-tall statue in a horizontal position to a Y-shaped sledge made from a forked tree trunk with cross pieces over the runners. Ropes were attached to the sledge, and between 75 and 180 people hauled it a few yards over flat ground.

Three additional methods of transportation have been suggested. American archaeologist William Mulloy, who directed the re-erection of statues on several restored sites, speculated that a 32-foot-tall, 89-ton statue called Paro could have been moved using a bipod of tree trunks about 30 feet tall. He believed the statue, suspended by ropes from the bipod, could have been inched forward by rocking it on its protruding belly. One or two of the larger statues lying along a transport road may have inspired Mulloy's fulcrum idea, but neither Paro nor the majority of the other larger-than-average statues have sufficient depth through the midsection to make the method feasible.

More recently, a crew directed by Thor Heyerdahl demonstrated that a 13-foot-tall moai could be inched forward in an upright position on completely flat terrain by tilting and rocking the statue back and forth while manipulating ropes attached to the statue's head and base, much as one would move a heavy piece of furniture. The statue they used, which now stands near Ahu Tongariki, was broken at the base during this operation.

Concrete replicas of moai, not particularly well designed or accurately proportioned, have been used in experiments similar to Heyerdahl's. American geologist Charles Love devised a variation on the upright, tilting method by attaching a pod—a small platform of short logs—to the base of his replica. Once upright on the pod, rollers were placed underneath and the replica was pulled forward over flat ground by attached ropes. This was an improvement over the tilting method, but spacing the rollers unevenly caused the replica to come crashing down.

These experiments were largely shots in the dark. I wanted to find a way to experiment with transport methods that didn't endanger a real statue and didn't depend on awkward and inexact replicas. It was also important to conduct experiments that were controlled and replicable, and which could be generalized from one statue to many. The moai measurements we so painstakingly gathered over the years would be used to build a computer-simulated moai.

Of the statues inventoried thus far, 134 have ten crucial measurements that define body and head shapes and allow us to determine volume, weight, and center of gravity. All 134 are found on ahu or lying "in transport" between Rano Raraku and various ahu. Analyses of size, shape, weight, and proportionate relationships of head to body have allowed us to clarify statue forms.

The statistically average statue for the whole island is 14 feet, six inches tall and weighs 14 tons. Of the dozen or more that we could have used as our reference moai, we chose Statue 01 at Ahu Akivi, a restored and dated ahu lying about 460 feet above sea level on the southwestern slope of Maunga Terevaka. Statue 01 is 13 feet tall and weighs 14 tons. It is five feet wide at its base, almost five feet wide at its head, and has a total depth of three feet through the midpoint of the body. It has a total volume of 210 cubic feet, and its center of gravity is at four and one-half feet. Metric and photogrammetric data collected in 1991 allowed artist Gary Lloyd to sculpt a 1:10 scale model of Statue 01. A computer image of the model produced by laser scan was used to experiment with a variety of hypothetical transport methods.

When Europeans entered the Pacific, the great double-hulled canoes for which Polynesia is now famous were few in number, seen mostly in Samoa, Tonga, and Fiji. Estimates of length vary, but 65 to 70 feet was typical. Canoe hulls from Fiji, Hawaii, and the Society Islands were hewn from massive hardwood tree trunks, weighed from 6 to 12 tons, and were between 108 and 118 feet long. Construction of such vessels was in the hands of master craftsmen with hereditary status and specialized knowledge. The work progressed in accordance with the availability of food. According to Fijian craftsmen, *"a tata tu i kete"* ("the chopping is in the belly"). Sometimes the canoes were built inland, where the best timber was available, and then hauled overland to a beach. In Fiji, the great war canoes are said to have been launched over the bodies of men, sacrificed to serve as rollers allowing the vessel to slide into the water. It is not unreasonable to speculate that moai were commissioned and paid for by Rapa Nui chiefs in much the same way that canoes were built and paid for elsewhere.

We can presume that the Rapa Nui called upon generations of experience in marine exploration and canoe construction and that principles of the fulcrum lever, forked lever, balance beam, pivot, and moving pivot would have been easily adapted to statue transportation. Ancient skills in the production of stone adzes and chisels, strong cordage, and boring and lashing techniques would have been utilized, as would methods for raising and securing masts using side, back, and fore stays. Fibers from the bark of the hau tree would have been twisted into long, strong ropes. Skilled master carvers would have employed a highly stylized design template, probably using

Rapa Nui surface map based on a computer-generated image shows locations of statues and alternative transport paths from Rano Raraku quarry to Ahu Akivi. Path 1 (the optimal path of about six miles) is at top.

knotted cords and charcoal to mark dimensions on the stone before a statue was roughed out.

We decided—based on Polynesian ethnographies, previous experimental archaeology projects in other megalithic societies, Rapa Nui terrain, and statue attributes—that a horizontal transport method was the most logical. The flat backs of the statues and lines of the shoulders were ideally shaped for such transport. Experiments with our scale model helped us to design a light and economical sledge. When transferred to our computer model, it consisted simply of two simulated nonparallel wood beams 18 feet long and almost ten inches in diameter. These were placed under our computer reference statue so that they extended and met about three feet beyond the statue's head. The V-shaped alignment of the transport beams would help in pulling the sledge. The weight of the statue alone would hold the beams

snugly in place. Fifteen to 20 "rollers" about ten inches in diameter were placed under the simulated beams. The statue was then "pulled" forward with ropes.

Of the 383 statues we have measured to date outside of Rano Raraku, 163 are lying face down, 122 are on their backs, and 31 are on their sides. Does the face down position of "in transport" statues mean they were being moved that way? Perhaps, although the experience of Hoa Hakananai'a being dragged with its nose "tracing a furrow in the ground" suggested to us that adjustments to our model would have to be made. To accommodate the face-down position, two crossbeams six and one-half feet long were required. One was placed at the neck to keep the nose and face clear of the ground, and the other, smaller one was placed at the base. Face-down or face-up, the stone experiences stress at the neck. In the face-up mode, a simple

padding of vegetable material under the back of the neck solves the problem, but in the face-down position, the stress is not completely relieved by padding. Some of the statues found "in transport" are broken at the neck, possibly from being transported face-down.

The most difficult aspect of moai transport was positioning and then erecting the statue on an ahu. The statues, whether they were in a face-up or face-down position on the sledge, were probably transported head-first. In the case of Ahu Akivi, statues could have approached the platform in either a face-up or face-down position and from either the front or the rear. Remaining on its transport sledge, the statue was aligned on the site with its base perpendicular to the platform. It was then pulled up a gently sloping earth ramp about three or four times the length of the statue. The base was raised about four feet and positioned on a flat pedestal on top of the platform. Using rocks, earth, rope stays, wedges, and levers, the statue would have been raised to an angle, where it was then guided slowly into place. At this point, the upright, tilting method would have been helpful in adjusting the statue's position on the flat pedestal. Any scars on the smoothly polished surface would have been abraded out with lumps of coral or pumice.

Some coastal ahu were built with high rear walls facing steep seaside cliffs. Moai were moved onto these platforms from the front. Houses and other structures were kept at a distance from the ahu, and the cleared, flat ground in front of the platforms provided ease of access. Earth ramps used in erecting statues were modified and beach cobble paving added to create platform extensions.

Katherine Scoresby Routledge, noting the patterns of breakage on some "in transport" statues, first considered and then rejected the idea that they were being transported upright. Instead, she believed that most had stood erect in place to form a ceremonial road to Rano Raraku. Testing this hypothesis, archaeologist Arne Skjølsvold of the Kon-Tiki Museum conducted excavations of two "in transport" statues in 1986. One had a patterned arrangement of stone at the base, suggesting that it had supported the weight of the upright statue, and lending some credibility to Routledge's hypothesis. Her excavations in Rano Raraku quarry, and Skjølsvold's own in 1955, revealed human bone, stone bowls, and tools associated with some moai standing on the volcano's slopes. In 1774 Captain Cook's party sought the lunchtime shade of a standing statue that may be one lying "in transport" near Ahu Oroi. This huge moai is almost 30 feet tall, more than double the height of the statistical average. It has a notched base, which suggests that levers were used to help move it while in a horizontal position, but it is shattered in such a way that it appears to have fallen from an upright position. All of this evidence suggests that at least some upright statues in the quarry, and others that *appear* to be "in transport," may actually have been deliberately placed

upright at their current non-ahu locations for use in ceremonial activity.

To test Routledge's idea of a ceremonial road further, we plotted the positions and orientations of moai lying along the main road from Rano Raraku to Rano Kau and the populous southeastern coast. The majority of statues either on their sides or face-down are lying with their heads oriented away from the quarry, while the heads of the face-up statues are toward the quarry. This means that nearly all of the statues, if standing upright, were looking southwest toward the massive bulk of the crater Rano Kau. There, from about A.D. 1450–1500 until well after contact with Europeans in 1722, the pan-island ceremonial center of Orongo flourished as the site of "birdman" rites. Predicated on the seasonal arrival of flocks of sooty terns and other birds following migratory schools of fish such as tuna, the birdman cult was a vital focus of Rapa Nui spiritual life. This cult emerged and evolved, in part, as a response to food resource scarcity and a changing sociopolitical environment. If Routledge's ceremonial road was, in fact, adorned with standing moai, the two spiritual centers of Rano Raraku and Rano Kau would have been visually linked in an extremely dramatic way.

The ahu to which the "in transport" statues were theoretically being moved were not prepared to receive them. None had been cleared of broken sculpture, and their walls had not been strengthened to support the new statues, all of which are larger than average. The cumulative evidence suggests that, at about the time Orongo became important, the ahu were adapted to uses that did not require moai. Instead, the statues remained in Rano Raraku, where many were used in new ways. Taking everything as a whole, it appears to me that Routledge's ceremonial road is a very real possibility.

In our computer modeling we sought the optimal path the Rapa Nui would have taken to haul Statue 01 from Rano Raraku to Ahu Akivi. We invited Zvi Shiller and his engineering graduate students at the University of California at Los Angeles Robotics Lab to participate in this stage of our research. First, they

digitized a topographic map of Rapa Nui to produce a three-dimensional map of the terrain. Using their computer programs and our statue data, they proposed three alternate routes.

Path 1 was the shortest, most direct route, requiring the least expenditure of energy. It ran westward and directly inland. Between 55 and 70 people would have been able to haul Statue 01 from Rano Raraku to Ahu Akivi along this route. A concerted pull on the hauling ropes would have moved the statue 14 feet. Taking into account pauses to adjust the statue, move the rollers, and tighten any lashings, the work could have been accomplished in five to seven days, calculated on the basis of a five-hour workday. Paths 2 and 3 were also viable, and neither required substantially more people to move the statue. However, Path 2 was longer and Path 3 the longest. Each demanded that laborers expend substantially more energy, thus requiring more food and water to get the job done.

The maximum force required to pull the statue in a horizontal position is two and one-half tons. In an upright position a 14-ton statue with a flat rectangular base requires two and one-third tons of force to tilt. Thus little energy is saved by tilting, although this transport method does not require wood. Pulling an upright statue on a "pod" over rollers requires nearly the same amount of wood as the horizontal method we designed. Manpower needs, however, are about half. The most obvious argument against upright transport is the Rapa Nui terrain. Our calculations show that an upright statue will fall often on a ten-degree slope and nearly all of the time on a 20-degree slope. Tilting an upright statue or pulling one on a "pod" of logs up or down even the gentlest slopes can be tricky and dangerous. Why would the Rapa Nui have resorted to such methods if, in fact, they even did? The only logical explanation would be a lack of wood and/or lack of sufficient manpower. The statues at Ahu Akivi were erected sometime after A.D. 1400 and before the mid-1600s, when the simple, rectangular stone platform was renovated to hold seven statues. Was wood available on Rapa Nui then?

Swamps and lakes in the craters of Rano Raraku and Rano Kau, and on Maunga Terevaka, hold thousands of years of pollen, evidence of the island's history of vegetation and ecological change. Pollen was collected by several investigators, including the Norwegian Archaeological Expedition in 1955. In the early 1930s John Flenley of Massey University in New Zealand and his colleagues analyzed core samples collected on Rapa Nui. They found that the island was once lushly if not lavishly forested, and that a species of palm similar to the gigantic *Jubaea chilensis* was once present, along with other trees.

More recently, Chilean agronomist Gerardo Velasco discovered dozens of large, round holes in ancient, hardened lava flows along the island's coast. The holes are the "prints" left by the trunks of trees once entombed in lava. Close examination reveals patterned ridges in the stone, clearly made by the distinctive trunks of palms. Velasco has measured dozens of these holes, which average 18 inches in diameter. This size is a great deal smaller than that of *Jubaea chilensis,* suggesting that more than one type of palm may have existed on the island. Eighteen inches, however, is a perfect size for transport frames and rollers.

Deforestation took place on the island in various locales at different times, with Rano Raraku probably stripped of its trees by A.D. 1000. American archaeologist Chris Stevenson has found evidence of palms and other as yet unidentified trees at inland sites dating to the 1400s and 1500s. It is safe to assume, therefore, that trees of appropriate dimensions were available for horizontal statue transport at about the time the Ahu Akivi statues were moved.

What about manpower? We used osteological data to calculate the stature of the prehistoric Rapa Nui man who would have transported and erected statues. Our Rapa Nui "reference man" was between the age of 18 and 30, in generally good health. He was five and one-half feet tall and weighed approximately 150 pounds. His daily nutritional requirement would have been 2,880 calories, of which he would have expended roughly 50 percent in energy. According

to the ethnographer Alfred Métraux, the typical Rapa Nui family consisted of nine members. Data from western Polynesia clearly show an extended family could be expected to have 45 to 50 members. Virtually every member contributed some form of labor to the economic life of the whole. Conservatively, each extended family would have had eight males of appropriate age and vigor available to haul statues, meaning that between eight and nine extended families would have had to cooperate to move the average moai.

We calculated an optimal daily diet for our Rapa Nui reference man. About 25–35 percent of the 2,880 calories would have been provided by fat. In order to replace the energy and body tissue he was expending in the work task, he would have needed 65–75 grams of protein and 15 grams of iron, in addition to calcium, phosphorous, carbohydrates, and various vitamins. To accomplish this each man would have had to consume either 200 grams of chicken or an equal amount of non-oily fish (preferably tuna or something similar) to gain 500–600 calories of protein. The remaining calories would have been supplied by sweet potatoes, sugar cane, and bananas, all important Rapa Nui crops with a high water content—a key factor in avoiding work fatigue. Water was also available in the crater lake of Rano Raraku and in the vicinity of Ahu Akivi.

To meet the food requirements of the laborers, a Rapa Nui chief (*ariki*) who commissioned an average statue and had it moved along Path 1 would have needed three to six acres per crop above and beyond the normal one-half acre required to feed each person. He would also have required a surplus of crops at least equal to what he was dispensing to pay for the fish or other protein. It is a conservative estimate that agricultural resources provided by 50 acres, or about double the extended family norm, were required to complete the Ahu Akivi transport task.

In the same way that Polynesian chiefs throughout the Pacific commissioned and paid for canoes, Rapa Nui chiefs called upon their communities to make and move statues. Work parties

were formed of combined, co-resident family groups or cooperating extended family units at the behest of chiefs who exploited ties of kinship, shared religious beliefs, and personal status to marshall the resources of lineage lands and fishing grounds. Master craftspeople with extensive, formal, and institutionalized knowledge, training, talent, and skill directed work crews. Food, water, and timber were produced on lineage lands or traded for by chiefs, and appropriate ceremonies were conducted at all stages of the work. Polynesians distinguish between food needed for sustenance and feast food, and prodigious amounts of both were required for statue transport.

Transporting and raising seven statues at Ahu Akivi is typical of what a Rapa Nui chief could do, and is no small accomplishment. Transport methods used by Rapa Nui experts would logically have been those that were most efficient and of proven utility, and the horizontal method seems most appropriate. Adaptation to time, manpower, or resource shortages would have required flexibility and could have produced individual innovations.

The evidence throughout the Pacific is that limited island ecosystems with short food chains were dramatically transformed by humans. On Rapa Nui from about A.D. 1000, deforestation and agricultural land-use policies apparently caused serious soil erosion. Birds and eggs, once easily attainable foods, were significantly depleted and consequently more valuable. Natural disasters may have occurred that have not, as yet, been investigated. Rapa Nui cultural practices interacted with the island's marginal and isolated environment to precipitate a series of environmental problems, resource shortages, and probable social crises as yet not fully understood.

Not all Rapa Nui people experienced the same kind of problems at the same time, however. Polynesian people held their island homes in high regard, and chiefs were responsible for maintaining individual lineage land-use rights and managing resources. Some were more successful than others. There is direct archaeological evidence that many people tried to mitigate some of their environmental crises as they recognized and understood them. Practical innovations such as *manavai* (stone garden enclosures), which protected fragile plants from the wind, worked fairly well. The Rapa Nui also conceived the birdman cult and other dramatically new religious practices out of old ideas.

The moai were not abandoned, however. Instead of being transported to ahu, they were used in new ways. It appears that increasingly larger moai were erected on the slopes of Rano Raraku. This may reflect a general movement away from narrowly defined, ahu-based lineage concerns and toward more integrated, supralineage ideological practices concentrated on the two main sites of pan-island significance, Rano Raraku and Rano Kau. In the same time frame, however, and possibly less than 200 years before the 1722 arrival of Europeans, our simulated transport studies suggest that a typical Rapa Nui chief was still able to make and move an average-size statue.

The Rapa Nui courageously faced the open and empty sea when they founded and settled their tiny island. As they cleared and used the land and fished the surrounding ocean, they called upon their gods, their leaders, their families, and their own strengths. They interacted with their island environment in traditional ways. Their repertoire of coping skills was shaped by their heritage as Polynesians. European "discoverers" of Rapa Nui perceived the culture, with its fallen statues, as in a state of collapse. This is an ethnocentric Western interpretation rather than an archaeological one. As cultural outsiders, we can now see where the Rapa Nui went wrong. But because the course of Rapa Nui history was interrupted and redirected by the impact of Europeans, we will never know for certain just how successful they might have been in dealing with the environmental crises they faced.

Paleolithic Paint Job

Two French archeologists are trying to get closer—much closer—to an ancient act of creation.

Roger Lewin

Roger Lewin is a writer in Washington, D.C., who specializes in human prehistory. His most recent book on the subject, Origins Reconsidered, *written with anthropologist Richard Leakey, was published in 1992. In 1989 Lewin was the recipient of the inaugural Lewis Thomas Award for Excellence in the Communication of Life Sciences. "Ancient human fossils stir the imagination," Lewin says, "but nothing matches the immediacy of prehistoric cave paintings in their ability to connect us with our past."*

"You have to be dressed right for this job," says Michel Lorblanchet, whose beret-capped head and white goatee make him a virtual caricature of a Frenchman. Lorblanchet, an archeologist with France's National Center for Scientific Research, slips out of mud-caked overalls and, with a colleague's help, struggles free of a pair of snug rubber boots. "It's pretty tight in there," he says, referring to a cave he has been working in, not to his boots. "You have to crawl a long way," he adds. "That's how we get so filthy." Lorblanchet is describing his efforts to study the ancient paintings deep inside the caves of the Lot Valley in southwest France. These depictions of a lost world—of Ice Age bison, horses, mammoths, and deer—were painted between 30,000 and 10,000 years ago.

They remain among the most haunting of all archeological finds.

The region here, known as Quercy, is dominated by rugged gray limestone plateaus intermittently sliced by fertile valleys and farmland. The cuisine of the area—a matter of constant and weighty discussion among the locals—is rich and robust: truffles, foie gras, duck confit, deeply flavorful lamb, and strong, dark wines. There is an earthy sensuosity about the place. When Lorblanchet, a native son of the area, describes it simply as "my country," you know he is speaking not only for himself but for generations of people whose roots are planted in this land. The Quercy sensuosity also apparently imbues Lorblanchet's unorthodox approach to studying cave art.

Traditionally cave art archeologists, perhaps to beef up their scientific credentials, have striven to understand the meaning of these paintings through objective inquiry. They have relied heavily on statistical analysis (which animals were represented where in the caves, for example) to test their hypotheses about the art. Lorblanchet's approach, by contrast, is freewheeling, subjective, experimental. He wants to get inside the minds of the early artists by reproducing some of their most famous works—not merely by tracing their outlines onto paper, as others have done in the past, but by replicating whole paintings on rock. Although he hopes to gain new insights, he has

no theory to prove or disprove. "Some of my colleagues think that experimentation without a preliminary theory is a waste of time," says Lorblanchet, the usual soft timbre of his voice gaining a slight edge of defiance. "But I totally disagree with them. I don't know what I will learn by temporarily becoming a Paleolithic painter, but I know I'll learn something."

Actually, for all its apparent unorthodoxy, Lorblanchet's work fits right into a new trend in cave art archeology. The Quercy archeologist is interested in how the early artists went about painting. Jean Clottes, another French archeologist, working in the Pyrenees, studies what their pigments were composed of. Although the two men's styles could hardly be more dissimilar—one personal and intuitive, the other extremely high-tech—they converge on the same novel question: What can we learn from the *paint* in these paintings? This investigative avenue doesn't ignore all that has gone before, of course, but builds on it.

The scholarly study of Ice Age art began in the 1920s with the great French prehistorian Abbé Henri Breuil, who saw it as an expression of hunting magic. Breuil based his conclusions on contemporary anthropological observations of the Arunta aborigines in central Australia. To ensure a plentiful supply of prey, the Arunta performed rituals during which they painted images of the prey—principally kangaroos—on rock faces. (Rituals of this kind are now well known among many of the world's remaining foraging peoples.)

Gradually though, archeologists began to doubt that hunting magic alone could explain all prehistoric cave art. The overthrow of this hypothesis in the 1960s was led by another French prehistorian, André Leroi-Gourhan. After surveying more than 60 painted caves, Leroi-Gourhan came to see order in the images' distribution. Stags often appeared in entrance-ways, ibex at the caves' peripheries, and horses, bison, oxen, and mammoths in the main chambers. As Leroi-Gourhan saw it, this structure represented the division of the world into males and females—or, more mystically, maleness and femaleness. The horse, the stag, and the ibex embodied maleness; the bison, the mammoth, and the ox embodied femaleness. According to this "structuralist" interpretation, all caves were decorated systematically to reflect this male-female duality, which suffused the mythology of Upper Paleolithic people.

This mode of structuralism was eventually done in by its all-embracing scope. It could be true, but there was no way of knowing: How could you test a rule with no exceptions? These

days archeologists are taking more diverse approaches. Structure could still play a role, for example, but a more limited one—individual caves may well have been decorated with an overall pattern in mind. More attention is now being paid to the art's context. For example, Margaret Conkey, an archeologist at the University of California at Berkeley, argues that to understand what made the art meaningful you have to understand its social context. Which members of society produced the images? Was it the sacred right of a few important males? Were females involved, or even responsible for the art?

Still, even with a diversity of approaches, you can only hope for shadowy glimpses of Paleolithic life. "You know we should admit that it may never be possible to bridge the gap between the Paleolithic mind and the modern mind," cautions Lorblanchet. "There are many barriers that stop us." The most immediate barrier, he says, is that our perspective on the world is so utterly different from that of the Ice Age artists. The country here was once a frigid steppe, roamed by herds of exotic species that have long since gone extinct; and the lives of the hunters, so intimately attuned to the rhythms of nature, were vastly different from our own. "We are city dwellers, surrounded by angular build-

ings, following artificial rhythms of life," says Lorblanchet. "How can we expect to be able to view the art as Upper Paleolithic people did?" Lorblanchet hopes his new approach will help answer that.

Lorblanchet's recent bid to re-create one of the most important Ice Age images in Europe was an affair of the heart as much as the head. "I tried to abandon my skin of a modern citizen, tried to experience the feeling of the artist, to enter the dialogue between the rock and the man," he explains. Every day for a week in the fall of 1990 he drove the 20 miles from his home in the medieval village of Cajarc into the hills above the river Lot. There, in a small, practically inaccessible cave, he transformed himself into an Upper Paleolithic painter. And not just any Upper Paleolithic painter, but the one who 18,400 years ago crafted the dotted horses inside the famous cave of Pech Merle.

You can still see the original horses in Pech Merle's vast underground geo-

Spit-painting in action: Michel Lorblanchet blows paint under his left hand to achieve an outline with a soft lower edge for the horse's back; spits pigment between parallel hands to paint the legs; makes a handprint; and spits dots through a hole in an animal skin.

logic splendor. You enter through a narrow passageway and soon find yourself gazing across a grand cavern to where the painting seems to hang in the gloom. "Outside, the landscape is very different from the one the Upper Paleolithic people saw," says Lorblanchet. "But in here, the landscape is the same as it was more than 18,000 years ago. You see what the Upper Paleolithic people experienced." No matter where you look in this cavern, the eye is drawn back to the panel of horses.

The two horses face away from each other, rumps slightly overlapping, their outlines sketched in black. The animal on the right seems to come alive as it merges with a crook in the edge of the panel, the perfect natural shape for a horse's head. But the impression of naturalism quickly fades as the eye falls on the painting's dark dots. There are more than 200 of them, deliberately distributed within and below the bodies and arcing around the right-hand horse's head and mane. More cryptic still are a smattering of red dots and half-circles and the floating outline of a fish. The surrealism is completed by six disembodied human hands stenciled above and below the animals.

Lorblanchet began thinking about re-creating the horses after a research trip to Australia over a decade ago. Not only is Australia a treasure trove of rock art, but its aboriginal people are still creating it. "In Queensland I learned how people painted by spitting pigment onto the rock," he recalls. "They spat paint and used their hand, a piece of cloth, or a feather as a screen to create different lines and other effects. Elsewhere in Australia people used chewed twigs as paintbrushes, but in Queensland the spitting technique worked best." The rock surfaces there were too uneven for extensive brushwork, he adds—just as they are in Quercy.

When Lorblanchet returned home he looked at the Quercy paintings with a new eye. Sure enough, he began seeing the telltale signs of spit-painting—lines with edges that were sharply demarcated on one side and fuzzy on the other, as if they had been airbrushed—instead of the brushstrokes he and others had assumed were there. Could you produce lines that were crisp on both edges with the same technique, he wondered, and perhaps dots too? Archeologists had long recognized that hand stencils, which are common in prehistoric art, were produced by spitting paint around a hand held to the wall. But no one had thought that entire animal images could be created this way. Before he could test his ideas, however, Lorblanchet had to find a suitable rock face—the original horses were painted on a roughly vertical panel 13 feet across and 6 feet high. With the help of a speleologist, he eventually found a rock face in a remote cave high in the hills and set to work.

Following the aboriginal practices he had witnessed, Lorblanchet first made a light outline sketch of the horses with a charred stick. Then he prepared black pigment for the painting. "My intention had been to use manganese dioxide, as the Pech Merle painter did," says Lorblanchet, referring to one of the minerals ground up for paint by the early artists. "But I was advised that manganese is somewhat toxic, so I used wood charcoal instead." (Charcoal was used as pigment by Paleolithic painters in other caves, so Lorblanchet felt he could justify his concession to safety.) To turn the charcoal into paint, Lorblanchet ground it with a limestone block, put the powder in his mouth, and diluted it to the right consistency with saliva and water. For red pigment he used ocher from the local iron-rich clay.

He started with the dark mane of the right-hand horse. "I spat a series of dots and fused them together to represent tufts of hair," he says, unselfconsciously reproducing the spitting action as he talks. "Then I painted the horse's back by blowing the pigment

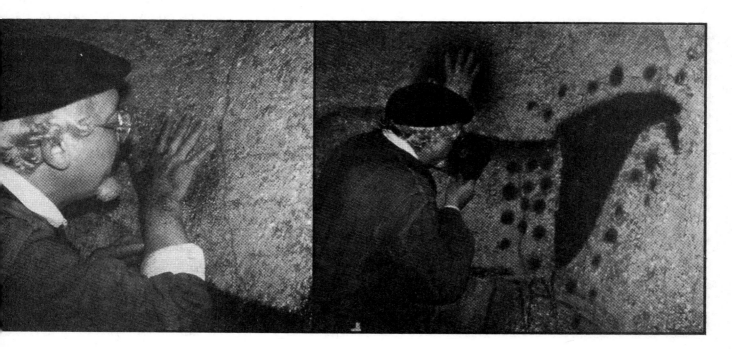

below my hand held so"—he holds his hand flat against the rock with his thumb tucked in to form a straight line—"and used it like a stencil to produce a sharp upper edge and a diffused lower edge. You get an illusion of the animal's rounded flank this way."

He experimented as he went. "You see the angular rump?" he says, pointing to the original painting. "I reproduced that by holding my hand perpendicular to the rock, with my palm slightly bent, and I spat along the edge formed by my hand and the rock." He found he could produce sharp lines, such as those in the tail and in the upper hind leg, by spitting into the gap between parallel hands. The belly demanded more ingenuity; he spat paint into a V-shape formed by his two splayed hands, rubbed it into a curved swath to shape the belly's outline, then finger-painted short protruding lines to suggest the animals' shaggy hair. Neatly outlined dots, he found, could not be made by blowing a thin jet of charcoal onto the wall. He had to spit pigment through a hole made in an animal skin.

"I spent seven hours a day for a week," he says. "Puff . . . puff . . . puff. . . . It was exhausting, particularly because there was carbon monoxide in the cave. But you experience something special, painting like that. You feel you are breathing the image onto the rock—projecting your spirit from the deepest part of your body onto the rock surface."

Was that what the Paleolithic painter felt when creating this image? "Yes, I know it doesn't sound very scientific," Lorblanchet says of his highly personal style of investigation, "but the intellectual games of the structuralists haven't got us very far, have they? Studying rock art shouldn't be an intellectual game. It is about understanding humanity. That's why I believe the experimental approach is valid in this case."

In contrast to Lorblanchet's freewheeling style, Jean Clottes's research looks much more like science as usual—technical and analytical. Clottes, a scientific adviser on rock art to the French Ministry of Culture, works in the Midi-Pyrénées, a wild and mountainous region that abuts France's border with Spain. Many of the caves in these mountains contain fine examples of Ice Age art. The most celebrated of the decorated caves is Niaux, which is approached by a gaping entrance on the steep northern slope of the Vicdessos Valley. About half a mile into this long, meandering cave is the Salon Noir, a towering cavern containing black images of horses, bison, ibex, and deer. Among the questions that preoccupied Clottes during his many visits to the Salon Noir was the age of these images. Were they all created at about the same time? And who created them?

One of the toughest problems in the study of rock art is accurately dating it. Radiocarbon dating, the surest method can be done only if charcoal is present in the paint. (The first such dates were obtained in 1989, when a technological advance—carbon dating by accelerator mass spectrometry—made it possible to use much smaller paint samples.) For the most part, however, archeologists have had to rely on what they term stylistic chronology. This basically depends on a subjective assessment of painting styles and on the assumption that particular conventions—such as the use of perspective—belong to particular periods. According to Leroi-Gourhan's chronology, nearly universally accepted, the paintings in the Salon Noir were painted in a uniform style typical of the period known as the Middle Magdalenian, which occurred some 13,000 to 14,000 years ago. But the pigment analysis that Clottes undertook with physicists Michel Menu and Philippe Walter revealed a different story.

Clottes's study was inspired by some work that Menu and Walter had done previously at the cave of La Vache, some 450 feet from Niaux, as the crow flies, on the southern side of the Vicdessos Valley. Although La Vache had no paintings, it did contain engraved bone objects, along with charcoal remains, that carbon dating established as being between 12,000 and 13,000 years old, an age corresponding to the period known as the Late Magdalenian. Trapped within the grooves of the engraved artifacts were residues of red and black paint Menu and Walter decided to find out what these paints were made from.

Back in Paris, at the Research Laboratory of the Museums of France, the

Lorblanchet's re-creation of the ancient dotted horses; it took him a week to complete his Paleolithic masterpiece.

Flightless Bird in Waterlogged Cave

The cave has been hailed as a sort of underwater Lascaux, the most exciting find since Lascaux's painted galleries were discovered five decades ago in southwest France. The hyperbole is understandable. The Cosquer cave, whose discovery was formally documented last year, can't really match Lascaux for artistry, but its images are unique and its place in prehistory is pivotal. The cave was found in 1991 by Henri Cosquer, a professional diver, while he was exploring the underwater grottoes at Cap Morgiu, near Marseilles. Its narrow entrance lies 121 feet below the surface of the Mediterranean, making it inaccessible to all but the most expert scuba divers—and enormously frustrating for landlubbing archeologists like Jean Clottes.

"I'd love to visit the Cosquer cave," says Clottes, who heads the committee formed by the French Ministry of Culture to plan future work at the promising site. "But I'm no diver, and the passage to it is very dangerous." Already the cave has claimed three lives. Shortly after its discovery, three diving enthusiasts died in the water darkness while worming their way along the 500-foot-long tunnel that leads from the entrance to the partially flooded inner caverns. The French government has since blocked the entrance to prevent further tragedy. Clottes himself has seen only video images of the paintings, transmitted by the cameras of the diving research team to a TV monitor on dry land.

The cave is important for several reasons, explains Clottes. While painted caves are common in southwest France and in the Pyrenees, nothing like Cosquer had ever been found in the country's southeast. Although Cosquer is half underwater, the walls above sea level are covered in decorations. There are hand stencils, finger tracings, cryptic symbols, and cross-hatchings and more than 100 engraved and painted animal images. Many of these show horses, bison, and ibex, which are typical of Ice Age art from Europe. But the images of marine animals—what look like jellyfish, and a kind of seabird—are unlike anything seen before. Early English-language reports referred to the large, portly birds with stunted wings as penguins. In fact, says Clottes, they are auks, flightless seabirds that became extinct in the Mediterranean about a century and a half ago.

The cave is all the more important because it is possible to carbon-date some of the images from charcoal flakes in the paint and from charcoal in hearths found on the cave floor. Carbon dating has shown that the hand stencils were done between 27,800 and 26,500 years ago, which makes them contenders for the oldest known paintings in the world. The animal images, some of which appear on top of the negative handprints, were crafted more than 8,000 years later. "In the short time since its discovery, Cosquer has become the most thoroughly dated painted cave known," observes Clottes.

Although getting to the cave is hard nowadays—a sort of athletic event in itself, as Clottes puts it—the prehistoric people who used the cave for their ancient rituals would have had no trouble reaching it. Sea levels at the time were at least 300 feet lower than they are today, so the cave was dry. Archeologists hope to make access easier by sinking a shaft through the limestone to a passage near the caverns. But first they will have to determine what effect such an opening would have on very fragile paintings that have been sealed in an air pocket for thousands of years. "Our first priority," says Clottes, "is the preservation of the paintings."

—Roger Lewin

two physicists used scanning electron microscopy, X-ray diffraction, and proton-induced X-ray emission to examine the physical and chemical properties of these paints. The pigment minerals held no surprises: the red was hematite and the black was basically manganese dioxide. The interest lay in the extender, a general term for materials that artists use to stretch pigment and, along with water, enhance its ease of application. Menu and Walter's analysis revealed that the extender in the La Vache paint was a mixture of biotite and feldspar, minerals easily obtained in the valley. But what intrigued the researchers was that biotite and feldspar don't occur together. "The

Paleolithic painters had to mix them together, then grind them with the pigment to form paint," says Clottes. Quartz grinding stones bearing traces of paint production were discovered in the caves. "This tells us that the Paleolithic painters didn't just use whatever was available," Clottes points out "They had a specific recipe."

Was the La Vache recipe—call it recipe B, for biotite and feldspar—also used at Niaux? "Because of their proximity, there seemed a good chance that the hunters of La Vache belonged to the same social group that frequented Niaux," explains Clottes. "If so, they probably used the same pigments."

Traditionally archeologists would have hesitated to take paint from prehistoric images to test the idea, but Menu and Walter's methods required only a tiny quantity—less than half a milligram. In 1989 they received permission to lift 59 pinhead-size pieces of pigment from images in the Salon Noir and other locations in the cave. When these paint samples were analyzed, Clottes's intuition was proved correct: most were indeed recipe B, suggesting that they, too, might be 12,000 to 13,000 years old, just like those in the cave across the valley. His deductions were recently confirmed in a follow-up study capitalizing on one of the surprises of the Niaux pigment analysis. Tests revealed that the recipe B paint was layered: there were traces of charcoal under the black manganese pigment. Carbon dating on the charcoal flakes under one of the images corroborated that the paint was 12,800 years old, consistent with the paint at La Vache.

The confirmation of Clottes's hunch, however, opened a can of worms. Based on Leroi-Gourhan's stylistic chronology, the Niaux paintings were up to 14,000 years old. Yet at least some of the Niaux paintings employed a paint recipe—recipe B—that carbon dating established as 12,000 to 13,000 years old. Did this mean that the recipe had been in use for at least 1,000 years? Or could there be something wrong with the chronology based on stylistic similarity?

"We didn't know what to make of it," says Clottes. "And the situation became more complicated, because in *some* paint samples from Niaux, we found a different recipe." In this paint mixture, call it recipe F the extender was only feldspar. It contained no biotite, and there was no charcoal beneath it. "We toyed with the idea of different paint recipes being used by groups of different social status, or even one recipe for men, the other for women. But it seemed just as likely that the different recipes were used during different periods."

To settle this puzzle, Clottes, Menu, and Walter analyzed the paint recipes from a wide range of decorated caves in the region that have been firmly carbon-dated. Would the two recipes at Niaux turn out to correspond to two different prehistoric periods? So far—and Clottes points out that the sample is small, about ten sites—recipe B has been found consistently with Late Magdalenian work (about 12,000 to 13,000 years old), while recipe F is exclusively Middle Magdalenian (about 13,000 to 14,000 years old). "We don't know why Paleolithic painters changed the recipe for the extender around 13,000 years ago," asserts Clottes. Perhaps, he speculates, it made the paint easier to apply or gave it a slightly different color. "But whatever the reason, it gives us a way of attaching a date to paintings when radiocarbon methods are not possible."

Thus the Niaux paint studies answered Clottes's question in a completely unexpected way: despite their similarity, the paintings in the cave were not all created within a short period of time. Many generations could have separated recipe B and recipe F paintings. The more general implication—one that archeologists will have to struggle with in the years to come—is that style is no certain guide to chronology. The methodology that supported years of archeological work has suddenly crumbled. But that isn't the only ripple the studies have left in their wake.

Archeologists have long believed that the Salon Noir at Niaux was a sanctuary—a sort of Ice Age cathedral where important ceremonies were held. Clottes himself subscribes to this gut feeling. "There is something special about the Salon Noir," he says, as he leads the way along the uneven corridor that takes you to the cave's inner chamber. "When you enter with a small lamp, you naturally follow the right-hand wall, retreating from that great black void to the left. Eventually, inevitably, you reach the Salon Noir, with its soaring ceiling beyond the reach of torchlight. It's as if the place draws you here." Clottes shifts the beam of light to the walls, dramatically revealing the panels of black bison, horses, ibex, and deer. He swings the beam from panel to panel, creating an eerie sense of movement in the ancient images as he points out how stylistically homogeneous they are. "This homogeneity," he explains, "has been very important to our perception of the cave as a sanctuary."

When archeologists speak of a sanctuary, they typically imagine a richly decorated cave in which the paintings seem to form a planned, cohesive body of work. The two most famous examples are Altamira in Spain, with its huge polychrome extravaganzas, and Lascaux in France, with its fabulous friezes. But by that logic, wouldn't the discovery of different paint recipes in the Salon Noir, spanning as much as two millennia, cast doubt on Niaux's status as a sanctuary? "That *seems* logical, but it turns out to be wrong," asserts Clottes. For evidence, he returns to the pigment studies that uncovered charcoal fragments under the most commonly used paint in the Salon Noir. "That indicated to us that the Upper Paleolithic artists first made a sketch using a charcoal stick, then painted over the outline," says Clottes.

This technique—a preliminary sketch followed by careful painting—is not common in Paleolithic art. The combination of sketch and painting not only takes more time, says Clottes, but also implies premeditation. It suggests that the artist had some sort of composition in mind, sketching first and only filling in the outlines with paint after he or she was satisfied with the overall effect. That kind of care, argues Clottes, is much more consistent with paintings found in heavily decorated sanctuaries than in the more run-of-the-mill caves with their scattered images that look as if they've been hastily dashed off on brief visits.

"I believe people repeatedly came to the spot we're standing on now," says Clottes. It was, he is sure, a gathering place of lasting social and mythological significance. "You know," he finally confides, "I've been in this cave many times. I've stood in the place where the Upper Paleolithic painter stood. I've traced the images. You put your hand where his or her hand once was; you move it, producing the same lines. Sometimes it feels uncanny. It brings you closer to them. Closer, but still frustratingly distant."

At moments like this the differences in style between Clottes and Lorblanchet seem to evaporate. "The first time I did my own hand stencil, I was shocked," recalls Lorblanchet. "There it was, my hand, separate and distant from me, but very definitely me, a more powerful signature than any writing. I had put myself into the rock, become part of another world." For Paleolithic people, that "other world," a potent mythological world mediated by simple images, was probably as real as life on the frigid steppe. Today we see only images on the rock.

BUSHMEN

John Yellen

John Yellen, director of the anthro-pology program at the National Sci-ence Foundation, has returned to the Kalahari four times since 1968.

I followed Dau, kept his slim brown back directly in front of me, as we broke suddenly free from the dense Kalahari bush and crossed through the low wire fence that separated Botswana from Namibia to the West. For that moment while Dau held the smooth wires apart for me, we were out in the open, in the full hot light of the sun and then we entered the shadows, the tangled thickets of arrow grass and thorn bush and mongongo trees once again. As soon as the bush began to close in around us again, I quickly became disoriented, Dau's back my only reference point.

Even then, in that first month of 1968, while my desert boots retained their luster, I knew enough to walk behind, not next to Dau. I had expected the Kalahari Desert to be bare open sand. I had imagined myself looking out over vast stretches that swept across to the horizon. But to my surprise, I found that the dunes were covered with trees and that during the rains the grasses grew high over my head. The bare sand, where I could see it, was littered with leaves, and over these the living trees and brush threw a dappled pattern of sunlight and shade. To look in the far distance and maintain a sense of direction, to narrow my focus and pick a way between the acacia bushes and their thorns, and then to look down, just in front of my feet to search out menacing shapes, was too much for me. Already, in that first month, the Bushmen had shown me a puff adder coiled motionless by the base of an acacia tree, but not until Cumsa the Hunter came up close to it, ready to strike it with his spear, could I finally see what all those hands were pointing at.

As Dau walked, I tried to follow his lead. To my discomfort I knew that many of these bushes had thorns—the Kalahari cloaks itself in thorns—some hidden close to the ground just high enough to rake across my ankles and draw blood when I pushed through, others long and straight and white so they reflected the sun. That morning, just before the border fence, my con-centration had lagged and I found my-self entangled in wait-a-bit thorns that curved backwards up the branch. So I stopped and this short, brown-skinned Bushman pushed me gently backwards to release the tension, then worked the branch, thorn by thorn from my shirt and my skin.

In the mid-1960s, the South African government had decided to accurately survey the Botswana border, mark it with five-strand fence, and cut a thin firebreak on either side. At intervals they constructed survey towers, strange skeletal affairs, like oil drilling rigs, their tops poking well above the highest mongongo trees. It was to one of these that Dau led me across the border, through the midday sun. Although he would not climb it himself, since it was a white man's tower, he assumed I would. I followed his finger, his chain of logic as I started rather hesitantly up the rusted rungs. I cleared the arrow grass, the acacia bushes, finally the broad leafy crowns of the mongongo nut trees. Just short of the top I stopped and sat, hooked my feet beneath the rung below, and wrapped my arms around the metal edges of the sides.

From *Science 85*, May 1985, pp. 41-48. © 1985 by John Yellen, National Science Foundation, Arlington, VA. Reprinted by permission.

4. EXPERIMENTAL ARCHAEOLOGY

For a month now I had copied the maps—the lines and the circles the !Kung tribesmen had drawn with their fingers in the sand. I had listened and tried to transcribe names of those places, so unintelligible with their clicks, their rising and falling tones. I had walked with Dau and the others to some of those places, to small camps near ephemeral water holes, but on the ground it was too confusing, the changes in altitude and vegetation too subtle, the sun too nearly overhead to provide any sense of where I was or from where I had come.

For the first time from the tower, I could see an order to the landscape. From up there on the tower, I could see that long thin border scar, could trace it off to the horizon to both the north and south. But beyond that, no evidence, not the slightest sign of a human hand. The Bushmen camps were too few in number, too small and well-hidden in the grass and bush to be visible from here. Likewise, the camp where we anthropologists lived, off to the east at the Dobe waterhole, that also was too small to see.

As Dau had intended, from my perch on that tower I learned a lot. At least now I could use the dunes, the shallow valleys, to know whether I was walking east and west or north and south.

In those first years with the Dobe Bushmen, I did gain at least a partial understanding of that land. And I learned to recognize many of those places, the ones that rate no name at all but are marked only by events—brief, ephemeral happenings that leave no mark on the land. I learned to walk with the Bushmen back from a hunt or a trip for honey or spear-shaft wood and listen. They talked, chattered almost constantly, decorating the bus, these no-name places as they went, putting ornaments of experience on them: "See that tree there, John? That's where we stopped, my brother and I, long before he was married, when he killed a kudu, a big female. We stopped under that tree, hung the meat up there and rested in the shade. But the flies were so bad, the biting flies, that we couldn't stay for long."

It took me a long time to realize that this chatter was not chatter at all, to

understand that those remarks were gifts, a private map shared only among a few, an overlay crammed with fine, spidery writing on top of the base map with its named waterholes and large valleys, a map for friends to read. Dau would see a porcupine burrow, tiny, hidden in the vastness of the bush. And at night he could sit by the fire and move the others from point to point across the landscape to that small opening in the ground.

But as an archeologist, I had a task to do—to name those places and to discover what life had been like there in the past. "This place has a name now," I told Dau when I went back in 1976. Not the chicken camp, because when I was there I kept 15 chickens, or the cobra camp, for the cobra we killed one morning among the nesting hens, but Dobe Base Camp 18. Eighteen because it's the eighteenth of these old abandoned camps I've followed you to in the last three days. See? That's what goes into this ledger, this fat bound book in waterproof ballpoint ink. We could get a reflector in here—a big piece of tin like some metal off a roof and get some satellite or a plane to photograph it. We could tell just where it is then, could mark it on one of those large aerial maps down to the nearest meter if we wanted.

We came back to these camps, these abandoned places on the ground, not once but month after month for the better part of a year. Not just Dau and myself but a whole crew of us, eight Bushmen and I, to dig, to look down into the ground. We started before the sun was too high up in the sky, and later Dau and I sat in the shade sipping thick, rich tea. I asked questions and he talked.

"One day when I was living here, I shot a kudu: an adult female. Hit it with one arrow in the flank. But it went too far and we never found it. Then another day my brother hit a wildebeest, another adult female and that one we got. We carried it back to camp here and ate it."

"What other meat did you eat here, Dau?"

"One, no two, steenbok, it was."
1948: 28 years ago by my counting was when Dau, his brothers, his family were here. How could he remember the

detail? This man sat in the shade and recalled trivial events that have repeated themselves in more or less the same way at so many places over the last three decades.

We dug day after day in the old camps—and found what Dau said we should. Bones, decomposing, but still identifiable: bones of wildebeest and steenbok among the charcoal and mongongo nut shells.

We dug our squares, sifting through the sand for bones. And when I dumped the bones, the odd ostrich eggshell bead, the other bits and pieces out onto the bridge table to sort, so much of what my eyes and ears told me was confirmed in this most tangible form. If excavation in one square revealed the bones of a wildebeest or kudi or other large antelope, then the others would contain them as well. In an environment as unpredictable as the Kalahari, where the game was hard to find and the probability of failure high, survival depended on sharing, on spreading the risk. And the bones, distributed almost evenly around the individual family hearths confirmed that. What also impressed me was how little else other than the bones there was. Most archeological sites contain a broad range of debris. But in those years the Bushmen owned so little. Two spears or wooden digging sticks or strings of ostrich eggshell beads were of no more use than one. Better to share, to give away meat or extra belongings and through such gifts create a web of debts, of obligations that some day would be repaid. In 1948, even in 1965, to accumulate material goods made no sense.

When it was hot, which was most of the year, I arranged the bridge table and two chairs in a patch of nearby shade. We sat there with the bound black and red ledger and dumped the bones in a heap in the center of the table, then sorted them out. I did the easy stuff, separated out the turtle shells, the bird bones, set each in a small pile around the table's edge. Dau did the harder part, separated the steenbok from the duiker, the wildebeest from kudu, held small splintered bone fragments and turned them over and over in his hands. We went through the piles then, one by one, moved each in its turn to the center of the table, sorted them into finer categories, body part by body part, bone by bone. Cryptic notes, bits of data that accumulated page by page. The bones with their sand and grit were transformed into numbers in rows and columns, classes and subclasses which would, I hoped, emerge from some computer to reveal a grander order, a design, an underlying truth.

Taphonomy: That's the proper term for it. The study of burial and preservation. Archeologists dig lots of bones out of the ground, not just from recent places such as these but from sites that span the millions of years of mankind's existence. On the basis of the bones, we try to learn about those ancient people. We try to reconstruct their diet, figure out how the animals were hunted, how they were killed, butchered, and shared.

What appealed to me about the Dobe situation, why I followed Dau, walked out his youth and his early manhood back and forth around the waterhole was the neat, almost laboratory situation Dobe offered. A natural experiment. I could go to a modern camp, collect those discarded food bones even before the jackals and hyenas had gotten to them, examine and count them, watch the pattern emerge. What happened then to the bones after they'd been trampled, picked over, rained on, lain in the ground for five years? Five years ago? Dobe Base Camp 21, 1971. I could go there, dig up a sample and find out.

What went on farther and farther back in time? Is there a pattern? Try eight years ago. 1968, DBC 18. We could go there to the cobra camp and see. Thirty-four years ago? The camp where Tsaa with the beautiful wife was born. One can watch, can see how things fall apart, can make graphs, curves, shoot them back, watch them arc backwards beyond Dau, beyond Dau's father, back into the true archeological past.

We dug our way through the DBCs, back into the early 1940s, listening day after day to the South African soap operas on the short-wave radio, and our consumption of plastic bags went down and down. Slim pickings in the

bone department. And the bones we did find tended to be rotten: They fragmented, fell apart in the sieve.

So we left the 1940s, collapsed the bridge table and the folding chairs and went to that site that played such a crucial role for anthropologists: DBC 12, the 1963 camp where those old myths about hunters and gatherers came up against the hard rock of truth.

They built this camp just after Richard Lee, the pioneer, arrived. They lived there through the winter and hunted warthog with spears and a pack of dogs so good they remember each by name to this day. Richard lived there with them. He watched them—what they did, what they ate, weighed food on his small scale slung with a rope from an acacia tree. He weighed people, sat in camp day after day with his notebook and his wristwatch and scale. He recorded times: when each person left camp in the morning, when each returned for the day.

In this small remnant group, one of the last in the world still living by hunting and gathering, it should be possible, he believed, to see a reflection, a faint glimmer of the distant universal past of all humanity, a common condition that had continued for millions and millions of years. He went there because of that and for that reason, later on, the rest of us followed him.

What he found in that desert camp, that dry, hard land, set the anthropological world back on its collective ear. What his scale and his wristwatch and his systematic scribbles showed was that we were fooled, that we had it all wrong. To be a hunter and gatherer wasn't that bad after all. They didn't work that hard, even in this land of thorns: For an adult, it came to less time than a nine-to-five office worker puts in on the job. They lived a long time, too, didn't wear out and die young but old-looking, as we had always thought. Even in this camp, the camp with the good hunting dogs, it was plants, not meat, which provided the staff of life. Women walked through the nut groves and collected nuts with their toes, dug in the molapos and sang to each other through the bush. Unlike the game, which spooked so easily and

followed the unpredictable rains, the nuts, roots, and berries were dependable, there in plenty, there for the picking. Another distinguished anthropologist, Marshall Sahlins, termed those DBC 12 people "the original affluent society"—something quite different from the traditional conception of hunting and gathering as a mean, hard existence half a step ahead of starvation and doom.

Over the years that name has held—but life in the Kalahari has changed. That kind of camp, with all the bones and mongongo nuts and dogs, is no more.

By the mid-1970s, things were different at Dobe. Diane Gelburd, another of the anthropologists out there then, only needed to look around her to see how the Bushman lifestyle had changed from the way Richard recorded it, from how Sahlins described it. But what had changed the people at DBC 12 who believed that property should be commonly held and shared? What had altered their system of values? That same winter Diane decided to find out.

She devised a simple measure of acculturation that used pictures cut from magazines: an airplane, a sewing machine, a gold mine in South Africa. (Almost no one got the gold mine right.) That was the most enjoyable part of the study. They all liked to look at pictures, to guess.

Then she turned from what people knew to what they believed. She wanted to rank them along a scale, from traditional to acculturated. So again she asked questions:

"Will your children be tattooed?"

To women: "If you were having a difficult childbirth and a white doctor were there, would you ask for assistance?"

To men: "If someone asked you for permission to marry your daughter would you demand (the traditional) bride service?"

Another question so stereotyped that in our own society one would be too embarassed to ask it: "Would you let your child marry someone from another tribe—a Tswana or a Herero—a white person?"

First knowledge, then belief, and finally material culture. She did the less sensitive questions first. "Do you

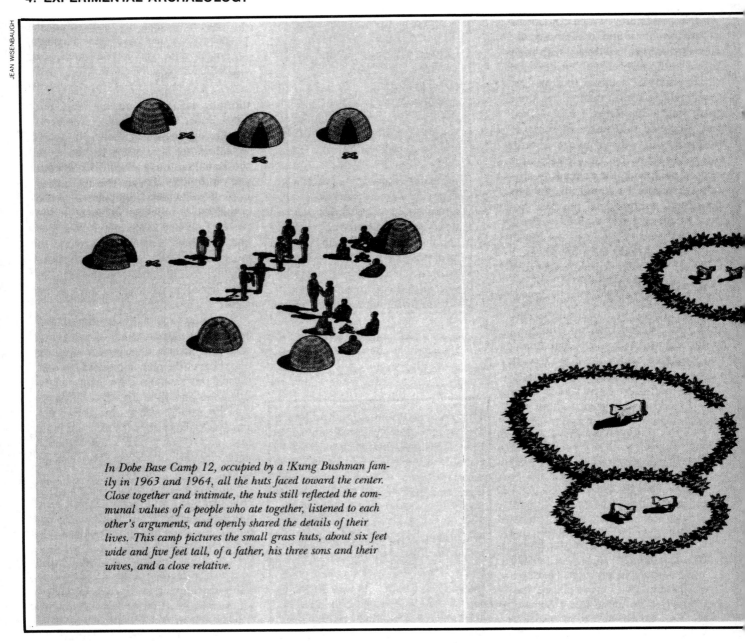

In Dobe Base Camp 12, occupied by a !Kung Bushman family in 1963 and 1964, all the huts faced toward the center. Close together and intimate, the huts still reflected the communal values of a people who ate together, listened to each other's arguments, and openly shared the details of their lives. This camp pictures the small grass huts, about six feet wide and five feet tall, of a father, his three sons and their wives, and a close relative.

have a field? What do you grow? What kind of animals do you have? How many of what?" Then came the hard part: She needed to see what people actually owned. I tagged along with her one day and remember the whispers inside one dark mud hut. Trunks were unlocked and hurriedly unpacked away from the entrance to shield them from sight. A blanket spread out on a trunk revealed the secret wealth that belied their statements: "Me? I have nothing." In the semidarkness she made her inventory. Then the trunks were hastily repacked and relocked with relief.

She went through the data, looked at those lists of belongings, itemized them in computer printouts. Here's a man who still hunts. The printout shows it. He has a bow and quiver and arrows on which the poison is kept fresh. He has a spear and snares for birds. He has a small steenbok skin bag, a traditional carryall that rests neatly under his arm.

He also has 19 goats and two donkeys, bought from the Herero or Tswana, who now get Dobe Bushmen to help plant their fields and herd their cows. They pay in livestock, hand-me-down clothing, blankets, and sometimes cash. He has three large metal trunks crammed full: One is packed to the top

with shoes, shirts, and pants, most well-worn. He has two large linen mosquito nets, 10 tin cups, and a metal file. He has ropes of beads: strand upon strand—over 200 in all, pounds of small colored glass beads made in Czechoslovakia that I had bought in Johannesburg years earlier. He has four large iron pots and a five-gallon plastic jerry can. He has a plow, a gift from the anthropologists. He has a bridle and bit, light blankets, a large tin basin. He has six pieces of silverware, a mirror and hairbrush, two billycans. His wife and his children together couldn't carry all that. The trunks are

Dobe Base Camp 36 was erected by the same extended family in 1978 and occupied until 1982. Fences of rail, thorn-bush, and barbed wire enclosing huts and goat and cattle kraals demonstrate their newly acquired ethic of privacy. The six huts clustered inside the large fence belonged to two of the sons and their grown and married children. Outside the group, a lone hut, unfenced, housed the third son. Another close relative occupied the last fenced hut. Now made of wattle and daub, the huts have doubled in size and spread apart. The family has even added wooden doors that can be closed and locked against intruders.

too heavy and too large for one person to carry so you would have to have two people for each. What about the plow, those heavy iron pots? Quite a job to carry those through bush, through the thick thorns.

But here is the surprising part. Talk to that man. Read the printout. See what he knows, what he believes. It isn't surprising that he speaks the Herero language and Setswana fluently or that he has worked for the Herero, the anthropologists. Nothing startling there. A budding Dobe capitalist. But then comes the shock: He espouses the traditional values.

"Bushmen share things, John. We share things and depend on each other, help each other out. That's what makes us different from the black people."

But the same person, his back to the door, opens his trunks, unlocks them one by one, lays out the blankets, the beads, then quickly closes each before he opens the next.

Multiply that. Make a whole village of people like that, and you can see the cumulative effect: You can actually measure it. As time goes on, as people come to own more possessions; the huts move farther and farther apart.

In the old days a camp was cosy, initimate and close. You could sit there by one fire and look into the other grass huts, see what the other people were doing, what they were making or eating. You heard the conversations, the arguments and banter.

We ask them why the new pattern?

Says Dau: "It's because of the livestock that we put our huts this way. They can eat the grass from the roofs and the sides of our houses. So we have to build fences to keep them away and to do that, you must have room between the huts."

I look up from the fire, glance around the camp, say nothing. No fences there. Not a single one around any of the huts, although I concede that one day they probably will build them. But why construct a lot of separate small fences, one around each hut? Why not clump the huts together the way they did in the old days and make a single large fence around the lot? Certainly a more efficient approach. Why worry about fences now in any case? The only exposed grass is on the roofs, protected by straight mud walls and nothing short of an elephant or giraffe could eat it.

Xashe's answer is different. Another brief reply. An attempt to dispose of the subject politely but quickly. "It's fire, John. That's what we're worried about. If we put our houses too close together, if one catches fire, the others will burn as well. We don't want one fire to burn all our houses down. That's why we build them so far apart."

But why worry about fire now? What about in the old days when the huts were so close, cheek by jowl? Why is it that when the huts were really vulnerable, when they were built entirely of dried grass, you didn't worry about fires then?

You read Diane's interviews and look at those lists of how much people own. You see those shielded mud huts with doors spaced, so far apart. You also listen to the people you like and trust. People who always have been honest with you. You hear their explanations and realize the evasions are not for you but for themselves. You see things they can't. But nothing can be done. It would be ludicrous to tell these brothers: "Don't you see, my friends, the lack of concordance be-

tween your values and the changing reality of your world?"

Now, years after the DBC study, I sit with data spread out before me and it is so clear. Richard's camp in 1963: just grass huts, a hearth in front of each. Huts and hearths in a circle, nothing more. 1968: more of the same. The following year though the first *kraal* appears, just a small thorn enclosure, some acacia bushes cut and dragged haphazardly together for their first few goats. It's set apart way out behind the circle of huts. On one goes, from plot to plot, following the pattern from year to year. The huts change from grass to mud. They become larger, more solidly built. Goats, a few at first, then more of them. So you build a fence around your house to keep them away from the grass roofs. The *kraals* grow larger, move in closer to be incorporated finally into the circle of huts itself. The huts become spaced farther and farther apart, seemingly repelled over time, one from the next. People, families move farther apart.

The bones tell the same story. 1947: All the bones from wild animals, game caught in snares or shot with poisoned arrows—game taken from the bush. By 1964 a few goat bones, a cow bone or two, but not many. Less than 20 percent of the total. Look then at the early 1970s and watch the line on the graph climb slowly upwards—by 1976 over 80 percent from domesticated stock.

But what explains the shattering of this society? Why is this hunting and gathering way of life, so resilient in the face of uncertainty, falling apart? It hasn't been a direct force—a war, the ravages of disease. It is the internal conflicts, the tensions, the inconsistencies, the impossibility of reconciling such different views of the world.

At Dobe it is happening to them all together. All of the huts have moved farther apart in lockstep, which makes it harder for them to see how incompatible the old system is with the new. But Rakudu, a Bushman who lived at the Mahopa waterhole eight miles down the valley from Dobe, was a step ahead of the rest. He experienced, before the rest of them, their collective fate.

When I was at the Cobra Camp in

1969, Rakudu lived down near Mahopa, off on his own, a mile or so away from the pastoral Herero villages. He had two hats and a very deep bass voice, both so strange, so out of place in a Bushman. He was a comical sort of man with the hats and that voice and a large Adam's apple that bobbed up and down.

The one hat must have been a leftover from the German-Herero wars because no one in Botswana wore a hat like that—a real pith helmet with a solid top and a rounded brim. It had been cared for over the years because, although soiled and faded, it still retained the original strap that tucks beneath the chin. The second hat was also unique— a World War I aviator's hat, one of those leather sacks that fits tightly over the head and buckles under the chin. Only the goggles were missing.

I should have seen then how out of place the ownership of two hats was in that hunter-gatherer world. Give two hats like that to any of the others and one would have been given away on the spot. A month or two later, the other would become a gift as well. Moving goods as gifts and favors along that chain of human ties. That was the way to maintain those links, to keep them strong.

When I went to Rakudu's village and realized what he was up to, I could see that he was one of a kind. The mud-walled huts in his village made it look like a Herero village—not a grass hut in sight. And when I came, Rakudu pulled out a hand-carved wood and leather chair and set it in the shade. This village was different from any of the Bushman camps I had seen. Mud huts set out in a circle, real clay storage bins to hold the corn—not platforms in a tree—and *kraals* for lots of goats and donkeys. He had a large field, too, several years before the first one appeared at Dobe.

Why shouldn't Bushmen do it—build their own villages, model their subsistence after the Herero? To plant a field, to tend goats, to build mud-walled houses like that was not hard to do. Work for the Herero a while and get an axe, accumulate the nucleus of a herd, buy or borrow the seeds. That year the rains were long and heavy. The sand held the water and the crickets and the birds didn't come. So the harvest was good, and I could sit there in the carved chair and look at Rakudu's herd of goats and their young ones and admire him for his industry, for what he had done.

Only a year later I saw him and his eldest son just outside the Cobra Camp. I went over and sat in the sand and listened to the negotiations for the marriage Rakudu was trying to arrange. His son's most recent wife had run away, and Rakudu was discussing a union between his son and Dau the Elder's oldest daughter who was just approaching marriageable age. They talked about names and Dau the Elder explained why the marriage couldn't take place. It was clear that the objection was trivial, that he was making an excuse. Even I could see that his explanation was a face-saving gesture to make the refusal easier for all of them.

Later I asked Dau the Elder why he did it. It seemed like a good deal to me. "Rakudu has all that wealth, those goats and field. I'd think that you would be anxious to be linked with a family like that. Look at all you have to gain. Is the son difficult? Did he beat his last wife?"

"She left because she was embarrassed. The wife before her ran away for the same reason and so did the younger brother's wife," he said. "Both brothers treated their wives well. The problem wasn't that. It was when the wives' relatives came. That's when it became so hard for the women because

Rakudu and his sons are such stingy men. They wouldn't give anything away, wouldn't share anything with them. Rakudu has a big herd just like the Herero, and he wouldn't kill goats for them to eat."

Not the way Bushmen should act toward relatives, not by the traditional value system at least. Sharing, the most deeply held Bushman belief, and that man with the two hats wouldn't go along. Herero are different. You can't expect them to act properly, to show what is only common decency; you must take them as they are. But someone like Rakudu, a Bushman, should know better than that. So the wives walked out and left for good.

But Rakudu understood what was happening, how he was trapped—and he tried to respond. If you can't kill too many goats from the herd that has become essential to you, perhaps you can find something else of value to give away. Rakudu thought he had an answer.

He raised tobacco in one section of his field. Tobacco, a plant not really adapted to a place like the northern Kalahari, has to be weeded, watered by hand, and paid special care. Rakudu did that and for one year at least harvested a tobacco crop.

Bushmen crave tobacco and Rakudu hoped he had found a solution—that they would accept tobacco in place of goats, in place of mealie meal. A good try. Perhaps the only one open to him. But, as it turned out, not good enough. Rakudu's son could not find a wife.

Ironic that a culture can die yet not a

single person perish. A sense of identity, of a shared set of rules, of participation in a single destiny binds individuals together into a tribe or cultural group. Let that survive long enough, let the participants pass this sense through enough generations, one to the next, create enough debris, and they will find their way into the archeological record, into the study of cultures remembered only by their traces left on the land.

Rakudu bought out. He, his wife, and his two sons sold their goats for cash, took the money and walked west, across the border scar that the South Africans had cut, through the smooth fence wire and down the hard calcrete road beyond. They became wards of the Afrikaaners, were lost to their own culture, let their fate pass into hands other than their own. At Chum kwe, the mission station across the border 34 miles to the west, they were given numbers and the right to stand in line with the others and have mealie meal and other of life's physical essentials handed out to them. As wards of the state, that became their right. When the problems, the contradictions of your life are insoluble, a paternalistic hand provides one easy out.

Dau stayed at Dobe. Drive there today and you can find his mud-walled hut just by the waterhole. But he understands: He has married off his daughter, his first-born girl to a wealthy Chum kwe man who drives a tractor—an old man, more than twice her age, and by traditional Bushmen standards not an appropriate match. Given the chance, one by one, the others will do the same.

Ancient Indians Sought Shadows and Ice Caves

**Daniel J. Lenihan and
James E. Bradford**

Shoveling dirt on a bright summer day in Canyon de Chelly, a deep ravine carved into the western slope of the Chuska Mountains of northern Arizona, archeological field crews cast longing glances at the approaching shadows. The prehistoric inhabitants who lived here also paid attention to solar orientation. On the arid Colorado Plateau, despite an average elevation of 5,000 feet, temperatures often exceed 100° F during the summer. In lower, moister locales, a thicker atmosphere tends to steam-cook a person more evenly, but in the Southwest the sun really counts.

The Anasazi ("ancient ones," in the Navajo language), first occupied Canyon de Chelly more than 2,000 years ago. The earliest Anasazi, known to archeologists as the Basket Makers, took advantage of subtle alignments of the landscape for protection from the sun at critical times of the year. Realizing that a narrow ledge in the canyon wall faced north, they would dedicate the entire site to the construction of storage units, digging small pits in the dirt and debris fallen from the overhanging roof of the rock-shelter. They lined the pits with sandstone slabs bonded by mud mortar and roofed them with beehive constructions of

sticks and mud. This enabled the Basket Makers to store food (corn, beans, pine nuts, squash) for a long time in a cool, dry environment in the middle of a sandstone hotbox.

In the winter months, the canyon rims and flat country outside the canyon entrance provided prehistoric inhabitants with easy exposure to the sun's warming rays, while the cooling shade of the canyon bottoms afforded refuge in the heat of summer. The later Anasazi, or Puebloans, constructed elaborate buildings of stone and mud mortar, which they nestled in shady canyon alcoves. To this day, the resident Navajo live on the canyon bottom in the summer and the rim in the winter.

Another basic strategy of Native Americans in the Southwest was to burrow into the earth, roofing semi-subterranean homes with earth-covered wooden frameworks or digging underground dwellings. In the earliest recorded description of a Navajo dwelling, dating to 1630, Fray Alonso de Benavides mentions a *vivienda debaxo de tierra,* "a dwelling under the ground" or "dwelling under earth." He probably was referring to an ancestral version of the hogan, perhaps a hole with hide stretched over the top. The typical hogan of today is constructed from logs, bark, earth, and stone and possesses a sunken floor that provides a cooler environment. Some hogans

have root cellars, rooms with still deeper floors insulated with additional dirt and logs. Their inside temperatures are significantly cooler for storage of perishable foods.

Caves, a source of protection from many types of meteorological mayhem, are also excellent insulators against heat. Limestone caves provide natural air conditioning, maintaining a nearly constant temperature year-round. The contrast is even more dramatic when the cave lies in dark rock, such as basalt, or hardened lava, whose surface absorbs much radiant heat.

Near Acoma, a still-occupied pueblo in western New Mexico, lies El Malpais—the badlands. The meager tree cover to be found, consisting of low-lying junipers, piñon pines, and ponderosas, affords little refuge from the black, jagged basaltic blanket. Not far below ground, however, are natural cavities that are oases of coolness. Lava tubes that hardened around molten rivers of rock provide makeshift thoroughfares to these sanctums, into which the dense, cold air of winter settles and remains. Ice forms in them as well, and depending on a cave's size and shape and the location of its entrance hole, it may be preserved throughout the year. Ice cave temperatures hover around freezing throughout the summer, in some cases maintaining ice that is 2,000 years old. A prehistoric woven mat, probably used to cushion and insulate the knees of an ancient ice gatherer, is still captured in the frozen interior of one such cave.

Through the centuries, the hundred-mile-long trail connecting the pueblos of Acoma and Zuni traversed El Malpais, presenting a formidable passage. With their ice, the caves provided not only respite from the heat but also a source of water. When the ancient icemen came, they chipped off a supply and apparently used fire to melt the precious resource. Nearly every ice-yielding cave contains charcoal from their fires. The drinking water thus obtained was consumed during the trip or sealed in pottery jars and cached for later use. Today, the Acoma, Zuni, and Navajo who hunt in El Malpais still use the caves to store their butchered meat until they are ready to return home.

The miracle of ice in an oven made of molten rock has engendered a sense of reverence in those who benefit from its presence. The Acoma, for instance, do not approach the caves without performing the requisite rites, including prayers and small offerings—gestures that acknowledge unique gifts, to be used within limits and with proper respect.

The now-dominant Anglo and Hispanic cultures in the Southwest have rediscovered some of the basic principles of the ancients. The homes of these newcomers (who will probably be known to future archeologists as the Plastic Makers) incorporate solar-design features. Although these are primarily aimed at keeping warm in the winter, rather than cool in the summer, most are fairly obvious extensions of Native American strategies.

But the newcomers have been slow to pick up on the ancient life style. One important key to keeping cool is choosing when to raise your metabolic rate. Just as the Arabs marveled at the propensity of English overlords to keep mad dogs company in the midday sun, many a Navajo has marveled at the antics of tourists—even some archeologists—who follow an activity schedule developed for use in Northern Europe.

History and Ethnoarchaeology

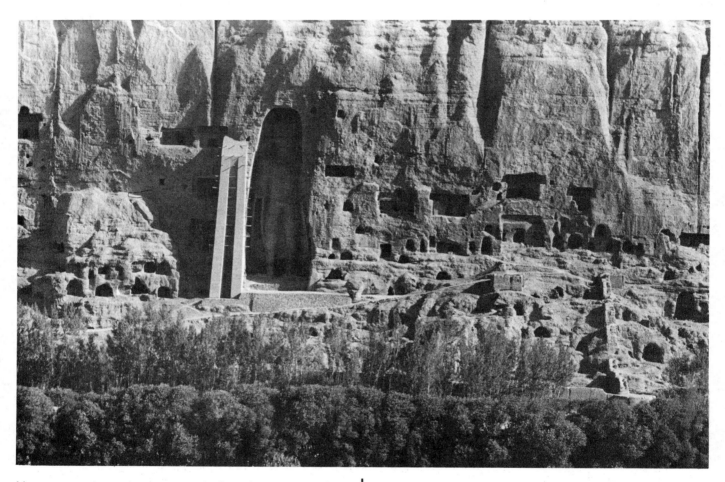

How many times have you misplaced your car keys? Locked yourself out of the house? Lost your wallet? Your address book? Sometimes these artifacts are recovered and brought back into the historical present. Sometimes they are lost forever, becoming part of the rubbish of an extinct culture. Have you ever noticed that lost things, when found, are always in the *last* place you look? Is this a law of science?

Here is an opportunity to practice historical archaeology. You may wish to try this puzzler in order to practice thinking like an archaeologist. (Do not forget to apply the basics discussed in unit 1.) The incident recounted here is true, only the names and places were changed to protect the privacy of the famous personages involved in this highly charged mystery.

Problem: Dr. Wheeler, an archaeologist at a large university, left his office on December 20, 1989, around 9 p.m., a cold Wednesday evening preceding the long holiday. He later stated that immediately before he left his office, he had placed a thin, reddish, three-ring notebook in an unlocked cupboard in his office.

Dr. Wheeler states he went directly to his designated campus parking lot, got into his car, and drove directly home to Marshalltown Goldens. When he arrived at home, he went straight to his study.

Dr. Wheeler had a great holiday with his family and thought nothing more of his notebook until the university resumed its session on Wednesday January 3, 1990. Upon returning to his office, Dr. Wheeler could not find his notebook in the cupboard, and he became very agitated. He chased his assistant, Miss Mortimer, around the office, wielding a wicked-looking Acheulean hand ax. Poor Miss Mortimer claimed she had no knowledge of the whereabouts of the notebook. But Dr. Wheeler had always suspected that Miss Mortimer pinched pens and pencils from his desk, so, naturally. . . . But Miss Mortimer protested so earnestly that Dr. Wheeler eventually calmed down, had a cup of tea, and decided that perhaps he had absentmindedly taken the notebook home after all.

However, a thorough search of his home indicated that the notebook was clearly not there. It was lost! Dr. Wheeler was also almost jolly well lost himself when his wife, Leonora, caught him excavating her rose garden in the vain hope that Tut, the family dog, had buried the lost article there. It was a professor's nightmare, since the notebook contained the only copy of all his class records for the entire term. What could he do? He knew he was in danger of being fired from his chair for ineptitude.

So, of course, Dr. Wheeler approached the problem in the manner of a proper, eccentric archaeologist. He had another cup of tea and generated several hypotheses about where his notebook might be. He tested these hypotheses, but none of them yielded his notebook. So, being a good archaeologist, he kept on generating hypotheses.

Now, as is sometimes the case, Lady Luck intervened and his faithful assistant Miss Mortimer received a phone call on January 9 from a woman who had found the missing notebook on the evening of December 31, in a gutter! To be precise, she found it in a family neighborhood located on the corner of Olduvai Drive and East Turkana Avenue in Hadar Heights, about one mile from the university. Please note that this area is in the opposite direction from Dr. Wheeler's home in Marshalltown Goldens. The notebook was wet and muddy, and it was wedged down on a gutter grid. The woman, a grammar school teacher, had been trying to call the university during the holiday without success.

Greatly relieved, the next day Dr. Wheeler sent Miss Mortimer over to the kind lady's home, and thus he retrieved his class records. Dr. Wheeler was so happy when Miss Mortimer returned with the notebook that he invited her to sit and join him for a cup of tea. But Dr. Wheeler was not satisfied with merely recovering his notebook. He was curious to know what had happened to it and why. He continued to generate more sophisticated hypotheses until . . . ?

The Challenge: Now it is your turn to be Dr. Wheeler. Trace the whereabouts of the lost three-ring notebook from the night of Wednesday, December 20, 1989, to the time of its return to Dr. Wheeler on January 10, 1990.

How do you do this? Review everything you know to be true, carefully. Using this as your initial database, set up a hypothesis to account for the lost notebook. This means a plausible series of events to account for the mysterious traveling notebook. Continue to refine your hypothesis and/or make alternative hypotheses until you arrive at the simplest possible explanation that is largely supported by direct or deduced data.

Consider that you are doing historical archaeology. Ask your living informant(s) for information first. What could you ask Dr. Wheeler? You could ask, Did you go to the restroom before you left the building on December 20? Where was your car parked? Was it raining? Did you stop and talk to anybody on your way to the car? Where were you on December 31? And don't forget Miss Mortimer. And the lady who found the notebook. Let your imagination run free. Creativity is the core of all science.

Hints: Dr. Wheeler's university office was never broken into. Poor Miss Mortimer and the kind lady who found the notebook had nothing to do with the whereabouts of the notebook. Dr. Wheeler's family and his dog Tut were not involved with the missing notebook. Don't look now, but you are thinking like an archaeologist. It is a lot of fun, and it will reward you well.

Looking Ahead: Challenge Questions

What is historical archaeology? How does it differ from other kinds of archaeology? What is the relationship between history and historical archaeology?

How was archaeology used as propaganda to fuel the Nazi movement in World War II? In your judgment, did the Nazi archaeologists really believe their own lies? Can you think of other instances where archaeology has been used as propaganda?

What happens when the archaeological record rewrites history? Give an example.

What kinds of evidence do forensic archaeologists use to solve past murders? Give examples.

How have recent excavations revised the stereotypes of the lives of slaves living on American plantations? Give examples.

What do ancient Peruvian textiles have to do with modern drug cartels?

How is predictability about human behavior revealed in the Donner Party incident?

Shungopovi—May 1970

Red Feathers from the South

Parrot Kachina Dance

Paul Coze

A century-old square of hard-beaten, sunbaked dirt is where the Kachinam will dance. It is still early, only a few people are sitting along the walls or peering through the windows. Some children play, a few dogs move about. In this quietness, everything is ochre, golden dust, clean as the air except when the sand blasts through the streets.

Slowly some boys and men have appeared above the rooftops and a few ladies with children are settling on the stone benches in front of their houses. Others will bring folding chairs or very low, small wood benches used for watching dances in all Pueblos. Old men take their places, here and there but many sit in one corner near a small room in ruins.

Color now is appearing in the village. Women are draped in flowery shawls, red and green mostly; here and there, bright blue or yellow. Some will open small umbrellas of any hue. This is a very silent place, not like any other in these United States. Today the dry air of the 6,000-foot altitude makes things feel different. Occasionally the distant trail of a jet plane contrasts to the impressive quietness.

Because of the massive structure of the houses, the narrow passage ways of some opening toward the cliff, one cannot hear, back of us, the arrival of pickups and cars. So here we are, as if in church, respectful, meditating, expecting, remembering, and for some of us, not able to imagine, what we came to see. It is a strange feeling: all those people, and for a long time, a nearly complete immobility.

There is no announcement, but somehow everyone feels an immediacy. There is a small opening between houses sheltered by a heavy roof. Suddenly, calm, but determined, a man walks in, carrying a cotton bag in his left hand. His grey hair is loose, past his shoulders. An eagle breast tied on the top of his head shows that he was initiated. He wears a clean shirt outside his Levis and terra cotta mocassins. He makes a trail by sprinkling cornmeal. On this trail walk the Messengers of the Gods, Living Spirits of the mysterious Forces of Nature: Kachinam. Then one by one, they come! One by one they bring magic. Some small, some tall, some slim, some heavy. All alike in their dissemblance. Yes, they do wear the same kilt of white cotton. All their bodies are painted red and yellow.

Black and yellow faces, with thin red ears standing out above necks lost in heavy wreaths of evergreen, have parrot beaks and snow designs on each cheek above long, mysterious, geometrical eyes. On top of the head dominating all is another parrot beak from which projects a mass of colorful feathers and a trail of flame: the tail feathers of the macaw. They are all alike with their turquoise ceremonial moccasins; two rings of sleigh bells tied around the calves; greenery in the left hand, gold rattle in the other. A large necklace of loose hair, red as rain in sunset. All alike and yet none are. The hues vary slightly, even the designs on the headgear and, above all, the arrangement of the feathers, the jewels and the heavy bow guard on the left wrist. Color is spilling everywhere as they keep on coming, crowding the court until they line up in single file, immobile now, therefore silent.

An imperative, powerful talk is given by the *Fathers*. Their voices explode, drag, then reach a powerful climax. They thank the Messengers who have come. They talk in the name of the peaceful people. He, a priest, is a humble delegate of the village. Some clans are blessed by his mission of asking and offering blessings to all. Then the Mother Earth trembles; the Song leader in the center has shaken his rattle, opening his arm like a wing. In this manner he says, "Yes, we will do as the People ask. We have come, we shall dance and take back their messages." That is what is meant and that is why he hit the ground with his foot; and the dynamic motion vibrates all over, giving life and meaningfulness with the gods to pulse in the heart of the village.

Of course, some people said that the Blue Flute, or the Grey, or is it both, have a parrot painted on their altar. This old man remembered what his grandfather used to say about the old days when Hopi traders traveled to Old Mexico, where there used to be a very large center for any kind of trade. Pottery was exchanged as well as ideas and techniques, shells from the oceans, weaving, but not moccasins because they did not exist until the "Castille" came with their heelless boots. They wore sandals then. There was richness of all kinds of feathers and especially the macaw. But Arizona was green and yellow with its own parrots, many of them in his grandfather's time. Now the "Nature-Killer" has destroyed them. Some of the clan people kept the birds alive in their homes. Now the "Nature-Killer" has made laws. Parrots and feathers cannot come into our Indian Land from our "uncle" in Mexico. They also make laws about the eagles, in spite of our religion, but the "Hopi Way" will go on strong, for the parrots come to bless their clans and all of us. Now the Parrot Kachinam are dancing; the people, their heads erect, their eyes watching the perfection of it all, feel good, feel goodness, feel sanctified because the beautiful, wonderful *Kayzo* have come from the south to *Kyasnyam*, their Clan.

Post-mortem at the Little Bighorn

Archeologists sift for clues at Custer's fatal battleground.

**Douglas D. Scott and
Melissa A. Connor**

The anniversary of the Battle of the Little Bighorn falls on June 26, the day 110 years ago when George Armstrong Custer led some 210 men to their death in the Montana Territory. In the years that followed, the story of Custer's Last Stand assumed legendary proportions, while much of the hard evidence of the battle remained unexamined. Then in August 1983, a wildfire scorched four-fifths of the 760 acres of Custer Battlefield National Monument (a cigarette tossed from a car on nearby State Route 212 may have ignited the drought-stricken vegetation), and the National Park Service, which administers the Monument, enlisted local archeologist Richard Fox to see whether artifacts might be recovered from the denuded landscape. The result has been a full-fledged study by the Midwest Archeological Center of the National Park Service and the University of Nebraska.

Along with Dick Harmon, of the U.S. Geological Survey, and Richard Fox, and aided by many volunteers, we have spent two field seasons encouraging the earth to yield its secrets about this historic battle. We chose to view the battleground as a crime scene, and by using forensic techniques, such as microscopic examination of firing-pin marks on cartridge cases and rifling marks on bullets, we have been able to determine the weapons used by the various participants. These techniques, combined with the standard archeological practice of recording where artifacts are found, have enabled us to deduce the movement of individual firearms over the field of battle, verify cavalry positions, and pinpoint the previously unknown placement of the Indian warriors. Many human skeletal remains were also found, and these tell us of the wounds the men received, as well as the soldiers' general health and condition at the time of death.

The story of the battle begins in 1868, when the Treaty of Fort Laramie was signed with the Sioux and Chey-enne. Among other things, the treaty granted the Black Hills area to the Sioux for "as long as the grass was green and the sky was blue." In the early 1870s, however, rumors spread of gold in the Black Hills, and white miners began slipping into the reservation. In 1874, the U.S. government sent a geological team under Custer to check out these rumors. Gold was among the minerals found, and thereafter there was no stopping the hordes of miners who flowed onto the Indians' land.

The Sioux were disgusted with the government's inability to keep white people from trespassing, especially in the Black Hills, which they considered sacred. As the whites did not seem to be respecting the treaty, many of the Indians saw no reason to abide by its terms and stay on the reservation. Along with Cheyenne from other Indian agencies, thousands of Sioux spent the winter of 1875–76 on their traditional hunting grounds in Montana and the Dakotas, despite a government warning that unless they returned immediately, they would be considered hostile and subject to military action.

In May of 1876, a three-sided campaign was launched to shepherd the Sioux and Cheyenne back to their assigned lands. One column, under Gen. John Gibbon, marched east from Fort Ellis (near present-day Bozeman, Montana). A second column, led by Gen. Alfred Terry and including Custer, headed west from Fort Abraham Lincoln (near present-day Bismarck, North Dakota). The third column departed from Fort Fetterman (near present-day Sheridan, Wyoming) under the command of Gen. George Crook and moved north into Montana. These three units, totaling about 3,000 men, were to meet near the end of June in the vicinity of the Little Bighorn River.

Unknown to Terry and Gibbon, Crook encountered Indians near Rosebud Creek in southern Montana, was defeated by them on June 17, and withdrew his men to Wyoming. Meanwhile, Terry, with some 921 men, mostly cavalry, was moving west up the Yellowstone River to the Little Bighorn. On June 22, the cavalry, led by Custer, left Terry's command to scout ahead.

The 7th Cavalry consisted of twelve companies, each authorized to contain fifty to sixty-four men. In reality, most field units never operated at authorized strength, owing to low budget allotments from Congress, high desertion rates, and men on detached duty. Custer commanded about 715 men, about 160 men under authorized strength. Custer's rank was lieutenant colonel (brevet major general). A brevet rank was an honorific and temporary grade given for special service and as an award for gallantry in action. Custer's second-in-command was Maj. Marcus Reno. Next in line was Frederick Benteen, the regiment's senior captain.

Early on the morning of the 25th, the 7th Cavalry was on high ground, with Rosebud Creek behind them to the east and the Little Bighorn about sixteen and a half miles to the west. From a spot subsequently dubbed the Crow's Nest, Custer observed a large Indian camp on the far side of the Little Bighorn. Worried that the Indians might escape, Custer decided to attack

and descended westward into the valley. Near the Crow's Nest, Captain Benteen was ordered to take three companies and keep to the south, to block a possible escape route. The pack train, carrying ammunition and guarded by one company, followed Benteen, while the other companies went ahead. At midday, a few miles from the Little Bighorn, Custer again divided his command, ordering Major Reno to take three companies along the river bottom and attack the Indian camp on its southern end. The remaining five companies followed Custer westward along the ridge to the north, preparing to support Reno.

About 3:00 P.M., Indian warriors engaged Reno and his men, forcing them to retreat back across the river and up the bluffs to a defensible position. Meanwhile, Custer must have realized the gravity of the situation as the north end of the Indian camp came into view. About 3:30, Custer's adjutant sent a message to Benteen: "Benteen, Come on. Big village, be quick, bring packs. P.S. Bring pacs [sic]. W. W. Cooke." The messenger, bugler John Martin, was the last to see Custer and the men in his five companies alive.

Summoned by the message, Benteen's forces and the pack train arrived some forty-five minutes later, joining Reno and his men on the hilltop. All were pinned down for two days, fighting to keep their defensive position and wondering when Custer would relieve them. The Indians finally retreated on June 27, when General Terry arrived, joined by General Gibbon's column. Reno sent two men to meet the advancing column, and they found Terry and Gibbon near the abandoned Indian camp. Here, a scout brought the news: Custer and his men lay dead on a ridge above the Little Bighorn.

From that moment until the present, Custer's movements after the messenger left him have been the subject of hot debate. Soon after the battle ended, however, eyewitness accounts began to appear in newspapers across the country. The witnesses were the survivors—the Indians. Weary of army pursuit, the warriors had returned to their reservations, where Indian agents interviewed them. Only then did the warriors learn for certain the identity of the commander they had defeated.

Different versions of Indian accounts of the battle appeared in differ-

Joe LeMonnier

In May of 1876, approximately 3,000 soldiers, commanded by Generals Gibbon, Terry, and Crook, set out to round up Plains Indians who had left their reservations. The three columns were to meet near the Little Bighorn River in late June. The ill-fated 7th Cavalry, under Custer, made up the majority of Terry's command.

ent papers and journals, and many began to question their accuracy. People suspected distorted reporting by glory-seeking correspondents or faulty translations of Indian words or signs. The Indians, fearing retribution from the army, may also not have told the whole truth. As a result, the Indian accounts were long scorned, although in the past fifteen years, historians who have reviewed them have concluded that the gist of the reports rings true.

The Indians' accounts, collected from survivors up until the middle of this century, state that the camp on the Little Bighorn was established shortly after Crook's defeat at Rosebud Creek, and included the Sioux who had fought in that confrontation. Nevertheless, Custer's arrival apparently took the camp by surprise. As Custer and his men moved north along the ridge, a large contingent of Sioux pressed the attack from the south. A group of Cheyenne and some Sioux also attacked the soldiers from the north and northwest.

At first the shooting was from a distance, but as the soldiers stood their ground, apparently in a V-shaped formation, the intense fire thinned their ranks. It was then that the warriors were able to move in and essentially surround the cavalry. Once many of the soldiers were dead or wounded, the Indians swooped in on those that remained, finishing them off in hand-to-hand combat. Accounts tell of killing wounded soldiers and of stripping the dead of their guns, ammunition, clothing, and other useful items. Some warriors scalped the dead or mutilated their remains, as was their custom in warfare.

In an attempt to make the battleground speak for itself, during the summers of 1984 and 1985 we used the techniques of archeology to unearth thousands of artifacts, despite events that had disturbed the area over the intervening years. After the battle, the Indians removed their dead and wounded, but the dead soldiers lay in the hot Montana sun for nearly three days. When the surviving members of the 7th Cavalry began the onerous task of burying the dead, the bodies were bloated, blackened, and almost unrecognizable. Because there were few

As he approached the Little Bighorn, Custer divided up the twelve companies under his command. While Captain Benteen trailed behind with four companies and a pack train, Custer ordered Major Reno to take three companies and attack the Indian camp from the south. Custer himself led the remaining five companies farther north. Reno and his men were driven back to a defensive position, where they were eventually joined by Benteen's forces. The detail map shows the battlefield where Custer deployed his men. One company, under Lieutenant Calhoun, was arranged in an arc, facing south. Another company, under Captain Keogh, was positioned farther north. Custer's other three companies stretched in a line from Deep Ravine to Last Stand Hill, confronting Indians attacking from the north and west.

Joe LeMonnier; Detail Map after Midwest Archeological Center, National Park Service

Archeological Finds at Custer Battlefield National Monument

Concentration of Cavalry Materials   Concentration of Indian Materials

shovels or other tools with which to do a proper job, cups, plates, and other available implements were used to mound dirt over the bodies. Afraid that the Indians would return and attack again, the soldiers covered most of the dead with just a little soil and sagebrush.

The powdery soil was not enough to keep coyotes and other scavengers from the graves, and the action of wind, rain, and snow compounded the

problem of keeping the men buried. In 1877, the army reburied the exposed bones. All the officers' remains, however, were exhumed and shipped home, except those of Lt. John Crittenden, whose father asked that he be left where he fell. Persistent reports of exposed remains brought the army back in 1879 for another reburial. Finally, in 1881, the army exhumed all the remains from the battlefield and reburied them in a mass grave on Last

Stand Hill, near where Custer's body had been found. A large granite marker was placed over the grave that same year.

While the reburial teams stripped the battlefield of its most conspicuous bones and artifacts, many important clues were left to await archeological exploration. We divided our work into three parts. The first was a metal detector survey of the battlefield. Volunteers, often experts in the use of detectors, walked about five yards apart, covering the field. Where their detectors beeped, they flagged the spot. Behind them came a recovery crew that excavated cautiously, searching for the object that had caused the detector to signal, but not moving it out of place. Finally, the survey crews came along to plot each artifact's position on a grid system. This crew also recorded the depth at which the artifact lay and, in the case of bullets and cartridges, noted the orientation and the declination of the piece. Only then was the artifact collected.

The second part of the project was a search in a gully known as Deep Ravine, where twenty-eight men were said to have been buried in place and never subsequently exhumed. At first, we thought that the metal detectors would locate these men, but even after several close examinations, only a handful of scattered artifacts came to light. In 1985, C. Vance Haynes, a geomorphologist from the University of Arizona, volunteered to examine the ravine. Haynes found a deeply buried area that conforms to the historic descriptions of the burial locale; we hope to excavate it in a future field season.

In the third part of our work, we excavated the immediate areas around marble markers that had been placed to commemorate the locations where Custer's men fell. Set in place fourteen years after the battle and more than nine years after the bodies were disinterred and placed in a mass grave, these marble markers replaced wooden ones, many of which had fallen down or been burned by wildfire. Two hundred fifty-one markers dot the main battlefield, yet only about 210 men fell with Custer. One reason to excavate

around the markers was to test the appropriateness of their locations.

These three activities—the metal detector survey, the search in Deep Ravine, and the excavations near the markers—uncovered about 2,200 artifacts, 300 human bones, and 200 bones of horses and other animals. Additional materials (still being analyzed) were collected in 1985 at the Reno-Benteen defense site.

The metal detector survey located hundreds of bullets and cartridge casings. In most cases we could assume that spent cartridges from Springfield carbines and Colt revolvers—the regulation cavalry weapons—had fallen in cavalry positions, and that bullets from these guns had been fired toward the Indians. Conversely, we assumed that bullets found in association with cavalry remains and artifacts came from Indian fire, and that cartridges of the corresponding calibers indicated the Indian positions.

Even before the analyses were complete, we knew that the Indians were much better armed than had been previously documented. The subsequent firearms analyses have identified twenty-five different types of guns used by the warriors. Metal arrowheads were also found, showing that the stereotypical bow and arrow was also used.

Indian arms included army issue Springfield carbines and Colt revolvers. These could have been captured either in the Rosebud skirmish with General Crook's forces or in the valley fight against Reno; some were no doubt taken from Custer's men. Antiquated muzzle-loading firearms were also well represented. Other Indian arms included the .44-caliber Henry, the .44-caliber Model 1866 Winchester, and the .44-caliber Model 1873 Winchester, all repeating rifles. The army did not issue repeating rifles in 1876. The army's single-shot Springfield was not as fast as the repeating rifles, although it was more powerful and more accurate than the majority of the Indian arms.

By using crime laboratory firearms-identification techniques, we could determine how many individual weapons

were represented by the archeological artifacts. We estimate that if 1,500 Indian warriors took part in the battle (a conservative number by historical accounts), then about 375 would have been armed with muzzle-loaders and single-shot rifles such as Sharps and Ballards, and about 192 would have been armed with repeating weapons. The rest may have used bows and arrows and a few old pistols and revolvers. Based on these minimal figures, we can conclude that in terms of carbines, Custer's men were outgunned two to one.

There is historical information on the battle that derives from the examination of the battleground at the time of its discovery (including where the bodies of the officers and men were found) and from Indian accounts. Combining this information with the distribution of the recently uncovered buttons, spurs, bullets, and cartridge cases, we are able to make a detailed reconstruction of the battle.

The Indian camp that Custer sought to attack contained perhaps 3,000 to 4,000 people, including some 1,500 warriors. The Indians belonged to a number of different bands whose members were affiliated by common language and family ties. The majority were Sioux (Lakota, Teton, Brulé, and Blackfoot), a lesser number of Cheyenne occupied the northern end of the camp, and there were also a few Arapahos. Although camped together for protection, the various bands lacked an overall organization. There were a number of important leaders—Sitting Bull, Crazy Horse, and Gall for the Sioux; Lame White Man and Two Moon for the Cheyenne—but in battle, strategy was determined by individual initiative and charisma, not by a chain of command. According to Indian accounts, Sitting Bull, sometimes thought of as Custer's adversary in battle, did not participate in the fighting but occupied himself with making medicine to strengthen the Indian warriors.

Our reconstruction begins after the messenger left Custer, with the command apparently moving aggressively toward the Indian camp. Encountering Sioux and Cheyenne warriors directed by Gall at about 4:00 P.M., Custer moved north and gained high ground at areas now known as Greasy Grass Ridge and Custer Ridge. Here he deployed one company, led by Lt. James Calhoun, in a broad, south-facing arc some 400 yards long. Then, probably to confront a group of Indians attacking from the north and west, Custer took the rest of his men and wheeled north. Leaving Capt. Myles Keogh in charge of a company between himself and Calhoun, Custer deployed his remaining three companies between a high point and a ravine, now called Last Stand Hill and Deep Ravine, respectively.

These deployments formed a broad V-shaped pattern—a classic offensive formation—with the angle to the north, at Last Stand Hill. The cartridge cases attributed to the soldiers are generally in the area of this V. There is very little archeological evidence to document any further troop movement. Although the fight may have been a running one until this final deployment, after this, the units apparently stood their ground.

We determined the soldiers' positions from the presence of spent cartridges from government-issue guns. Bullets fired from the soldiers' guns were found embedded in the ground, often within, or in front of, the areas in which quantities of Indian cartridge cases were found. Bullets corresponding to the calibers of cartridge cases at Indian positions were found embedded in army positions. A few were associated with human remains.

The most intense Indian fire came from a position about 300 feet southeast of Calhoun's position, where perhaps as many as sixty .44-caliber Henry and Winchester rifles were being fired. A second Indian position, on Greasy Grass Ridge, was southwest of Calhoun's men. A minimum of forty-five guns using .44-caliber rimfire ammunition were fired here, as well as at least seven other types of weapons. Calhoun's men probably were overrun by Indians firing from these two positions.

The only physical evidence we found for any movement among the soldiers' positions consists of some .45-caliber cartridge cases (U.S. Army issue for the Springfield carbine), fired from the same weapons. These were found, first, in the Calhoun position, then scattered along a line toward the Keogh position, and finally, intermixed with cartridges belonging to the Keogh group. Several of Calhoun's men, watching their comrades and then their position fall, must have finally retreated under fire to Keogh's position.

Some Indian weapons fired toward Calhoun's men were also fired toward the cavalry line that stretched from Deep Ravine to Last Stand Hill. This cavalry line was also under attack from the north and west by Crazy Horse, Two Moon, Lame White Man, and other Sioux and Cheyenne warriors. Judging by the numbers of cartridges that we found, these warriors were not as well armed as those fighting Calhoun's men. Indians joining the attack from the south, after Calhoun's position collapsed, may have added the firepower and numbers needed to overwhelm the cavalry.

The documented movement of a number of Indian weapons indicates that as the battle progressed, the Indians moved upslope toward Custer's final position on Last Stand Hill. Some of the Indians converged at a knoll north and east of the hill to shoot down into the knot of remaining men. We found little evidence that the soldiers fired their handguns. Indian accounts of the battle, gathered many years afterward, state that the soldiers only used their Colts near the end of the battle, when hand-to-hand fighting began, and that after emptying their Colts, the soldiers did not have time to reload before the Indians were upon them. The paucity of Colt bullets and casings among the archeological finds confirms these accounts. The battle was all over sometime between 5:00 and 6:00 in the afternoon.

Our excavations around the markers confirm that most were placed where a soldier fell, as shown by pieces of uniforms, weapons, and human bone found nearby. About thirty-eight pairs of markers (markers placed by twos around the battlefield) usually indicated a single soldier, thus accounting for many of the excess markers.

Although Custer's men were reburied in a mass grave in 1881, we found human remains belonging to at least thirty-two individuals. Dr. Clyde Snow, a forensics expert who is interpreting the remains, says this is not unusual. Whenever untrained people gather up bones, they may overlook small ones, such as hand and foot bones, or not recognize them as human. These were most of the bones we found.

The skull fragments we uncovered showed that the bone had been broken while still green, indicating what Dr. Snow calls "perimortem blunt instrument trauma." An Indian warrior, Black Elk, recounting the final moments of the battle, described how the Indians used hatchets and clubs to finish off the surviving soldiers. While some of the evidence of trauma we found was undoubtedly induced at the time of death, many of the cut marks and crushed skulls may have resulted from mutilation of the dead, a normal cultural expression of victory for Sioux and Cheyenne warriors. This battle was not exceptional in this regard, but to the soldiers who buried Custer's dead on June 28, 1876, the field was a scene of ghastly and sickening horror.

The excavations around one pair of markers near the Deep Ravine yielded many bones from one individual, some uniform buttons, bullets, and a metal arrowhead. Taking this data, the relative placement of the artifacts, and a little imagination, we could put together the following scenario. The soldier was about twenty-five years old and robust—probably strong for his 5' 8" stature. He wore regulation coat and pants and was hit by a bullet from a .44-caliber repeating rifle. The bullet was associated with a few rib bones, suggesting the shot was to the chest and may have been the mortal wound. Whether the man was dead or dying, someone also shot him in the head with a Colt revolver. When the Indians overran his position, they crushed his skull with a war club and hacked at his front and back with knives. The Indians did not remove his uniform for cloth; perhaps it was too bloody to be worthwhile.

So far the archeological data support much in the Indian accounts of the battle and contradict none of them. As the analysis of the material collected in 1985 progresses, we will learn more details of Custer's fight, as well as what happened to Reno and Benteen. The archeological finds provide historians with a new resource in the study of the battle. By itself, each button, bullet, or cartridge may seem unimportant, but both the Indians and the cavalry left behind arrangements of artifacts that reflected their fighting styles, their ideas of leadership, and their concepts of battle.

The Battle of the Little Bighorn epitomized the clash of cultures—the Native American versus the Euro-American—that differed in hundreds of ways, including perceptions of land ownership, treaties, and boundaries. It may not have been of strategic importance in military history, but it did affect the course of this struggle. In the years preceding the battle, individuals sympathetic to the Indians' plight had determined government dealings with them. If the debacle at the Little Bighorn did nothing else, it galvanized the anti-Indian forces in the U.S. government, influencing official policy toward the Plains Indians until nearly the close of the nineteenth century.

Germany's Nazi Past
The Past as Propaganda

How Hitler's archaeologists distorted European prehistory to justify racist and territorial goals.

Bettina Arnold

The manipulation of the past for political purposes has been a common theme in history. Consider Darius I (521–486 B.C.), one of the most powerful rulers of the Achaemenid, or Persian, empire. The details of his accession to power, which resulted in the elimination of the senior branch of his family, are obscured by the fact that we have only his side of the story, carved on the cliff face of Behistun in Iran. The list of his victories, and by association his right to rule, are the only remaining version of the truth. Lesson number one: If you are going to twist the past for political ends, eliminate rival interpretations.

The use of the past for propaganda is also well documented in more recent contexts. The first-century Roman historian Tacitus produced an essay titled "On the Origin and Geography of Germany." It is less a history or ethnography of the German tribes than a moral tract or political treatise. The essay was intended to contrast the debauched and degenerate Roman Empire with the virtuous German people, who embodied the uncorrupted morals of old Rome. Objective reporting was not the goal of Tacitus's *Germania;* the manipulation of the facts was considered justified if it had the desired effect of contrasting past Roman glory with present Roman decline. Ironically, this particular piece of historical propa-

ganda was eventually appropriated by a regime notorious for its use and abuse of the past for political, imperialist, and racist purposes: the Third Reich.

The National Socialist regime in Germany fully appreciated the propaganda value of the past, particularly of prehistoric archaeology, and exploited it with characteristic efficiency. The fact that German prehistoric archaeology had been largely ignored before Hitler's rise to power in 1933 made the appropriation of the past for propaganda that much easier. The concept of the *Kulturkreis,* pioneered by the linguist-turned-prehistorian Gustav Kossinna in the 1920s and defined as the identification of ethnic regions on the basis of excavated material culture, lent theoretical support to Nazi expansionist aims in central and eastern Europe. Wherever an artifact of a type designated as "Germanic" was found, the land was declared to be ancient Germanic territory. Applied to prehistoric archaeology, this perspective resulted in the neglect or distortion of data that did not directly apply to Germanic peoples. During the 1930s scholars whose specialty was provincial Roman archaeology were labeled *Römlinge* by the extremists and considered anti-German. The Römisch Germanische Kommission in Mainz, founded in 1907, was the object of numerous defamatory attacks, first by Kossinna and

later by Alfred Rosenberg and his organization. Rosenberg, a Nazi ideologue, directed the Amt Rosenberg, which conducted ethnic, cultural, and racial research.

Altered prehistory also played an important role in rehabilitating German self-respect after the humiliating defeat of 1918. The dedication of the 1921 edition of Kossinna's seminal work *German Prehistory: A Preeminently National Discipline* reads: "To the German people, as a building block in the reconstruction of the externally as well as internally disintegrated fatherland."

According to Nazi doctrine, the Germanic culture of northern Europe was responsible for virtually all major intellectual and technological achievements of Western civilization. Maps that appeared in archaeological publications between 1933 and 1945 invariably showed the Germanic homeland as the center of diffusionary waves, bringing civilization to less developed cultures to the south, west, and east. Hitler presented his own views on this subject in a dinner-table monologue in which he referred to the Greeks as Germans who had survived a northern natural catastrophe and evolved a highly developed culture in southern contexts. Such wishful thinking was supported by otherwise reputable archaeologists. The *Research Report of the Reichsbund for German Prehistory,*

July to December 1941, for example, reported the nine-week expedition of the archaeologist Hans Reinerth and a few colleagues to Greece, where they claimed to have discovered major new evidence of Indogermanic migration to Greece during Neolithic times.

This perspective was ethnocentric, racist, and genocidal. Slavic peoples occupying what had once been, on the basis of the distribution of archaeological remains, Germanic territory, were to be relocated or exterminated to supply true Germans with *Lebensraum* (living space). When the new Polish state was created in 1919, Kossinna published an article, "The German Ostmark, Home Territory of the Germans," which used archaeological evidence to support Germany's claim to the area. Viewed as only temporarily occupied by racially inferior "squatters," Poland and Czechoslovakia could be reclaimed for "racially pure" Germans.

Prehistoric archaeologists in Germany, who felt they had been ignored, poorly funded, and treated as second-class citizens by colleagues specializing in the more honored disciplines of classical and Near Eastern archaeology, now seemed to have everything to gain by an association with the rising Nazi party. Between 1933, the year of Hitler's accession to power, and 1935, eight new chairs were created in German prehistory, and funding became available for prehistoric excavations across Germany and eastern Europe on an unprecedented scale. Numerous institutes came into being during this time, such as the Institute for Prehistory in Bonn in 1938. Museums for protohistory were established, and prehistoric collections were brought out of storage and exhibited, in many cases for the first time. Institutes for rune research were created to study the *futhark,* or runic alphabet in use in northern Europe from about the third to the thirteenth centuries A.D. Meanwhile, the Römisch Germanisches Zentral Museum in Mainz became the Zentral Museum für Deutsche Vor- und Frühgeschichte in 1939. (Today it has its pre-war title once again.)

Open-air museums like the reconstructed Neolithic and Bronze Age lake settlements at Unteruhldingen on Lake Constanz were intended to popularize prehistory. An archaeological film series, produced and directed by the prehistorian Lothar Zotz, included titles like *Threatened by the Steam Plow, Germany's Bronze Age, The Flames of Prehistory,* and *On the Trail of the Eastern Germans.* The popular journals such as *Die Kunde (The Message),* and *Germanen-Erbe (Germanic Heritage)* proliferated. The latter publication was produced by the Ahnenerbe ("Ancestor History") organization, run as a personal project of Reichsführer-SS and chief of police Heinrich Himmler and funded by interested Germans to research, excavate, and restore real and imagined Germanic cultural relics. Himmler's interests in mysticism and the occult extended to archaeology; SS archaeologists were sent out in the wake of invading German forces to track down important archaeological finds and antiquities to be transported back to the Reich. It was this activity that inspired Steven Spielberg's *Raiders of the Lost Ark.*

The popular journals contained abundant visual material. One advertisement shows the reconstruction of a Neolithic drum from a pile of meaningless sherds. The text exhorts readers to "keep your eyes open, for every *Volksgenosse* [fellow German] can contribute to this important national project! Do not assume that a ceramic vessel is useless because it falls apart during excavation. Carefully preserve even the smallest fragment!" An underlined sentence emphasizes the principal message: "Every single find is important because it represents a document of our ancestors!"

Amateur organizations were actively recruited by appeals to patriotism. The membership flyer for the official National Confederation for German Prehistory (*Reichsbund für Deutsche Vorgeschichte*), under the direction of Hans Reinerth of the Amt Rosenberg, proclaimed: "Responsibility with respect to our indigenous prehistory must again fill every German with pride!" The organization stated its

goals as "the interpretation and dissemination of unfalsified knowledge regarding the history and cultural achievements of our northern Germanic ancestors on German and foreign soil."

For Himmler objective science was not the aim of German prehistoric archaeology. Hermann Rauschning, an early party member who became disillusioned with the Nazis and left Germany before the war, quotes Himmler as saying: "The one and only thing that matters to us, and the thing these people are paid for by the State, is to have ideas of history that strengthen our people in their necessary national pride. In all this troublesome business we are only interested in one thing—to project into the dim and distant past the picture of our nation as we envisage it for the future. Every bit of Tacitus in his *Germania* is tendentious stuff. Our teaching of German origins has depended for centuries on a falsification. We are entitled to impose one of our own at any time."

Meanwhile archaeological evidence that did not conform to Nazi dogma was ignored or suppressed. A good example is the controversy surrounding the Externsteine, a natural sandstone formation near Horn in northern Germany. In the twelfth century Benedictine monks from the monastery in nearby Paderborn carved a system of chambers into the rock faces of the Externsteine. In the mid-1930s a contingent of SS Ahnenerbe researchers excavated at the site in an attempt to prove its significance as the center of the Germanic universe, a kind of Teutonic mecca. The excavators, led by Julius Andree, an archaeologist with questionable credentials and supported by Hermann Wirth, one of the founders of the SS Ahnenerbe, were looking for the remains of an early Germanic temple at the Externsteine, where they claimed a cult of solar worshipers had once flourished. The site was described in numerous publications as a monument to German unity and the glorious Germanic past, despite the fact that no convincing evidence of a temple or Germanic occupation of the site was ever found.

So preposterous were the claims made by Andree, Wirth, and their associates that numerous mainstream archaeologists openly questioned the findings of the investigators who became popularly known as *German omanen* or "Germanomaniacs." Eventually Himmler and the Ahnenerbe organization disowned the project, but not before several hundred books and pamphlets on the alleged cult site had been published.

By 1933 the Nazis had gone a step further, initiating a movement whose goal was to replace all existing religious denominations with a new pseudo-pagan state religion based loosely on Germanic mythology, solar worship, nature cults, and a Scandinavian people's assembly or *thing,* from which the new movement derived its name. Central to the movement were open-air theaters or *Thingstätten,* where festivals, military ceremonies, and morality plays, known as *Thingspiele,* were to be staged. To qualify as a Thingstätte, evidence of significant Germanic occupation of the site had to be documented. There was considerable competition among municipalities throughout Germany for this honor. Twelve Thingstätten had been dedicated by September 1935, including one on the summit of the Heiligenberg in Heidelberg.

The Heiligenberg was visited sporadically during the Neolithic, possibly for ritual purposes; there is no evidence of permanent occupation. It was densely settled during the Late Bronze Age (1200–750 B.C.), and a double wall-and-ditch system was built there in the Late Iron Age (200 B.C. to the Roman occupation), when it was a hillfort settlement. Two provincial Roman watchtowers, as well as several Roman dedicatory inscriptions, statue bases, and votive stones, have been found at the site.

When excavations in the 1930s failed to produce evidence of Germanic occupation the Heiligenberg was granted Thingstätte status on the basis of fabricated evidence in the published excavation reports. Ironically, most of the summit's prehistoric deposits were destroyed in the course of building the open-air arena. The Heiligenberg Thingstätte actually held only one Thingspiel before the Thing movement was terminated. Sensing the potential for resistance from German Christians, the Ministry of Propaganda abandoned the whole concept in 1935. Today the amphitheater is used for rock concerts.

Beyond its convenience for propaganda and as justification for expansion into countries like Czechoslovakia and Poland, the archaeological activities of the Amt Rosenberg and Himmler's Ahnenerbe were just so much window dressing for the upper echelons of the party. There was no real respect for the past or its remains. While party prehistorians like Reinerth and Andree distorted the facts, the SS destroyed archaeological sites like Biskupin in Poland. Until Germany's fortunes on the eastern front suffered a reversal in 1944, the SS Ahnenerbe conducted excavations at Biskupin, one of the best-preserved Early Iron Age (600–400 B.C.) sites in all of central Europe. As the troops retreated, they were ordered to demolish as much of the site's preserved wooden fortifications and structures as possible.

Not even Hitler was totally enthusiastic about Himmler's activities. He is quoted by Albert Speer, his chief architect, as complaining: "Why do we call the whole world's attention to the fact that we have no past? It's bad enough that the Romans were erecting great buildings when our forefathers were still living in mud huts; now Himmler is starting to dig up these villages of mud huts and enthusing over every potsherd and stone axe he finds. All we prove by that is that we were still throwing stone hatchets and crouching around open fires when Greece and Rome had already reached the highest stage of culture. We should really do our best to keep quiet about this past. Instead Himmler makes a great fuss about it all. The present-day Romans must be having a laugh at these revelations."

"Official" involvement in archaeology consisted of visits by Himmler and various SS officers to SS-funded and staffed excavations, like the one on the Erdenburg in the Rhineland, or press shots of Hitler and Goebbels viewing a reconstructed "Germanic" Late Bronze Age burial in its tree-trunk coffin, part of the 1934 "Deutsches Volk—Deutsche Arbeit" exhibition in Berlin. Party appropriation of prehistoric data was evident in the use of Indo-European and Germanic design symbols in Nazi uniforms and regalia. The double lightning bolt, symbol of Himmler's SS organization, was adapted from a Germanic rune. The swastika is an Indo-European sun symbol which appears in ceramic designs as early as the Neolithic in western Europe and continues well into early medieval times.

German archaeologists during this period fall into three general categories: those who were either true believers or self-serving opportunists; those (the vast majority) who accepted without criticism the appropriation and distortion of prehistoric archaeology; and those who openly opposed these practices.

Victims of the regime were persecuted on the basis of race or political views, and occasionally both. Gerhard Bersu, who had trained a generation of post–World War I archaeologists in the field techniques of settlement archaeology, was prematurely retired from the directorship of the Römisch Germanische Kommission in 1935. His refusal to condone or conduct research tailored to Nazi ideological requirements, in addition to his rejection of the racist Kossinna school, ended his career as a prehistorian until after World War II. The official reason given for the witch-hunt, led by Hans Reinerth under the auspices of the Amt Rosenberg, was Bersu's Jewish heritage. By 1950 Bersu was back in Germany, again directing the Römisch Germanische Kommission.

It should be noted that some sound work was accomplished during this period despite political interference. The vocabulary of field reports carefully conformed to the dictates of funding sources, but the methodology was usually unaffected. Given time this would have changed as politically motivated terms and concepts altered the intellectual vocabulary of the discipline. In 1935, for example, the entire prehistoric and early historic chronologies were officially renamed: the Bronze and pre-Roman Iron Ages became the "Early Germanic period," the Roman Iron Age the "Climax Germanic period," the Migration period the "Late Germanic period," and everything from the Carolingians to the thirteenth century the "German Middle Ages."

It is easy to condemn the men and women who were part of the events that transformed the German archaeological community between 1933 and 1945. It is much more difficult to understand the choices they made or avoided in the social and political contexts of the time. Many researchers who began as advocates of Reinerth's policies in the Amt Rosenberg and Himmler's Ahnenerbe organization later became disenchanted. Others, who saw the system as a way to develop and support prehistory as a discipline, were willing to accept the costs of the Faustian bargain it offered. The benefits were real, and continue to be felt to this day in the institutions and programs founded between 1933 and 1945.

The paralysis felt by many scholars from 1933 to 1945 continued to affect research in the decades after the war. Most scholars who were graduate students during the 12-year period had to grapple with a double burden: a humiliating defeat and the disorienting experience of being methodologically "deprogrammed." Initially there was neither time nor desire to examine the

reasons for the Nazi prostitution of archaeology. Unfortunately prehistoric archaeology is the only German social-science discipline that has still to publish a self-critical study of its role in the events of the 1930s and 1940s.

The reluctance of German archaeologists to come to terms with the past is a complex issue. German prehistoric archaeology is still a young discipline, and first came into its own as a result of Nazi patronage. There is therefore a certain feeling that any critical analysis of the motives and actions of the generation and the regime that engendered the discipline would be ungrateful at

---

The reluctance of German archaeologists to come to terms with the past is a complex issue.

---

best and at worst a betrayal of trust. The vast majority of senior German archaeologists, graduate students immediately after the war, went straight from the front lines to the universities, and their dissertation advisers were men whose careers had been determined by their connections within the Nazi party.

The German system of higher education is built upon close bonds of dependence and an almost medieval fealty between a graduate student and his or her dissertation advisor. These bonds are maintained even after the graduate student has embarked on an

academic career. Whistle-blowers are rare, since such action would amount to professional suicide. But in the past decade or so, most of the generation actively involved in archaeological research and teaching between 1933 and 1945 have died. Their knowledge of the personal intrigues and alliances that allowed the Nazi party machine to function has died with them. Nonetheless, there are indications that the current generation of graduate students is beginning to penetrate the wall of silence that has surrounded this subject since 1945. The remaining official documents and publications may allow at least a partial reconstruction of the role of archaeology in the rise and fall of the Nazi regime.

The future of prehistoric archaeology in the recently unified Germany will depend on an open confrontation with the past. Archaeologists in the former East Germany must struggle with the legacy of both Nazi and Communist manipulation of their discipline. Meanwhile, the legacy of the Faustian bargain struck by German archaeologists with the Nazi regime should serve as a cautionary tale beyond the borders of a unified Germany: Archaeological research funded wholly or in part by the state is vulnerable to state manipulation. The potential for political exploitation of the past seems to be greatest in countries experiencing internal instability. Germany in the years following World War I was a country searching for its own twentieth-century identity. Prehistoric archaeology was one means to that end.

Murders From the Past

Sleuthing crimes of the past, forensic anthropologists open up files on Lizzie Borden, the Colorado Cannibal, Zachary Taylor, and Huey "Kingfish" Long, among others.

James Dickerson

An electric saw buzzed through a lead container that had been sealed for 150 years. Slowly, the liner lid was removed, exposing the remains of Zachary Taylor, the twelfth president of the United States. Face to face with the former president, a blue-ribbon panel of investigators was surprised to see a thick mass of dark hair and a large cloth bow under the chin. Since the president's visit was meant to be brief, his hosts went to work immediately. University of Florida forensic anthropologist Bill Maples methodically cut away the president's clothing, finding abundant body hair beneath the one-piece, pleated shroud. Then he took hair, nail, and tissue samples, hoping they would prove whether the president had succumbed to arsenic poisoning or died of natural causes.

Ghoulish? Perhaps to most. But to forensic sleuths like Maples, who focus on murders and other mysteries a century or more old, exhuming and examining the remains of celebrities from presidents to political assassins is business as usual.

In another case, for instance, Maples seeks to identify the remains of Francisco Pizarro, the Spanish conqueror of Peru. And his colleague James Starrs, a lawyer and forensic scientist at George Washington University in Washington, DC, has exhumed the remains of Dr. Carl Austin Weiss, the alleged assassin of the controversial U.S. senator from Louisiana, Huey

Long. When held up to the scrutiny of modern science, Weiss's remains and other buried evidence may show whether the doctor was truly Long's assassin or was innocent, as his descendants have claimed.

It's possible to resolve such issues today, thanks to the extraordinary range and power of modern forensic techniques. Today's high-resolution microscopes, for instance, can analyze knife marks on bone, distinguishing between different knives or the marks left by animals. X-rays can probe beneath the surface of grave sites. Sophisticated chemical and nuclear technologies can detect trace amounts of incriminating poisons. And using computers, experts can superimpose old photos of a victim or suspect on top of x-ray images of facial bones, determining whether or not the identities are a match.

In fact, whether it's determining the identity of an eighteenth-century cannibal or investigating the fate of the princess Anastasia Romanov, forensic anthropologists have begun to rewrite the history of murder, mayhem, and sensational crime. For a look at some of the most fascinating investigations to date, open *Omni*'s murder dossier, and read on.

WHO KILLED THE KINGFISH?

VICTIM: Huey Long, U.S. senator and former governor from Louisiana.
DEATH NOTES: The politically powerful Long was shot and killed while

visiting the Louisiana State Capitol on September 8, 1935. The presumed assassin, a 29-year-old physician named Carl Weiss, was killed by Long's bodyguards in a hail of gunfire at the scene.
MURDER MYSTERY: Although the case against Weiss was considered open and shut at the time, questions began to emerge. First of all, officials were never able to establish a genuine motive. In addition, though police said Weiss's gun was found at the scene, no one could prove he had carried the gun into the Capitol. Did Carl Weiss really kill Huey Long, or was he just a patsy, a fall guy set up by one of the many bitter political enemies Long had cultivated over the years?
FORENSIC SLEUTHS: James Starrs, forensic scientist, George Washington University, Washington, DC; Douglas Ubelaker, curator of anthropology, National Museum of Natural History, Smithsonian Institution, Washington, DC; Lucien Haag, freelance "criminalist" and weapons expert, Phoenix; Irvin Sother, state medical examiner, West Virginia; and Alphonse Poklis, toxicologist, Medical College of Virginia at Richmond.
CLUES UNEARTHED: Weiss's remains were exhumed on October 20, 1991, at the Roselawn Cemetery in Baton Rouge and transported first to the Lafayette, Louisiana, pathology lab for cleaning, then to Ubelaker's lab at the National Museum of Natural History. To identify the remains as those of Weiss, Ubelaker used the technique of photographic imposition to

match the skull with old photos of the suspect. To rule out the likelihood that Weiss committed the act as a result of a brain tumor or while under the influence of drugs, toxicologist Poklis examined the anatomy of the skull and analyzed the chemical content of tissue and bones. Examining the remains, he also discovered that Weiss had been shot a minimum of 23 times, with half the wounds inflicted on his back. Several bullet wounds were found in his arms, suggesting a defensive posture. Ubelaker also found that Weiss had been shot from a "variety of angles, implying that his assailants came from many directions."

Then Haag, an expert in firearms and tool marks, stepped in to examine the contents of files squirreled away by

the police superintendent. Perhaps most telling was a .32-caliber bullet thought to have come from the scene of the crime. After testing the bullet at the laboratory in Phoenix, Haag concluded it did not come from Weiss's gun. Since Long's bodyguards carried only larger .38- and .45-caliber pistols, Haag notes, the mysterious bullet raises the question of a second, never-reported .32-caliber pistol somewhere on the scene. It's possible, he proposes, that Weiss's gun was simply a plant to protect the identity of the true killer, the one that got away. Anyone who knew that Weiss carried a piece could have found one like it and committed the crime themselves, setting Weiss up for the fall, Haag says.

CONCLUSION: As a result of all the

new evidence, the seemingly solid case against Weiss has been riddled with doubt.

WILL THE REAL PIZARRO PLEASE STAND?

VICTIM: Francisco Pizarro, Spanish conqueror of Peru.

DEATH NOTES: Francisco Pizarro, despised by native Peruvians because of his brutal reign, was stabbed to death by a crowd of angry subjects in 1541 at the age of 71 in full view of numerous witnesses. Pizarro subsequently faded into history where he remained a topic for academicians and scholars for more than 350 years.

QUESTION OF IDENTITY: The cir-

Back in time: To resolve some of the most gruesome and enigmatic murder mysteries of the past, physical anthropolo-

gists like Bill Maples, top center, are digging up remains of both killers and victims as well as old murder weapons and more. Maples' colleagues, for instance, have exhumed the body of Dr. Carl Austin Weiss, top left, convicted, perhaps wrongfully, of assassinating the controversial U.S. senator Huey Long. Weiss's x-rayed

skull is depicted, bottom right. Experts also want to study the hatchet supposedly used by Lizzie Borden, next page, top right, to kill her father, whose skull is shown, top right, and her stepmother, whose skull

is depicted on the next page, bottom left. Bottom center on this page is another focus for forensic sleuthing: One Alferd Packer, convicted of the gruesome, cannibalistic murder of five prospectors seeking gold and silver in Colorado's San

Juan Mountains. Though Packer was convicted by a jury of his peers, he always maintained his innocence and was eventually paroled. Packer died in 1907, leaving unanswered the question of whether he truly was the vicious killer who ate his unwitting victims' remains. Shown above is a photo of the remains of the five victims shortly after

exhumation in 1989. Another historical figure currently the subject of investigation is Meriwether Lewis, of Lewis and Clark fame, at right, who died of two gunshot wounds. The

death was declared a suicide at the time but is now considered a murder. Also the topic of study was

former U.S president Zachary Taylor, bottom right, who died suddenly, allegedly of gastroenteritis; despite this official cause of death, some experts have suggested arsenic poisoning instead. To unearth the truth, a team of forensic sleuths exhumed Taylor's remains in 1991, almost a century and a half after his

untimely death. It's interesting to note that detailed chemical and nuclear tests at the Louisville medical examiner's office and at the Oak Ridge National Laboratory in Tennessee yielded

no evidence of arsenic poisoning. But despite these results, say some experts, it's remotely possible that Taylor was poisoned with arsenic after all and that the evidence has simply leached from his body over the years.

cumstances of Pizarro's death are not in question, having been well documented at the time by the Spanish, who tortured witnesses to elicit the details. However, in the 1890s, Peruvian officials decided to put Pizarro's remains on exhibit as part of an upcoming celebration of Columbus's voyage. They asked officials at the Cathedral of the Plaza de Aramis in Lima for Pizarro's body and were directed to a mummy, which they put on view. Then, in 1978, workers in the cathedral uncovered a secret niche that had been walled over. On a shelf inside the niche was a lead box with a skull and an inscription identifying the contents as the head of Pizarro. Alongside this first box was another, this one containing the bones of several unidentified individuals. Who was the real Pizarro? The mummy that had been on display

for nearly a century or the skull and bones found in the cathedral crypt?
FORENSIC SLEUTHS: Bill Maples, anthropologist, University of Florida, Gainesville, and Bob Benfer, anthropologist, University of Missouri, Columbia.
CLUES UNEARTHED: A preliminary investigation by one of Benfer's students showed that postcranial bones in the second box matched the skull in the first. The matching bones were then assembled with the skull. The challenge for Maples and Benfer: determining whether the newly discovered bones contained marks consistent with knife or sword wounds and then determining whether similar wounds appeared on the mummy. Using straightforward visual observation, the researchers determined that the skeleton had been stabbed multiple times, consistent with

the reported demise of Pizarro. From the location of the wounds, Maples and Benfer concluded that Pizarro had been stabbed about the head and body and apparently had tried to shield himself with his arm, a reaction that is common in stabbing deaths. The mummy, on the other hand, exhibited no injuries whatsoever and could not have been Pizarro at all.

CONCLUSION: The remains of Pizarro had been hidden in the Cathedral crypt all along. The mystery solved, Peruvian officials exchanged the mummy with the bones, which are now on display instead. As for the mummy, it's on a piece of plywood down in the crypt. "Fame is fleeting," Maples observes, "even after death."

SEARCH FOR ANASTASIA

VICTIMS: Czar of Russia, Nicholas II; his wife, Alexandra; their five children, Olga, Tatiana, Marie, Anastasia, and Alexis; the royal physician; and several royal servants.

DEATH NOTES: On July 17, 1918, during the Bolshevik Revolution, the Russian czar and his family along with the royal physician and some servants were awakened and taken to the basement of the house in which they stayed. There, they were greeted by a hail of bullets and then stabbed with bayonets. According to one account, their bodies were hacked to pieces and soaked in acid. Two were burned.

MURDER MYSTERY: In what may have been the ultimate game of Russian roulette, the assassins assigned to wipe out the royal family may have let two members slip through the cracks. According to rumors that have persisted ever since the fateful day, the princess Anastasia Romanov and her brother Alexis may have survived their grievous injuries and lived to tell the tale. One observer, for instance, recalled the czar's youngest daughter sitting up and screaming after the initial volley of bullets. And in the years that followed, a number of people have claimed to be Anastasia herself. Anna Anderson Manahan, who died in Charlottesville, Virginia, in 1984 at the age of 82, was probably the most publicized claimant. For 60 years she tried to convince people she was Princess Anastasia and even filed a lawsuit in Germany for an $85 million dowry supposedly held in trust. German bankers were vague about the existence of a trust fund, however, and she lost the case. Although a movie was made of her struggle, her claims were discounted, primarily because she could not speak Russian. Was Manahan or another claimant the true Anastasia Romanov? Did the youngest czarist princess survive?

FORENSIC SLEUTHS: Bill Maples; Lowell Levine, codirector of the New York State Police Forensic Sciences Unit in Albany; Michael Baden, New York City pathologist; and Catherine

Francisco Pizarro, top left, Spanish conqueror of Peru, stabbed to death by native Peruvians who despised his brutal reign. While the circumstances of Pizarro's death are not in question, experts have debated the legitimacy of the explorer's mummified remains, put on exhibit at the Cathedral of the Plaza de

One of the biggest mysteries of the past involved the lost remains of

Aramis in Lima. The mummy in question showed no evidence of a brutal attack, and when workers found another batch of remains hidden behind a secret cathedral wall, the identity of the true Pizarro was up for grabs. A bit of forensic sleuthing proved the mummy an imposter and the bones behind the hidden wall real.

The mystery solved, Peruvian officials put the true remains on display. "Fame is fleeting," observed investigator Bill Maples, "even after death." This page, center, is George Washington University lawyer and forensic scientist James Starrs, who investigated the murder of Huey Long, bottom left, and the true guilt of his experts trying to solve a royal murder mystery have compared photos of Anna Anderson Manahan, right, with depictions of her royal highness Anastasia Romanov, bottom right, said to have been killed with the rest of the Russian royal family during the Bolshevik revolution. To her dying day, Manahan claimed she was the real Anastasia, whose remains have never been identified.

murderer, Carl Weiss, whose dead body is shown on the previous page on a Baton Rouge Capitol corridor floor. Forensic slueths investigating the Colorado Canni-

bal have studied this sketch, above, created by artist John Randolph, the man said to have discovered the remains of the five unlucky victims brutally killed and then apparently filleted and eaten by Packer.

Photograph of the skull of victim George Noon, below, shows numerous hatchet marks. Finally,

Did Anastasia survive? To get to the truth, scientists are hoping to find and study more royal bones at the bottom of a firepit.

Oakes, microtomist, New York State police.

CLUES UNEARTHED: In 1991, Russian authorities exhumed the remains of nine bodies thought to be the czar and those who perished with him. Also retrieved from the grave site were bullets and a broken acid jar. Soon after exhumation, American experts, including Maples and Levine, arrived at a lab in Yekaterinburg, a city some 800 miles east of Moscow. Their goal: to identify the bodies and determine the cause of death. The Americans quickly declared that historical accounts of the assassination were born out by the condition of the remains. "Three of the skulls showed clear evidence of gunshot wounds," Maples says, "and teeth

and skulls showed evidence of etching and erosion by acid." There was even enough tissue on the remains of what was certainly the royal physician to hold the lower torso together. In fact, there was only one part of the story that could not be verified: the death of Anastasia. The skeleton of a 17-year-old female could not be found. Maples sees one last way to prove that Anastasia died: Locate a firepit containing the two bodies that were supposedly burned. According to historical accounts, the burned bodies belonged to Alexis, the czar's son, and a maid. But Maples says one of the burned bodies could turn out to be Anastasia. "If we found the bodies of two teenagers in a fire pit," he says, "I would feel confident that Anastasia did not survive."

CONCLUSION: DNA analysis conducted by British scientists confirmed the findings of forensic sleuths who went to Russia. After comparing blood samples taken from Prince Philip, a blood relative of the czar's wife, with tissue samples taken from the remains at Yekaterinburg, scientists were able to get a match. At the moment, the fate of Anastasia has been thrown into question. Russian investigators say Anastasia's remains were among those found. American experts are unsure. Recently, a lock of hair said to belong to Anna Anderson Manahan has been produced and will soon be subjected to DNA analysis. Hopefully, say the experts, they will be able to tell whether her genes and those of Prince Philip match.

PRESIDENTIAL POISON

VICTIM: Zachary Taylor, twelfth president of the United States.

DEATH NOTES: On July 4, 1850, President Taylor dedicated the cornerstone for the Washington Monument. After walking home from the ceremony, he ate a bowl of cherries and drank a glass of cold milk. A short while later, he became violently ill with diarrhea, severe vomiting, and dehydration. Five days later he died.

MURDER MYSTERY: At the time, Taylor's death was attributed to deadly gastroenteritis. But according to pundits, the same symptoms are characteristic of arsenic poisoning, and, they say, Taylor may have been murdered by enemies wishing to do him in. Historical novelist Clara Rising even has two prime suspects: then–Vice President Millard Fillmore and Kentucky senator Henry Clay. Taylor was opposed to the extension of slavery, Rising explains, and supported the admission of California as a free state, something that would have made free states more numerous than slave ones. After Taylor's death, however, Fillmore supported a compromise proposal by Clay in which California, a free state, was paired with New Mexico, a slave state; the balance of power was kept intact. Motive enough to assassinate a president? Rising and others say maybe so.

FORENSIC SLEUTHS: Clara Rising, Louisville; Bill Maples; Dr. Richard Greathouse, Jefferson County coroner, Louisville; Dr. George Nichols, medical examiner, Commonwealth of Kentucky, Louisville; and Dr. William Hamilton, medical examiner, Gainesville, Florida.

CLUES UNEARTHED: Before exhuming Taylor on June 17, 1991, researchers checked with White House historical records to determine if the president had been embalmed. In the 1800s, embalming almost always involved the use of arsenic, and if he had been embalmed, it would have been impossible to tell whether Taylor had in fact been poisoned. According to Rising, records show that Taylor's wife would not allow him to be embalmed.

Oxidation of the coffin's lead liner caused by large quantities of seeping body fluids offers additional evidence that embalming did not occur. The researchers also sent tissue samples to the Louisville medical examiner's toxicology lab and to the Oak Ridge National Laboratory in Tennessee, where it was placed in a powerful research reactor and bombarded with neutrons. When bombarded with neutrons, different metals give off different levels of radiation; arsenic, of course, has its own telltale signature. When the results were in, both the chemical and nuclear tests revealed only "normal levels of arsenic" consistent with neither embalming nor poisoning. The labs also checked for the presence of other heavy metals, including mercury and antimony, and found none.

CONCLUSION: The detailed tests found no evidence of arsenic poisoning. But despite the results, says Maples, it's remotely possible that Taylor was poisoned with arsenic after all and that the evidence has simply leached from his body over the years.

COLORADO CANNIBAL

VICTIMS: Shannon Bell, Israel Swan, James Humphrey, George Noon, and Frank Miller, five prospectors seeking gold and silver in Colorado's San Juan Mountains.

DEATH NOTES: In the winter of 1874, the five victims hired one Alferd Packer to guide them through the mountains. But when Packer returned to town after six weeks, he said he had lost the others in a snow storm. There had, indeed, been a raging storm, but authorities were suspicious because of Packer's appearance: Despite his claims of hardship and a shortage of food, he was noticeably fat and more interested in drinking than eating. In addition, he seemed to have far more money than he'd had *before* the trip. When a traveling artist located the remains of the missing men, he discovered evidence of foul play and even sketched the scene for *Harper's Weekly*. Finally authorities reported "marks of extreme violence" on the

bodies of the victims and concluded that they had been murdered by ax or hatchet.

FORENSIC SLEUTHS: James Starrs; Douglas Ubelyker; Walter Birkby, forensic anthropologist, University of Arizona, Tucson; tool-mark expert Lucien Haag; and archeologist James Ayres, Tucson, Arizona.

MURDER MYSTERY: Before he could be charged with the murders, Packer escaped from authorities and remained at large for nine years. He was finally captured in 1883 and at his trial declared that four of the men had been murdered by Shannon Bell. He himself shot and then hacked Bell to death in self-defense, he claimed, after Bell attacked him. Packer was convicted and sentenced to death but won a new trial on a technicality. He was convicted a second time and sentenced to 40 years hard labor. At the turn of the century, however, a Denver newspaper columnist raised doubts about his guilt and succeeded in getting him paroled in 1901. He died in 1907. Was Packer innocent, or was he a vicious killer who ate the remains of his victims?

CLUES UNEARTHED: After the remains of the five prospectors were exhumed in July 1989, they were taken to the University of Arizona, where Walter Birkby is curator of physical anthropology. According to Birkby, the remains were in good condition, the result of soil with especially low levels of acid at the grave site. None of the bodies had been dismembered, he noted, but all had hatchet-like marks on the skull and had been defleshed. After the skeletons were assembled, Lucien Haag was called in to identify the marks found on the bones. Haag used a microscope to study the tool patterns and then made silicone rubber casts to preserve the marks for additional study.

According to investigators, the number, type, and location of implement marks leave no mystery as to how the prospectors died and what happened to them after death. "These individuals were all murdered," said Birkby. "All of them exhibited evidence of sharp implement marks on their bones, which is consistent with defleshing.

One individual had 14 hatchet marks on his skull." Some of the marks are clearly defensive, indicating some of the victims had held up their arms to ward off the blows of an ax or hatchet. Others received blows on the head, indicating they may have been sleeping when attacked. Many of the bones also showed very fine knife marks, Haag adds, an indication that these victims had, like steak, been filleted.

What about Packer's claim that Bell shot the others, causing him to shoot Bell in self-defense? Not likely, say the investigators. One individual probably committed all the murders, they explained, because the injuries were consistent from one cranium to the next. What's more, the researchers found only one bullet wound amongst all the victims—and that individual had been shot years before his death.

CONCLUSION: Packer's story did not hold up to scientific scrutiny. The jury that convicted him was right and his defenders were wrong. Alferd Packer was, indeed, "the Colorado Cannibal."

ON THE DOCKET:

Thanks to modern technology, the skeletal remains of historical figures have the potential to rewrite history by answering questions unanswerable at the time of death. Several cases still under study could rattle the cages of historians and law-enforcement officials:

Lizzie Borden. After an inept police investigation and a sensational murder trial in 1893, Lizzie Borden was found not guilty of hacking her father and 200-pound stepmother to death with an ax at their home in Fall River, Massachusetts. Despite her acquittal, Lizzie remained guilty in the eyes of the popular press and some historians. Enter forensic investigator James Starrs, who is convinced Lizzie Borden may have been innocent. Starrs wants permission from Borden family members to exhume the skulls of Lizzie's parents. If Lizzie is innocent, it can be proven scientifically, he says, "by comparing available physical evidence, such as the famous 'hoodoo hatchet,' with scientific analysis of the remains."

Meriwether Lewis. Also on Starrs' list of unsolved mysteries is the death of Meriwether Lewis (of Lewis and Clark fame). Lewis died in 1809 at an inn on the Natchez Trace southwest of Nashville, Tennessee. Governor of the Louisiana Territory at the time, he was on his way to Washington, DC, to meet with officials when he died of two gunshot wounds, one to the side and the other to the head. The death has long been labeled a suicide, but Starrs states that "the scientific evidence that he committed suicide is entirely deficient." Lewis may have been murdered,

> *'James Starrs hopes to exhume the skulls of Lizzie Borden's parents to compare with physical evidence such as the famous hoodoo hatchet.'*

says Starrs. With the permission of Lewis's descendants, he hopes to exhume the remains and find out.

John Wilkes Booth. Abraham Lincoln was assassinated in April 1865 by John Wilkes Booth, who 12 days later was gunned down by soldiers in a barn—right? Wrong, according to Hugh Berryman, director of the Regional Forensic Center in Memphis; Nathaniel Orlowek, a religious educator at Beth Shalom Congregation in Potomac, Maryland; and Arthur Chitty, historian at the University of the South. They believe Booth may have escaped capture and lived another 38 years using the name John St. Helen before confessing his identity and committing suicide in Enid, Oklahoma. After his death, St. Helen's body was embalmed. But when the government showed no interest in investigating the claims, the lawyer to whom St. Helen confessed stored the mummy in his basement for 29 years. Eventually, the mummified body was sold to a carnival and then slipped out of sight. If the mummy can be recovered, says Berryman, it would be possible, using mod-

ern forensic technology, to make comparisons with known photographs of Booth. Meanwhile, Orlowek is attempting to exhume the body thought to belong to Booth and determine whether it is truly his.

Wild Bill Longley. On October 11, 1878, a notorious Texas outlaw named Wild Bill Longley was convicted of murder and hanged under the watchful eye of the local sheriff. His body was then buried in a cemetery near Giddings. Or was it? Family legend has it that he escaped the hangman's noose and relocated in Iberville Parish, Louisiana, where he adopted the sheriff's last name of Brown and lived a long life as a respected member of the community. According to family legend, in fact, Longley made a deal with the sheriff to fake the hanging using a harness to break his fall. Before burial, he escaped while the coffin was weighted with stones. The sheriff was subsequently killed in a gunfight with police in Chicago, and a man calling himself John Calhoun Brown began a new life in Louisiana. He fathered ten children, ran a successful timber business, and died around 1923.

These claims by the families of both the "original" Longley and the Brown descendants in Louisiana prompted Dr. Douglas Owsley, a forensic anthropologist at the Smithsonian Institution, to organize an investigative team. The first step was using a computer to compare photographs of the two men. "I was taken aback by the correspondence of the fit," he says. "They were very, very similar. "Betting on the "probability" that Longley and Brown were one and the same, Owsley worked with geologist Brooks Elwood at the University of Texas and Pat Mercado-Allinger of the Texas Historical Commission to excavate 25 graves at the cemetery where the outlaw's coffin, filled with stones, was said to lie. The outlaw's marker had been moved at least twice in more than a century, so it's no surprise that none of the 25 coffins turned out to be his. But the team will do some more historical research and then return to the cemetery, hoping to find a coffin full of stones.

Bones and Bureaucrats

New York's Great Cemetery Imbroglio

Spencer P. M. Harrington

The bones of 420 enslaved Africans found last year under a parking lot two blocks north of New York's City Hall comprise the largest and earliest collection of African-American remains, and possibly the largest and earliest collection of American colonial remains of any ethnic group. The excavation of the old Negros Burial Ground has challenged the popular belief that there was no slavery in colonial New York, and has provided unparalleled data for the Howard University scholars who will study the remains of New York's first African Americans. But as archaeologists removed the remains one by one, they dug up age-old resentment and suspicion with every trowel-full of earth. Scholarly excitement was tempered by the protest of the city's black community, which felt its concerns were not being addressed in decisions about the excavation and disposition of the remains. In the flurry of protests, negotiations, and political maneuverings, the controversy took on an undeniably racial cast. The African Burial Ground, as it is known today, became a "microcosm of the issues of racism and economic exploitation confronting New York City," says Michael L. Blakey, a Howard University anthropologist and the burial ground's scientific director.

In a national context, the controversy over the burial ground excavation became an important episode in a larger struggle of descendant communities to reclaim their heritage. But more specifically, the story was about African-American empowerment: about how a black congressman, acting on the advice of New York City's first black mayor, stopped the excavation of the burial ground; about how the African-American community chose Washington D.C.'s Howard University, the country's most prestigious black research university, as a venue for the study of the remains, thereby ensuring that black researchers and students would study and interpret the remains of their ancestors; and about how the city's black community lobbied for and received a $3 million appropriation from Congress for a memorial and commemorative museum. Equally important were the hard lessons learned by the General Services Administration, the federal agency that supervised the excavation—lessons about the importance of descendant-community involvement in salvage archaeology.

The story of the African Burial Ground begins in 1626, when the Dutch West Indies Company imported its first shipment of slaves, 11 young men from today's Congo-Angola region of Africa. Two years later, the company brought over three African women "for the comfort of the company's Negro men," according to Dutch West Indies records. Like the British who governed Manhattan after them, the Dutch encountered difficulties attracting European settlers to the new colony. Grave manpower shortages threatened the profitability of the Dutch West Indies trading enterprise, and the company was quick to import slave labor to farm its fields. In 1664, just before the Dutch ceded Manhattan to the British, enslaved Africans made up about 40 percent of the colony's total population. The British continued the slave trade, importing as many as 6,800 Africans between 1700 and 1774, many of whom had worked previously on Caribbean plantations. By the mid-eighteenth century, New York had become a thriving port town, and enslaved Africans loaded and unloaded cargo at the docks, wharves, slips, and warehouses along the East River. They also piloted boats ferrying produce from the farming villages of Long Island, repaired and expanded city streets, and worked in shipbuilding and construction. On the eve of the American Revolution, New York City had the largest number of enslaved Africans of any English colonial settlement except Charleston, South Carolina, and it had the highest proportion of slaves to Europeans of any northern settlement. Though seldom acknowledged, Africans were essential to the functioning, as well as the building of colonial New York.

In November 1697, New York City adopted a policy of mortuary apartheid, declaring lower Manhattan churchyards off-limits to blacks. Forced to look for a place to bury its dead, New York's African population, which then numbered about 700, chose unappropriated property outside city limits two blocks north of today's City Hall. There, from 1712 until 1790, in an area characterized by David Valentine, an early city historian, as "unattractive and desolate," Africans conducted last rites for their people. "So little seems to have been thought of the race that not even a dedication of their burial place was made by church authorities," wrote Valentine of what was known then as the Negros Burial Ground. Under the British, Africans were subject to a sunset curfew and city ordinances that prohibited unsupervised gatherings of more than three slaves. They were, however, allowed to gather in large numbers and with regularity at the burial ground. Some 10,000 to 20,000 people, both black and lower-class white, are believed to have been buried in the five-to-six-acre plot of land.

The growth of the city's population in the late eighteenth and early nineteenth centuries led to a northward expansion along main thoroughfares such as Broadway. Street plans were drafted, and blocks over the burial ground were divided into lots for residential and commercial development. By the end of the century, ten- and 15-story buildings with deep foundations and with vaults that were used for storage and coal delivery were going up. The Negros Burial Ground, now paved or built over, was all but forgotten, noted only in a few historical maps and documents. Meanwhile, African Americans were now burying their dead on the Lower East Side, near what are now Chrystie and Delancey streets.

Nearly 200 years later a section of the burial ground lay beneath a parking lot between Duane and Reade streets. In December 1990, New York sold this property and another plot on nearby Foley Square to the General Services Administration (GSA), the federal agency charged with constructing and managing government buildings. The GSA paid $104 million for both properties, which it hoped to develop simultaneously. It planned to build a $276 million, 34-story office tower

and adjoining four-story pavilion on the parking lot area. A federal courthouse was envisioned for the Foley Square property. The tower, designated 290 Broadway, would contain the offices of the United States Attorney, a regional office of the Environmental Protection Agency, and the downtown district office of the Internal Revenue Service. The pavilion would house a day-care center, an auditorium, and a pedestrian galleria.

Five months before the GSA bought the sites from the city, the agency hired Historic Conservation and Interpretation (HCI), an archaeological salvage and consulting firm, to write the archaeological portion of an environmental impact statement for the 290 Broadway site. Such statements are a legal requirement before any new construction using federal funds can begin. HCI's report identified the area as a section of the old Negros Burial Ground and included historical maps indicating its approximate location. But the impact statement predicted that nineteenth- and twentieth-century construction at the site would have destroyed any significant archaeological deposits. It read in part: "The construction of deep sub-basements would have obliterated any remains within the lots that fall within the historic bounds of the cemetery."

Still, the statement left open the possibility of some human remains being preserved under an old alley that once bisected Duane and Reade streets. That the GSA purchased the land despite this possibility suggests that the agency was betting on HCI's overall assessment that few, if any, human remains would be found there. In retrospect, GSA regional director William Diamond admits that the agency would never have bought the land if it had known it would have to remove hundreds of skeletons before sinking the office tower foundation.

In May 1991, six months after purchasing the land, the GSA hired HCI to investigate the possibility that there were undisturbed burials in the alley area. By the end of the summer the firm started to find human bones. In September a full-scale excavation was

underway, and on October 8 Diamond held a press conference to announce the discovery of the remains. One year later, the last of some 420 skeletons had been removed from the site to Lehman College in the Bronx, where they were undergoing conservation before being transferred to Howard University for more detailed study.

African-American outrage over the handling of the excavation stemmed from a perception that the black community had no control over the fate of its heritage—that decisions about the burial ground were being made by white bureaucrats with little insight into African-American history and spiritual sensitivities. "Religious, Afrocentric people believe that to disturb burials in any way is the highest form of disrespect," says Gina Stahlnecker, an aide to State Senator David Patterson, who represents Harlem and the Upper West Side. "There were some people who believed the archaeologists were releasing evil." According to Peggy King Jorde, of the Mayor's Office of Construction, an early monitor of the project, the GSA initially was calling the site a "potters' field," which she felt divorced it from its African origin and diminished its importance. There were even rumors, she says, that the bones were to be removed without any archaeological study. Jorde says that the GSA had only vague ideas about what to do with the remains that were coming to light.

The black community was also upset because it was not alerted at the outset to what might lie beneath the parking lot between Duane and Reade streets. While the GSA did distribute both draft and final environmental impact statements to more than 200 federal, state, and city agencies and local community groups, the agency did not alert civic groups in predominantly black neighborhoods that the buildings would be constructed on top of the old burial ground. "I spoke to hundreds and hundreds of people in the black community, and no one had ever heard about it," says Stahlnecker. While distributing environmental impact statements to descendant communities may seem like a good idea, it is not customary for private or government developers to do so. Peter Sneed, the GSA's planning staff director, argues that the distribution list was formulated in accordance with federal regulations. "We didn't include the Harlem community board because the project isn't in Harlem, it's in lower Manhattan," he says. "We felt it was incumbent upon the Mayor's office to spread the word. It's unreasonable to expect a federal agency to know every interest group in the community."

African-American fury over the excavation increased dramatically after a backhoe operator digging the tower's foundation accidentally destroyed several of the burials. The incident was reported by Dan Pagano, an archaeologist for the city's Landmarks Preservation Commission, who was photographing the site through a telephoto lens when he spotted HCI archaeologists sifting through human remains outside the excavation area, where the backhoe had scooped up earth so that a concrete footing could be poured for the tower. Pagano says jawbones and leg and arm bones were among the remains scooped up by the backhoe. The GSA blamed the accident on an out-of-date drawing that the construction crews were using to determine which part of the site was "culturally sterile." Diamond halted tower construction pending further investigation by archaeologists. The incident led State Senator David Patterson to form an oversight committee to monitor the burial ground excavation.

Miriam Francis, a member of Patterson's committee, says that the involvement of African-American anthropologists in the excavation was among the group's most pressing concerns. "If it was an African find, we wanted to make sure that it was interpreted from an African point of view," she says. But the committee soon learned that the GSA had picked physical anthropologists from the city's Metropolitan Forensic Anthropology Team (MFAT) to conduct field analyses of the remains and that the bones would be stored at the group's Lehman College facility. "We didn't know anything about MFAT whether they were

butchers, bakers, or candlestick makers," says Francis. She notes that when the committee introduced the GSA to African-American specialists like Howard University's Michael Blakey, it was either stonewalled or ignored.

Meanwhile, the GSA was having difficulty getting HCI, its archaeological salvage contractor, to produce a research design stating conservation measures and scientific study goals for the burial project. The GSA had managed to obtain extensions on the report's due date from the Advisory Council on Historic Preservation, the government agency that reviews all federal projects that might have an impact on historic sites. Still, the missing research plan sent further signals to the black community that something was wrong with the way work was progressing. "Any archaeological excavation is useless without a research design," noted Landmarks Preservation Commission Chair Laurie Beckelman at a congressional hearing on the burial ground. "It's like driving a car in a foreign country without a road map or destination."

HCI's Edward Rutsch, the project's archaeologist, says that although he was responsible for the research design, he felt too overworked to get it done properly. "They [GSA] had us working seven days a week and overtime every day," says Rutsch. "Many times it was expressed to me that millions of dollars of public money were being lost. There was terrific pressure to get the excavation done—to finish it."

Last April, black activists staged a one-day blockade of the site in an effort to prevent the GSA from pouring concrete for the tower's foundation. Among other things, they were concerned that there was little African-American involvement in the scientific aspects of the excavation; they were visibly unhappy at the choice of Lehman College as the site for the conservation of the remains. Bones from the site had been wrapped in newspaper and placed in cardboard boxes before being shipped to Lehman. One problem, according to Dan Baer of Ed-

wards and Kelcey, an engineering firm hired to manage the site, was that "We were digging them out faster than [storage] cases could be made." But in the African-American community there was concern that the bones were being damaged at Lehman. "They had some remains up there in boxes ten or 11 months," says Abd-Allah Adesanya, director of the Mayor's Office of African American and Caribbean Affairs. "They were wrapped in newspaper longer than they should have been. They had to be rewrapped in acid-free paper." Baer says, "The bones were stored in newspaper, which may be scientific protocol, but it didn't appear respectful to those who visited the site. It was a mistake that was made. But the bones were in good shape and Dr. Blakey said so after touring the facility."

Blakey's tour of Lehman resulted from pressure by Senator Patterson's committee. "We kept asking them [MFAT], 'Can we go up there?' And that involved more waiting, more delays," says Miriam Francis. "It wasn't that we were against Lehman, we just wanted to see how our ancestors were being stored." Blakey's visit to the facility confirmed the community's suspicion of inadequate conservation. In a letter to ARCHAEOLOGY, Blakey wrote "We intervened in time to prevent the potential for further deterioration, such as the spread of mold in the skeletal remains due to inadequate environmental controls, and improper storage of skeletal materials on top of fragile bone."

As the excavation progressed, the GSA began briefing the public on the burial project's progress. But there was a widespread perception among African Americans that the GSA was merely paying lip-service to the public, that they were digging the bones as fast as they could so the tower foundation could be poured. "People would tell them [the GSA] their gripes, then they went off and did what they wanted," says Adesanya. "The community wanted to be let in on the decision-making process, to influence the direction of the project." While descendant-community input into decisions about

STORIES THE BONES WILL TELL

The skeletal remains and associated artifacts from the African Burial Ground are the only concrete evidence recovered to date of the life of Africans who lived in colonial New York City. The burials were found 16 to 28 feet below street level, many coffins stacked one on top of another—an urban mortuary practice of the period. Although the majority of burials are people of African descent, about seven percent appear to be Europeans. Physical anthropologists determine racial differences by studying characteristic features of the skull, pelvis, and limb bones. The 420 skeletons found at the New York City site represent a fraction of the entire graveyard population. The condition of the remains varies considerably, from good to extremely poor. There were no grave markers or burial maps, and other than wood, coffin nails, and shroud pins, few artifacts associated with the burials were found. "These were not wealthy graves," says Howard University's Michael L. Blakey, the African Burial Ground's scientific director. "The most striking artifacts were the glass beadwork on one woman, and cowrie shells," he says. "Cowrie shells had a symbolic function in West African funeral practice. They were symbols of the passage in death across the sea and have been variously interpreted as a return to Africa or the afterlife."

In the vast majority of the burials the deceased's head faces west, which prompted journalists to report that the bodies were arranged according to Christian burial practice so that they could sit up and see the rising sun on Judgment Day. But Blakey warns that there was considerable overlap between African and Western burial practices during this period, and it is unclear just how Christianized the Africans were. Blakey points out that a few graves facing east may indicate Moslem burials.

Spencer Turkel, an anthropologist with the Metropolitan Forensic Anthropology Team, estimates two-thirds of the remains found at the site were male, and that 40 percent of the sample were children. He says that sex ratios may change after lab study because the hard physical labor demanded by slavery affected the musculoskeletal structure in such a way that some female skeletons look male. The soil in which the bodies were buried was highly acidic and corrosive to human bone, causing further complications for researchers. "One problem we've been having is trying to determine the difference between damage to the bone caused by life experience and that caused by post-mortem soil exposure," says Turkel.

He notes that field examination revealed some obvious causes of death—a musket ball lodged in a rib cage, and a case of rickets, a nutritional deficiency. Diagnosis of other causes of death will have to await further study. "The major epidemics of that period were cholera and yellow fever, but here we're dealing with vague written descriptions," he says. "Many of the children would have died from diarrhea, which is a form of malnutrition. Poorly nourished children would also have been susceptible to pneumonia."

Meanwhile, Howard University scientists are contemplating the skeletal sample's research potential. Because seventeenth- and eighteenth-century historical sources tend to dismiss or ignore New York's enslaved Africans, anthropological research becomes all the more important for scholars interpreting what their life was like. "This is a unique opportunity to gain a better understanding of the biology, health, and culture of the first generation of people who would become the African-American people," says Blakey.

The primary focus of the research conducted at Howard, will be the social and economic conditions affecting the health of the enslaved Africans. The interdisciplinary team studying the skeletal population will consider questions dealing with demography, epidemiology, nutrition, social history, and cultural transformation. Demographic research will attempt to provide information on the African ethnicity of the sample. "We hope to bring attention to the great variety of cultural groups that were brought over from Africa," says Blakey. "Some of these individuals may have spent time in the West Indies or South America, and we may be able to pick that up," he says. Meanwhile, epidemiologists will study the Africans' adjustment to New York's disease environment. Turkel notes that such bone-scarring diseases as tuberculosis and syphilis were relatively rare in Africa, and finding them in this population would yield interesting data on the community's acculturation to Western diseases. Research on the skeletons may also reveal information about nutrition in the colonial period, while study of mortuary practices at the site will show the extent to which African burial traditions were retained or modified.

Because the sample is large enough to account for human variation, accurate statistical analysis will be possible. And because of the age of the burial population, the sample provides baseline data against which hypotheses about the development of specific pathologies in the African-American population can be tested, such as the relatively high incidence of hypertension in today's black community. The data will also yield information on toxic-element levels in preindustrial America.

The draft research design submitted by Blakey this past fall notes that earlier studies of African-American skeletal populations tended to be descriptive of physical characteristics such as sex, age, and height rather than focused on biohistorical information such as diet, African nationality, and adaptation to disease. According to Blakey, carefully conceived, large-scale academic research plans for African-American archaeological sites are rare. "The growth of African-American archaeology reflects the randomness of the discoveries resulting from development projects," he says, adding that specialists in African-American archaeology often find themselves responding to "emergency situations," in which burial grounds or other sites are threatened by development projects. Theresa Singleton, an archaeologist at the Smithsonian Institution, says that "quick and dirty" salvage archaeology has compromised historical sites in general, and African-American sites in particular, because "you need time to study sites thoroughly, and most contractors don't have time." She adds that "many contract archaeologists don't know much about African-American archaeology." Blakey notes that contract archaeologists "have not often taken advantage of the rich literature and perspectives of Afro-American scholarship on Afro-Americans. That needs to change. And that's one of the things all the protest in New York brought about."

—S.P.M.H.

the course of contract excavations seems desirable when human remains are involved, consultation is not part of standard archaeological practice. Nonetheless "the [African-American] community was very unhappy," says Diamond, "and I understood that and kept saying to them, 'I wish I could help you with this but my obligations by law are contrary to your wishes, and the only way we can get this changed is by an act of Congress or an agreement from the administrator of the GSA.' And I was in consultation with them [GSA administrator Richard G. Austin and members of Congress] and they were telling me to continue the construction."

At the GSA's public meetings, African Americans also questioned the propriety of continuing with the removal of remains from the area where the pavilion would be built. They also hoped that the GSA would consider not building the pavilion, or at least modify the plans so there would be no further removals. "There were several conflicting demands," recalls Diamond. "Some wanted the exhumation to stop, others wanted nothing built on the site, and still others wanted a museum built on the site. . . . But I had no authority but to continue under the law with the construction."

The GSA eventually replaced Historic Conservation and Interpretation with John Milner Associates (JMA), a West Chester, Pennsylvania, archaeological contractor. JMA had recently completed a successful excavation of an early nineteenth-century cemetery associated with the First African Baptist Church in Philadelphia that brought to light information on that city's early black history. "JMA had done this sort of job before," says Baer. "We didn't feel we had involved the community enough and we thought that JMA would improve that situation."

But reports by agencies monitoring the excavation were becoming increasingly critical. One report filed by the Advisory Council on Historic Preservation stated, in part, that: " . . . the GSA was proceeding without any clear focus on why the remains were being removed; how they were to be an-

alyzed; how many more bodies were involved; or, what the African-American community's desire was for the treatment of the burials." Mayor David Dinkins sent a letter to Diamond complaining about the lack of a research design and requesting "that the GSA suspend all excavation and construction activities in the pavilion area and bring the project into compliance with the terms outlined in the Memorandum of Agreement [a document specifying the terms of archaeological work to be undertaken in advance of construction]. . . ." There is "no basis for discontinuance of ongoing excavations" was Diamond's response a week later. "I would not be put in a position of abrogating important government contracts because of political pressure," he later recalled.

The final act in the drama was played out before the congressional committee that appropriates funds for the GSA, the House Subcommittee on Public Buildings and Grounds. Meeting in New York, the subcommittee was chaired by former Representative Gus Savage, an Illinois Democrat, who heard testimony from the GSA, the Advisory Council, the city's Landmarks Preservation Commission, and concerned citizens. At the meeting, the GSA argued that stopping the excavation would jeopardize the exposed human remains, and it estimated that relinquishing the pavilion site would cost taxpayers as much as $40 million: $5 million in interest payments, $10 million in land acquisition costs, and $25 million in initial construction costs.

Savage then subjected GSA representatives to intense questioning, during which it became apparent that at the outset the GSA was aware that a historic burial ground had once occupied the land it intended to purchase and develop, and that the agency had made no contingency plans for construction in the event that human remains were found. The meeting also revealed that the building prospectus for 290 Broadway the GSA had submitted for Congressional approval did not mention the burial ground, nor was Savage's subcommittee alerted by the

agency when HCI's impact statement mentioned the possibility of intact graves. Savage ended the hearing early, noting that he would not approve any further GSA projects until he received "a more honest and respectful response" from the agency regarding its excavation of the burial ground. "And don't waste your time asking this subcommittee for anything else as long as I'm chairman, unless you can figure out a way to go around me! I am not going to be part of your disrespect," Savage said.

Three days later, Savage halted excavation on the pavilion site, and last October former President Bush signed Public Law 102-393, ordering the GSA to cease construction of the pavilion portion of the project and approving $3 million for the construction of a museum honoring the contribution of African Americans to colonial New York City. Meanwhile, JMA removed the last of the exposed burials.

In a statement to the House Subcommittee on Public Buildings and Grounds, GSA head Richard G. Austin acknowledged that "in hindsight we could have handled some things better." Austin's statement made it clear to all parties that the GSA recognized the need for descendant-community cooperation in salvage excavations. Its office tower would be built, but African Americans would determine the course of research on the remains. The agency hired Blakey to develop a research design, which he produced in consultation with JMA and numerous black scholars. Blakey was also appointed scientific director of a five-year research program on the remains that will take place at Howard University. Sherill D. Wilson, an urban anthropologist and ethnohistorian, calls the sudden involvement of black scholars "very revolutionary." Such scholarship, she says, "is going to set a precedent for what happens to African burial grounds in the future, and how African heritage will be viewed by the public."

Meanwhile, a chastened GSA has also set up a federal advisory committee chaired by Howard Dodson of New York's Schomburg Center for Research in Black Culture that will address plans for reburial of the remains, an African Burial Ground memorial, a burial ground exhibition in the office tower, and a museum of African and African-American History in New York City. State Senator David Patterson's burial ground oversight committee seeks to create a museum that will honor African-American heritage, "a place similar to Ellis Island, something that can attest to Afro-American history." The city Landmarks Preservation Commission has also proposed that the burial ground be designated a city landmark and has requested that it be considered for National Historic Landmark status. These efforts stemmed in part from a massive petition drive spearheaded by Senator Patterson's oversight committee and jazz musician Noel Pointer that yielded more than 100,000 signatures.

Among other things, the petition called for the creation of a museum and landmark status for the burial ground.

The burial ground controversy and its attendant publicity have had important repercussions nationwide. "The media exposure has created a larger, national audience for this type of research," says Theresa Singleton, an archaeologist at the Smithsonian Institution who has done pioneering research on African-American sites. "I've been called by dozens of scholars and laypeople, all of them interested in African-American archaeology, all of them curious about why they don't know more about the field. Until recently, even some black scholars considered African-American archaeology a waste of time. That's changed now."

Things have indeed changed. Public curiosity about this country's African-American past has been aroused by the New York experience. And it is probably safe to assume that in the future government and private developers will take a hard look at how to include descendant communities in their salvage excavations, especially when human remains are concerned. "Everyone could have talked more to everyone else," concludes the GSA's planning staff director Peter Sneed. "There would have been a lot less heartache . . . the GSA has certainly been sensitized to archaeology."

DOMINIC G. DIONGSON *helped in the reporting of this article. Research assistance was provided by* ANDREW D. REINHARD.

The Earth Is Their Witness

Archaeology is shedding new light on the secret lives of American slaves

Larry McKee

Larry McKee is staff archaeologist at the Hermitage in Hermitage, Tennessee, and adjunct assistant professor of anthropology at Vanderbilt University. He is working on a book about the Hermitage slave community, with support from the Ladies' Hermitage Association, the National Endowment for the Humanities and Earthwatch.

In the spring of 1835, as Andrew Jackson approached his last year in the White House, his mind was already back at the Hermitage, the cotton plantation near Nashville where he would die ten years later. In a letter to Andrew Jackson Jr., his adopted son and temporary master of the Hermitage, the president tried to pass on some of what he had learned about plantation management. "One willing hand is really worth two who only does what labour he is forcibly compelled to perform," he wrote, after praising the plantation overseer, who had "reduced the hands to good subordination, and in doing this [had] obtained their confidence and attachment."

Jackson's "hands" were, of course, slaves. In the first half of the nineteenth century the Hermitage was home to more than 130 slaves and one of the largest plantations in the fertile central basin of Tennessee. In contrast to Thomas Jefferson, who compared his own slave ownership to holding a "wolf by the ears," Jackson never questioned his right to own other human beings. Fervently populist yet racist to his

bones, pragmatic yet prone to furious rages that often ended in fisticuffs and in one case a formal duel, Jackson was a great champion of the southern status quo. Slave ownership was a purely practical matter to him, an organizational problem no more anguishing than the weather or the price of cotton.

In an earlier letter to his son, Jackson had declared without irony that slaves "will complain often, without cause." To a modern reader, taught to think of slavery as a nightmare of backbreaking labor and unrelenting brutality, that statement seems shockingly insensitive. If Jackson seems to have been blind to the psychological horror of slavery, however, the modern understanding of plantation life too often translates that horror into physical terms. Slaves were the most valuable assets on any plantation: common sense required planters to provide them with adequate food, clothing and shelter, and to keep workloads moderate, and brutal, corporal punishments to a minimum. Plantation life, however demeaning, must have also fostered at least a fragile consensus between blacks and whites. Why else would the great majority of slaves never have run away or directly revolted against their oppressors? How else could a handful of white owners and overseers have controlled hundreds of slaves twenty-four hours a day?

Making sense of Jackson's offhand comments requires a calm, nuanced assessment of slavery, one that moves beyond the inflammatory rhetoric that has always surrounded the subject.

From the start, studies of slavery have been hampered by a dearth of hard data or reasonably objective accounts by contemporary observers. In delivering speeches, writing letters or even filling out the pages of diaries, participants in the slavery debate seem to have been always conscious of the eyes of history upon them, of the need to record for posterity their most extreme—and often, therefore, their least objective—arguments.

Those in the pro-slavery camp stressed the humane paternalism of plantation owners and their role in "civilizing" a "savage" people. As one planter wrote in 1846:

Our slaves will bear a favorable contrast with that of any other laboring population in the world, so far as comfort and happiness is concerned, and will not fall below them in any other point of view than that of mere abstract notions of human rights, about which, it is true, there has been much nonsensical prating in this as well as in other countries.

Abolitionists, for their part, usually matched their opponents' rhetorical excesses. Frances Anne Kemble, author of *Journal of a Residence on a Georgian Plantation in 1838–1839* put it this way:

Though the Negroes are fed, clothed, and housed, and though the Irish peasant is starved, naked, and roofless, the bare name of freemen . . . are blessings beyond food, raiment, or shelter; possessing which, the want of every comfort of life is yet more tolerable than their fullest enjoyment without them.

Reprinted with permission from *The Sciences*, March/April 1995, pp. 36-41. © 1995 by the New York Academy of Science. Individual subscriptions are $21.00 per year. Write to: *The Sciences*, 2 East 63rd Street, New York, NY 10021 or call 1-800-THE-NYAS.

To withstand the buffeting winds of such rhetoric, an understanding of slavery needs to be anchored in simple facts about day-to-day plantation life. Because the historical documents are nearly devoid of such facts, one has to examine the actual remains of slave life—the bones, potsherds, bottle glass and broken trinkets buried on plantation grounds throughout the South. Paltry, as they seem, such remains, together with information gathered from documents, folklore, anthropological theory and whatever else may be of use, can help build (to use a term coined by the anthropologist Clifford Geertz of the Institute for Advanced Study in Princeton, New Jersey) "thick descriptions" of the world that slave and master made and occupied together.

The archaeological study of slavery began in the late 1960s, with the pioneering work of the late Charles H. Fairbanks along the southeastern coastal lowlands. In the quarter-century since that time, the study has spread through all former slaveholding regions of the United States and the Caribbean, as well as parts of Central and South America. Archaeologists have excavated the remains of dozens of slave quarters and have pieced together an understanding of power structures, trade networks and social relations within slave communities.

The permanent, family-based slave quarters built later in the nineteenth century were a result of complicated, mostly indirect negotiations.

In the 1980s, excavations of slave dwellings at Monticello, by William M. Kelso of the Association for the Preservation of Virginia Antiquities, added a new dimension to the understanding of Thomas Jefferson. More recently, excavations at the colonial-period African Burial Ground site in lower Manhattan provided a sobering reminder that slavery was not confined to the South. Poor interdisciplinary communication and the usual scholarly turf wars have kept mainstream historians from appreciating the significance of such discoveries, much less incorporating them into their work. It now seems, however, that in the next decade archaeology will be firmly accepted as an indispensable tool in the study of slavery.

My own work, as staff archaeologist at the Hermitage since 1988, has uncovered dramatic evidence of initiative and autonomy among Hermitage slaves. In hunting for wild meat after work, surreptitiously bartering for goods or observing their ancestors' beliefs, Hermitage slaves refused to accept their dispossession, and they strove to improve their lives rather than submit passively to their owner's orders. If Jackson's overseer did indeed reduce Hermitage slaves to "good subordination," the slaves' remains show that he often did so by subordinating his own wishes to their needs.

A visitor taking the current public tour at the Hermitage gets little sense that 130 slaves once lived on the property. Most of the tour is devoted to the Jackson family's Greek Revival mansion, set within a bucolic landscape. Gone are the rutted roads, squealing hogs and crowds of slaves toiling in the fields to make the planters' high life possible. A log cabin behind the mansion provides the only hint of slavery on the tour. Signs describe it as the home of Alfred Jackson, a Hermitage slave who stayed on after emancipation until his death in 1901. His gravestone, in the garden near the family tomb, commemorates him as "Uncle Alfred, faithful servant of Andrew Jackson."

No other African-Americans are buried in the garden, and the slave burial ground has never been found. Lacking any antebellum maps of the Hermitage slave quarters, or any diaries or letters written by the slaves themselves, historians have been largely at a loss to recover the slaves' side of the plantation's history. But archaeologists, by locating the remains of the slave quarters, have begun to clarify Jackson's intentions toward his slaves.

Like many planters, Jackson divided his slaves into two groups: those assigned to household duties lived in cabins set up near the mansion; those assigned to farming lived in cabins in the fields, clustered in two subgroups, one 250 yards and the other 600 yards from the mansion. In designing the cabins, Jackson almost certainly consulted southern farm journals in the Hermitage library. Constructed of brick and, in plan, nearly always a square twenty feet on a side, the cabins bespeak an effort at "social engineering" of the kind advocated by essays in those journals.

"The ends aimed at in building negro cabins should be: First, the health and comfort of the occupants," one planter wrote in 1856. "Secondly, the convenience of nursing, surveillance, discipline, and the supply of wood and water; and Thirdly, economy of construction." Like plain, sturdy stables built to shelter valuable livestock, such housing kept slaves literally and figuratively in their place, implying that the contrast between shabby slave quarters and the grand mansion was part of an immutable natural order.

In Jackson's time each slave family at the Hermitage occupied a single 400-square-foot room with a wooden floor, an attic loft, one door and one window. Larger Hermitage families, which had as many as ten children, according to the 1850 farm census, must have found life in such cramped quarters chaotic. Yet the cabin design Jackson chose was a product of more than a century of give-and-take between owner and slave. As late as 1820, our excavations show slaves on the Hermitage (as elsewhere in the South) were crammed together in hut-like log buildings that offered families little or no privacy.

The permanent, family-based slave quarters built later in the nineteenth century, like many other improvements in slave life, were a result of complicated, mostly indirect negotiations. Surly behavior, work slowdowns, theft, sabotage or flight were the slaves' only weapons in this cold war. The owners might have retaliated with whippings or worse, but more often they tried gentler methods. Coaxing was preferable to coercing, three planters wrote in 1846, in "promoting [the slaves'] happiness, and consequently their usefulness to us." Compliant slaves might be allowed to travel off the property when not at work, or to take extra time off following the harvest or during holidays. They might get cash bonuses for chopping extra firewood or for producing crafts. Such noblesse oblige was meant to win the slaves' "confidence and attachment" while demonstrating the owner's self-confident authority and managerial savvy.

Like military barracks, the rows of identical slave cabins at the Hermitage seem to suggest lives shaped and dictated by a local authority. But beneath their façades, the cabins hid evidence of less regimented lives, conducted in near secret. The most direct gateways to those secret lives were found under each cabin floor: small squared-off pits dug into the stiff clay soil and sometimes lined with brick. Such pits served primarily as cool, dry root cellars, but they were often also used as places for items (and, on occasion, people) that had to be kept hidden from master and overseer.

Jackson and many other plantation owners allowed slaves to dig the pits for food storage, although they probably knew that the "hidey holes" could also be used for clandestine activities and stolen goods. One planter, writing in 1851, cautioned that houses should have "no place to stow away anything." Another, writing the year before, recommended that slave dwellings be placed on piers: "When thus elevated, if there should be any filth under them, the master or overseer, in passing, can see it and have it removed."

Small game and baskets of root crops were among the most common items stored in the pits, and their remains are among the most revealing to the archaeologist. Food was always a major point of contention on any plan-

tation. Planters disagreed with slaves as well as with one another about what constituted adequate rations and how those rations ought to be distributed. Some thought it best to distribute a week's worth of raw rations at a time, whereas others favored a central kitchen where slaves could go for their meals. Although it appears that many planters believed, in the words of one essayist, that "A negro slave is so constituted that he is dependent in a great measure for happiness on his food," the rations provided hardly seem to bear out that dictum. Research into plantation records from all over the South shows that between thirty-two and forty-eight cups of cornmeal and three and a half pounds of meat a week was all a slave could expect to receive from his owner.

Contrary to popular belief, however, few slaves were content to eat only their rations. Of the more than 100,000 animal bones we have excavated so far, most came from pigs. Moreover, in some years, according to Hermitage records, more than nine tons of pork was processed on the property; Those numbers imply that every household at the site, including the Jackson family itself, chose pork for 70 to 80 percent of its meals. Mutton and beef were about equally favored as alternatives. Each slave family rounded out those provisions with foods as varied as family members were resourceful. Depending on which cabin site we excavated, we found bones from chickens; geese, ducks and other wild birds; opossums, raccoons, groundhogs and other small mammals; and turtles, fish, shellfish and other aquatic animals.

Secret trade networks, run by the slaves, moved goods all over the South from ports as distant as Europe and the Caribbean.

By allowing slaves to hunt and collect wild foods and to raise garden crops and livestock, the planters saved

the cost of providing truly sufficient rations and, perhaps, promoted a sense of self-satisfaction within the plantation community. Keeping rations to a minimum also enabled planters to reward good behavior and added effort with extra rations. "If occasionally a little molasses be added to the allowance," an essayist wrote in 1850, "the cost will be but a trifle, while the negro will esteem it a great luxury."

Such rewards may have helped fulfill Jackson's goal of creating "willing hands," but at a cost of some loss of authority and control. Slaves often chose to sell their personal produce rather than consume it themselves. As one planter from Alabama put it:

A privilege to work in their patches until 9 or 10 o'clock at night is often construed into a privilege to visit a neighbor's hen house or pig yard; or perhaps to get a mule and take a turn of corn to some market and barter it for a jug of whiskey, or something of little more value.

If slaves stashed important items beneath cabin floors, one might assume the cabins themselves held little of value. But excavations at the Hermitage have revealed an astonishing wealth of artifacts among cabin remains, and in one slave cabin at Monticello archaeologists unearthed fragments of fifteen matching porcelain dinner plates from China. Jackson and Jefferson were particularly wealthy planters, able to offer their slaves gifts of chipped or outmoded objects along with a few basic furnishings. But mansion castoffs alone cannot account for all the Hermitage artifacts, including coins, bone-handled cutlery and combs, a brass thermometer backing plate, glass beads in a variety of styles and colors, and 1,190 ceramic shards, mostly from refined white earthenware vessels made in England.

Some of those items might have made their way to Tennessee with new slaves from Florida or New Orleans. Given their diverse origins, however, many items probably arrived through surreptitious trade networks run by the slaves themselves. Passing from hand to hand, coat lining to coat lining, in a continual yet ephemeral system of barter and trade, goods reached slaves all over the South from ports as distant as Europe and the Caribbean. Cities such as Nashville, Memphis and New Orleans, linked by land and river, were key nodes in the trade network.

Among the Hermitage slaves, as among their white owners, success at trade would have been regarded as one sign of social rank. Given the conventional wisdom that house slaves were better treated and generally more comfortable than field slaves, one would expect their material remains to be richer. At the Hermitage, however, cabins belonging to house slaves and cabins belonging to field slaves yielded equally impressive artifacts. Such evidence seems to suggest that class structure at the Hermitage had less to do with the social order Jackson tried to impose than with the slaves' own reckoning of their talents and achievements. Field slaves might have received fewer castoffs from the mansion, but living further from the overseers eyes gave them more freedom to hunt and trade.

Such discoveries serve as reminders that plantation slaves, against all odds, formed true communities, complete with social mobility, scandal, gossip and ceremony. Bones and trade goods document the daily struggle for food and minor liberties, but the most intriguing artifacts offer a window on those parts of slave life that made bondage bearable. In the course of three excavating seasons, for instance, our teams have uncovered three beautifully wrought brass amulets shaped like human fists. Only one similar charm has been recovered by archaeologists—on the grounds of a house in Annapolis, Maryland, occupied by white families and their slave attendants during the eighteenth and nineteenth centuries. Elsewhere in the world, however, hand images are common and are often believed to confer spiritual power. In Islamic folklore, the "Hand of Fatima" is used to ward off the evil eye. In Brazil and elsewhere in Latin America, hand-shaped charms and votive items, known as *figas* and *mil-*

agros, respectively, are still widely used to confer good luck and fertility, as defenses against witchcraft and as religious offerings. The meaning that Hermitage slaves probably bestowed on their charms is clearly linked to the use of the word *hand* in African-American folklore as a generic term for any item intended to bring good luck or to ward off evil.

Hundreds of other items uncovered at the Hermitage and at other southern plantations were probably thought to have similar spiritual powers: quartz crystals, medicine vials, lumps of sulfur, cut silver coins and a pierced coin-like medallion, glass beads used to protect slaves from witchcraft, gaming pieces made from shards of European pottery, prehistoric projectile points, and a smoothed and polished raccoon penis bone. More than any other artifacts, such spiritual items show how slaves created an independent world within the bounds of their bondage—a culture within a culture, defined by its own beliefs concerning supernatural powers.

When the issue of race so deeply divides society, common sense about slave life has a hard time escaping the distorting gravity of myth.

Slave owners usually dismissed slave superstitions as primitive and childlike, forbidding them to be openly observed for fear they might disrupt plantation discipline. That slaves almost uniformly ignored such orders demonstrates how spirituality helped build solidarity in the slave community and thus provided a moral compass in a world that must have seemed largely senseless and evil.

To nurture a culture in the heart of oppression, slaves had to become masters of disguise, shielding their inner lives from prying eyes, hiding or even burying their most precious belongings, assuming the trappings

of obedience while secretly subverting their role. Archaeologists can sometimes get to the truth behind those disguises, but not without getting fooled themselves from time to time. Am I right in thinking the odd smooth stones sometimes found at the Hermitage are spiritual items—akin to similar stones found in medicine bundles used by African curers—or are they just leftovers from a child's collection of curios? If Hermitage slaves managed to conduct trade networks and forbidden rituals beneath their owners' noses, might they not easily deceive me a century later? I often imagine the slaves themselves watching me at work, listening to the tales I spin based on their garbage and ruins. Do they feel exposed—violated, even—watching me piece together the remains of their secrets? Or do they just laugh, shaking their heads at the persistence of delusion?

After spending more than a decade digging up slave quarters in Virginia and Tennessee, I realize that the "truth" of slavery will always remain elusive. As long as race, oppression and inequality remain burning, contemporary issues, the scholars of every generation will reinterpret slavery for their own time. In Tennessee today the world of plantation slavery seems simultaneously familiar and unthinkable. Blacks and whites live in relative harmony, yet they are only three or four generations removed from slaves and slave owners. Slavery may not be a constant topic of discussion, but a confederate flag, a hymn to old Dixie, or a hiring based on affirmative action can still stir up a fight.

When the issue of race so deeply divides society, common sense about slave life has a hard time escaping the distorting gravity of myth. On the one hand, a minister for Louis Farrakhan's Nation of Islam describes slavery as the worst crime "in the history of humanity. . . . The Holocaust did not equal it." On the other hand, some southern whites call slavery a necessary step in our national development. In comparison, the conclusions my colleagues and I have reached about life at the Hermitage may seem self-evident: anyone who has read a line of Faulkner knows that slaves and masters endlessly negotiated the details of daily life. For all its apparent mundanity, however, archaeology can help prepare new ground for such sensible old ideas, extinguishing the fires of ideology with a rain of specific detail.

To their credit, some plantation museums in the U.S. are evolving from shrines for southern myths into places where visitors can confront facts about the past. At the Hermitage, on a busy day in the summer, more than a thousand people stop by to watch the excavations behind the mansion. Some move on quickly; others stop just long enough to crack jokes about finding gold; a few pace along the edge of the excavation pit, asking questions that they have never had answered. Most of the truths they take away are only partial, but one is complete: that the Hermitage was a home to slaves as well as slave owners—elegance as well as injustice—although the mansion stands unblemished and the cabins are survived by holes in the ground.

Colorful Cotton!

*An ethnoarchaeologist tries to revive a 5,000-year-old
Peruvian textile tradition.*

Angela M. H. Schuster

A shaft of sunlight through the window of an adobe house illuminates the chalk-covered hands of an elderly weaver. Pulling and plying chocolate-colored fiber from a cone of raw cotton held in place by a large stone, she gathers it onto a weighted spindle, the chalk allowing the fiber to pass smoothly through her fingers. In a month she will have spun enough yarn to make a poncho of the type worn by the men of her community for more than three millennia. like her mother and her grandmother before her, Margarita Farfán, a Mochica, has spent the better part of a lifetime providing her family with clothes, blankets, saddlebags, and fishing nets, all woven of naturally pigmented cotton in shades of rust, beige, mauve, and chocolate.

The cultivation of multicolored cotton, *algodón nativo (Gossypium barbadense),* has been an integral part of Andean culture for millennia. Three-thousand-year-old mummies preserved in Peru's coastal sand dunes were wrapped in layer upon layer of colored cotton fabric; royalty buried in 1,500-year-old tombs at the Moche site of Sipán in the Reque Valley were draped in cotton shrouds and wore tunics of the native fiber bearing intricate anthropomorphic figures woven in dark chocolate; and, at the 4,500-year-old site of Huaca Prieta in northern Peru's Lower Chicama Valley, archaeologist Junius B. Bird recovered more than

9,000 textile fragments, presumably from mummy wrappings and funerary offerings, most of which were woven of cotton. At all of these sites, the cotton textiles had retained their natural pigmentation.

Known for its long staple and colorful fibers, algodón nativo is naturally

resistant to insects, and thrives on the eastern slopes of the Andes 3,000 feet above sea level, an elevation at which other varieties of cotton fail. The plant's deep root system allows it to survive on Peru's arid north coast, which receives less than one inch of rainfall per year. To grow the cotton

Margarita Farán pulls and plies fiber from a cone of algodón nativo. *Chalk on her hands facilitates handling the fiber.*

An Ancient Tradition

Several days before it is ginned, freshly picked cotton is laid out to cure in the sunlight. While paler shades of mauve and beige give up their seeds easily, the fragile rust and chocolate fibers, whose seeds are firmly embedded, are difficult to gin by hand. Cleaned locks of cotton are stretched out, flattened, and gathered into bundles weighing as much as a pound. These are beaten flat with sticks, folded and beaten again until the fibers are smooth and homogeneous. The flattened bundles are rolled into cones.

The spinning process is simple. A spindle is held in a horizontal and slightly inclined position while fibers are drawn from a cone of cotton tied to a stationary post, or distaff, or held in place under a heavy object such as a large stone. Cotton spinners on the north coast use smaller and lighter spindles (the sticks around which yarn is wound) and whorls (spindle weights) than those in the highlands, who work longer and heavier camelid fibers. Both cotton and camelid textiles are woven on a traditional backstrap loom anchored to a wall or tree.—A.M.H.S.

and produce a textile from it is time-consuming and arduous, especially if ginning (removing the seeds), carding (cleaning and straightening the fiber), and spinning are done by hand, as they are to this day in remote villages of Peru.

In antiquity an estimated ten percent of the land under cultivation was devoted to algodón nativo. Today, it grows only in small family gardens along with native food crops, and sometimes wild along country roads. Margarita Farfán and her seven daughters are among the last to spin and weave it. Peru's once dominant fiber has been displaced by the more familiar white tanguis and pima cottons—cultivated for their high yield, strong fiber, and ease of spinning—and commercially produced synthetics. In recent decades much of the farmland in the nearby Andean foothills, once used to grow the native cotton, has been turned over to coca leaf. A far more lucrative crop, it is Peru's leading agricultural export, supplying some 60 percent of the world market for cocaine.

Though extensive research has been carried out on Peru's highland textiles, most of which are woven of fibers from camelids—alpaca, llama, and vicuña—until recently little was known about the textiles of the north coast, especially those woven of multicolored

cotton. To document Preconquest use of the colored cotton fibers, anthropologist James Vreeland of the University of Texas, Austin, began working with traditional weavers in several coastal communities in the departments of Piura and Lambayeque. In two villages, Mórrope and Ferreñafe, he found that women still cultivated, spun, and wove the colored cotton and that more than three-quarters of them had worked the fiber in their youth. In documenting their methods of cultivation and the equipment used to spin and weave—distaffs, spindles, whorls, and looms—Vreeland noticed that in nearly every respect the tools and techniques were Precolumbian in origin, attesting an unbroken textile tradition in the region.

Vreeland's ethnographic research provided clues to an enigmatic archaeological find. During the 1970s archaeologists working in the Jequetepeque Valley had collected soil samples from a pre-Inka field system abandoned ca. A.D. 1250. Along with seeds of cotton and various squashes, crops traditionally grown in close proximity, they recovered remnants of the woody shrub *Lippia* sp., a relative of lemon verbena that seemed to serve no useful purpose. In a recent conversation with an elderly farmer in the Piura Valley, Vreeland learned that peasants in the

area grow the shrub near their cotton plants as a pesticide; smoke from burning these shrubs kills and repels a number of insects harmful to the plants.

In addition to its value as a textile fiber, algodón nativo has played an important role in traditional Mochica medicine, where it is still used to cure a host of illnesses. Recent research has revealed that cotton seed is rich in antibiotics, which may explain its widespread use in folk remedies. Women also use the ash of burned cotton to cure spider bites and tuck small wads of the chocolate fiber in their clothing for protection against *mal de ojo,* the evil eye. In some communities a small pad of the dark brown cotton is placed on a newborn's head to protect it from the nocturnal hoot of the two-horned owl, a sound thought to be capable of splitting open an infant's fragile skull. Vreeland also found that coastal fishermen still made nets of chocolate-colored cotton similar to those recovered by Junius Bird at Huaca Prieta. When he inquired about this use of the fiber, one octogenarian fisherman told him that nets made of the dark cotton are invisible to fish, especially those swimming near the surface.

What for Vreeland began as research into ancient textile production soon became a personal campaign to revitalize Peru's native cotton tradition. "The gene stock is here," he says, "as well as the knowledge of Prehispanic farming techniques that are less destructive than modern practices, which rely on fertilizers, harmful pesticides, and overtilling of the soil." In 1984 he co-founded La Sociedad de Investigacion de la Ciencia, Cultura, y Arte Norteño (SICAN), a nonprofit research institution, to promote a return to Precolumbian land-management techniques and provide a profitable alternative to growing coca leaf. With support from several nongovernmental organizations, Vreeland collected seed from family gardens and abandoned fields, and, with the help of peasant families, local graduate students, and Peruvian scientists, he planted 11 farmyard plots. Fiber generated from these plots was given to artisans to weave into traditional garments and blankets that were sold to handicraft stores in Lima and museum shops in the United States. Vreeland and his colleagues also began testing the fiber on modern spinning machines. The dark cotton tended to break when spun on machines. By blending the fiber with organically grown white cotton, they were able to strengthen it.

Last year some 500 families, both on the coast and in the Andean foothills, were involved in growing and weaving the native cotton, and the number is expected to double this year. Because the fibers and textiles are produced without chemical fertilizers, pesticides, or commercial dyes and fabric softeners, they have been favorably received by the environmentally minded in the United States, Europe, and Japan. Retailers such as L.L. Bean and Lands' End now carry socks and underwear made from the colored cotton. Vreeland, however, faces strong

opposition from drug cartels and commercial cotton producers. "It has been difficult to compete with coca as a cash crop," he says, "since it can yield $3,000–$4,000 per hectare [2.5 acres] annually, four times what a farmer can make from cotton, even if it is grown commercially." The United States Drug Enforcement Administration estimates that Peru now has more than 130,000 hectares under coca cultivation compared to 100,000 hectares for commercial cotton. Until recently farmers were heavily fined for cultivating algodón nativo in areas where tanguis and pima were grown for export. Commercial cotton producers feared cross pollination, resulting in undesirable intermediate varieties, weaker fibers, and muddled colors unacceptable in the highly competitive industrial market.

Meanwhile, farmers are under extreme pressure from the drug cartels to grow the coca leaf and to produce coca paste and refine cocaine from it. One

ginning company processing algodón nativo found rifle cartridges in its machines, presumably intended to damage the equipment. "But there is a quality-of-life issue here that many of the farmers are just now beginning to see," says Vreeland. "Though they earn more money growing coca leaf, it costs significantly more to provide for their families, since they have to purchase the food they once grew themselves. Moreover, being in business with the cartels places a great amount of strain on family life."

Cultivation regulations, the drug trade, and recent torrential rain and flash floods brought by El Niño—a climatic phenomenon caused by a periodic change in the Peru Current that runs along the Pacific coast—have significantly depleted the native cotton gene stock. In antiquity, Peruvians stored cotton seed so that crops could be replenished in the event of a disaster. During the past century, there has been virtually no preservation of seed

Seed Sleuths

When Spanish soldiers landed on Peru's north coast in 1531, they marveled at the fields of brown and mauve cotton, unknown in the Old World. The Spanish missionary Bernabé Cobo wrote in his seventeenth-century *History of the New World* that "the Indians dye the fibers of cotton on the plant." Early in the eighteenth century Spanish botanists Hipólito Ruiz and José Pavón reported the plant being grown in the valleys of Lima and Chancay, and sent specimens to the Spanish taxonomist Cavanilles for study. And at the end of the eighteenth century Bishop Martínez de Compañón included colored cotton in a book on north coast plants.

In 1983 James Vreeland of the Sociedad de Investigación de la Ciencia, Cultura, y Arte Norteño, Magda Chanco of the Museum of Natural History of Lima, Miguel Holle of the International Board for Plant Genetic

Resources/FAO, Felix Chicoma of Lambayeque University, and I began a systematic study of algodón nativo and its current distribution within Peru. We began collecting cotton from gardens in the Indian desert communities of Schura and Olmos. Seeds from plants with the most vivid fiber pigments were sown in an observation plot on the lemon plantation of Gustavo del Solar, where they survived the 1983 El Niño and the severe drought that followed. Additional seeds from Olmos were collected and planted at the Museum of Natural History of Lima.

During our decade-long project, we found that water supply and soil conditions dramatically affect the plant—it grows to a height of 18 feet on the desert coast but rarely more than six feet in jungle areas. We were surprised to find remnants of the species *Gossypium raimondii,* named for a nine-

teenth-century Italian botanist Antonio Raimondi, in the Saña Valley. Researchers had declared it extinct decades ago. On the Morañon River, a tributary of the Amazon, we found kidney cotton, a native variety whose seeds form a kidney-shaped mass.

To slow the erosion of the gene base of algodón nativo, we succeeded in having the plant declared a national plant patrimony in 1992. Today the plants that we collected can be examined in the Herbarium of the Museum of Natural History of the University of San Marcos, Lima. More than 700 samples of the cotton seed have been placed in an air-conditioned vault at the Peruvian Ministry of Agriculture for future generations to use and study.

Ramón Ferreyra *is director of the Museum of Natural History, University of San Marcos, Lima, Peru.*

stock. To remedy this, Vreeland and his colleagues collected seeds from throughout Peru hoping to recoup colors lost in antiquity. In 1992 SICAN succeeded in having native cotton declared a national plant patrimony under Peru's 1990 Environmental Code, and it can now be grown anywhere without penalty.

While peasant farmers are producing native cotton for export, personal use of the fiber among the indigenous population has declined. The villages of Mórrope and Ferreñafe, once isolated from mainstream Peruvian culture, are now connected by new roads to the Panamerican Highway. Villagers who once wore garments made of native cotton now prefer blue jeans and Michael Jackson T-shirts.

Esperanza Pisfil Capuñay is a weaver in Monsefú, a small town south of Chiclayo. She makes her living weaving dowries—tablecloths, napkins, bed linens, and doilies. "A generation ago women provided their own dowries," she says, "but today many of the young girls are going to work in Lima, Piura, or Trujillo and do not have the time or the inclination to spin and weave." Though the tradition of presenting a groom's family with a dowry remains strong, it is women like Esperanza who produce it. Weaving on a traditional backstrap loom, she works primarily with imported cotton fiber in brilliant shades of pink and green. She prefers the aniline-dyed cotton yarn, which she has to purchase, to the native cotton that grows wild near her house because the indigenous fiber is time-consuming and difficult to work. Commercially spun yarns, she says, are inexpensive and readily available at the local market. The most important factor, however, is color. "Only the elderly still wear the brown and mauve," she says. "It's old-fashioned."

While use of native cotton in the villages of the north coast may end with the demise of the older generation, the technology is being kept alive by a group of weavers in Chiclayo, who have found a growing market in replicating and restoring ancient textiles for museums. Clemencia Cabrera de Bautista is the director of the Puchka Cooperative, a weavers' group formed in 1983 to manufacture blankets and ponchos for the tourist trade. "They are producing beautiful goods," says Vreeland, "but they are in no way 'traditional.' Most of the Puchka weavers came from the highlands and originally worked in alpaca and llama wool. They were taught how to spin and weave algodón nativo by Margarita Farfán and her daughters. As a result, they are now producing cotton items whose designs are of highland origin." Cabrera agrees that the co-op has re-created many of the ancient highland patterns and that their work does not represent a continuity with the past. However, she says her weavers understand the methods used millennia ago and are comfortable deciphering lowland textiles and fragments found in excavations and replicating them. Their work can be seen in the *Royal Tombs of Sipán* exhibition now touring the United States.

While traditional spinning and weaving by hand are on the decline, Vreeland hopes that algodón nativo will prove a workable alternative to coca leaf. This past year sales of the fiber grown by the Indians exceeded $1 million and he expects to have some 10,000 hectares under cultivation next year. If he and others can continue to interest foreign markets in buying Peru's unique strain of cotton, it is conceivable that one of South America's oldest cultivars will one day help sustain a country now in urgent need of an alternative export.

Living Through the Donner Party

The nineteenth-century survivors of the infamous Donner Party told cautionary tales of starvation and cannibalism, greed and self-sacrifice. But not until now are we learning why the survivors survived.

Jared Diamond

Jared Diamond is a contributing editor of DISCOVER, *a professor of physiology at* UCLA *School of Medicine, a recipient of a MacArthur genius award, and the author of* The Third Chimpanzee.

> *"Mrs. Fosdick and Mrs. Foster, after eating, returned to the body of [Mr.] Fosdick. There, in spite of the widow's entreaties, Mrs. Foster took out the liver and heart from the body and removed the arms and legs. . . . [Mrs. Fosdick] was forced to see her husband's heart broiled over the fire." "He eat her body and found her flesh the best he had ever tasted! He further stated that he obtained from her body at least four pounds of fat!" "Eat baby raw, stewed some of Jake and roasted his head, not good meat, taste like sheep with the rot."*
>
> —GEORGE STEWART,
> *Ordeal by Hunger: The Story
> of the Donner Party*

Nearly a century and a half after it happened, the story of the Donner Party remains one of the most riveting tragedies in U.S. history. Partly that's because of its lurid elements: almost half the party died, and many of their bodies were defiled in an orgy of cannibalism. Partly, too, it's because of the human drama of noble self-sacrifice and base murder juxtaposed. The

Donner Party began as just another nameless pioneer trek to California, but it came to symbolize the Great American Dream gone awry.

By now the tale of that disastrous journey has been told so often that seemingly nothing else remains to be said—or so I thought, until my friend Donald Grayson at the University of Washington sent me an analysis that he had published in the *Journal of Anthropological Research.* By comparing the fates of all Donner Party members, Grayson identified striking differences between those who came through the ordeal alive and those who were not so lucky. In doing so he has made the lessons of the Donner Party universal. Under more mundane life-threatening situations, who among us too will be "lucky"?

Grayson's insights did not depend on new discoveries about the ill-fated pioneers nor on new analytical techniques, but on that most elusive ingredient of great science: a new idea about an old problem. Given the same information, any of you could extract the same conclusions. In fact, on page 165 you'll find the roster of the Donner Party members along with a few personal details about each of them and their fate. If you like, you can try to figure out for yourself some general rules about who is most likely to die when the going gets tough.

The Lewis and Clark Expedition of 1804 to 1806 was the first to cross the continent, but they didn't take along ox-drawn wagons, which were a requirement for pioneer settlement. Clearing a wagon route through the West's unmapped deserts and mountains proved far more difficult than finding a footpath. Not until 1841 was the first attempt made to haul wagons and settlers overland to California, and only in 1844 did the effort succeed. Until the Gold Rush of 1848 unleashed a flood of emigrants, wagon traffic to California remained a trickle.

As of 1846, when the Donner Party set out, the usual wagon route headed west from St. Louis to Fort Bridger in Wyoming, then northwest into Idaho before turning southwest through Nevada and on to California. However, at that time a popular guidebook author named Lansford Hastings was touting a shortcut that purported to cut many miles from the long trek. Hastings's route continued west from Fort Bridger through the Wasatch mountain range, then south of Utah's Great Salt Lake across the Salt Lake Desert, and finally rejoined the usual California Trail in Nevada.

In the summer of 1846 a number of wagon parties set out for California from Fort Bridger. One, which left shortly before the Donner Party, was guided by Hastings himself. Using his shortcut, the party would eventually make it to California, albeit with great difficulty.

The pioneers who would become the members of the Donner Party were in fact all headed for Fort Bridger to join the Hastings expedition, but they arrived too late. With Hastings thus unavailable to serve as a guide, some of these California-bound emigrants opted for the usual route instead. Others, however, decided to try the Hastings Cutoff anyway. In all, 87 people in 23 wagons chose the cutoff. They consisted of 10 unrelated families and 16 lone individuals, most of them well-to-do midwestern farmers and townspeople who had met by chance and joined forces for protection. None had had any real experience of the western mountains or Indians. They became known as the Donner Party because they elected an elderly Illinois farmer named George Donner as their captain. They left Fort Bridger on July 31, one of the last parties of that summer to begin the long haul to California.

Within a fortnight the Donner Party suffered their first crushing setback, when they reached Utah's steep, brush-covered Wasatch Mountains. The terrain was so wild that, in order to cross, the men had first to build a wagon road. It took 16 backbreaking days to cover just 36 miles, and afterward the people and draft animals were worn out. A second blow followed almost immediately thereafter, west of the Great Salt Lake, when the party ran into an 80-mile stretch of desert. To save themselves from death by thirst, some of the pioneers were forced to unhitch their wagons, rush ahead with their precious animals to the next spring, and return to retrieve the wagons. The rush became a disorganized panic, and many of the animals died, wandered off, or were killed by Indians. Four wagons and large quantities of supplies had to be abandoned. Not until September 30—two full months after leaving Fort Bridger—did the Donner Party emerge from their fatal shortcut to rejoin the California Trail.

By November 1 they had struggled up to Truckee Lake—later renamed Donner Lake—at an elevation of 6,000 feet on the eastern flank of the Sierra Nevada, west of the present-day California-Nevada border. Snow had already begun to fall during the last days of October, and now a fierce snowstorm defeated the exhausted party as they attempted to cross a 7,200-foot pass just west of the lake. With that storm, a trap snapped shut around them: they had set out just a little too late and proceeded just a little too slowly. They now faced a long winter at the lake, with very little food.

Death had come to the Donner Party even before it reached the lake. There were five casualties: on August 29 Luke Halloran died of "consumption" (presumably tuberculosis); on October 5 James Reed knifed John Snyder in self-defense, during a fight that broke out when two teams of oxen became entangled; three days later Lewis Keseberg abandoned an old man named Hardkoop who had been riding in Keseberg's wagon, and most of the party refused to stop and search for

---

They cut off and roasted flesh from the corpses, restrained only by the rule that no one partook of his or her own relative's body.

---

him; sometime after October 13 two German emigrants, Joseph Reinhardt and Augustus Spitzer, murdered a rich German named Wolfinger while ostensibly helping him to cache his property; and on October 20 William Pike was shot as he and his brother-in-law were cleaning a pistol.

In addition, four party members had decided earlier to walk out ahead to Sutter's Fort (now Sacramento) to bring back supplies and help. One of those four, Charles Stanton, rejoined the party on October 19, bringing food and two Indians sent by Sutter. Thus, of the 87 original members of the Donner Party, 79—plus the two Indians—were pinned down in the winter camp at Donner Lake.

The trapped pioneers lay freezing inside crude tents and cabins. They quickly exhausted their little remaining food, then killed and ate their pack animals. Then they ate their dogs. Finally they boiled hides and blankets to make a gluelike soup. Gross selfishness became rampant, as families with food refused to share it with destitute families or demanded exorbitant payment. On December 16 the first death came to the winter camp when 24-year-old Baylis Williams succumbed to starvation. On that same day 15 of the strongest people—5 women and 10 men, including Charles Stanton and the two Indians—set out across the pass on homemade snowshoes, virtually without food and in appallingly cold and stormy weather, in the hope of reaching outside help. Four of the men left behind their families; three of the women left behind their children.

On the sixth morning an exhausted Stanton let the others go on ahead of him; he remained behind to die. On the ninth day the remaining 14 for the first time openly broached the subject of cannibalism which had already been on their minds. They debated drawing lots as to who should be eaten, or letting two people shoot it out until one was killed and could be eaten. Both proposals were rejected in favor of waiting for someone to die naturally.

Such opportunities soon arose. On Christmas Eve, as a 23-year-old man named Antoine, a bachelor, slept in a heavy stupor, he stretched out his arm such that his hand fell into the fire. A companion pulled it out at once. When it fell in a second time, however, no one intervened—they simply let it burn. Antoine died, then Franklin Graves, then Patrick Dolan, then Lemuel Murphy. The others cut off and roasted flesh from the corpses, restrained only by the rule that no one would partake of his or her own relative's body. When the corpses were consumed, the survivors began eating old shoes.

On January 5, 23-year-old Jay Fosdick died, only to be cut up and boiled by Mrs. Foster over the protests of Mrs. Fosdick. Soon after, the frenzied

Mr. Foster chased down, shot, and killed the two Indians to eat them. That left 7 of the original 15 snowshoers to stagger into the first white settlement in California, after a midwinter trek of 33 days through the snow.

On January 31 the first rescue team set out from the settlement for Donner Lake. It would take three more teams and two and a half months before the ordeal was all over. During that time many more people died, either in the winter camp or while fighting their way out with the rescue teams. There was never enough food, and by the end of February, cannibalism had established itself at the lake.

When William Eddy and William Foster, who had gotten out with the snowshoers, reached the lake with the third rescue team on March 13, they found that Keseberg had eaten their sons. The Foster child's grandmother accused the starving Keseberg of having taken the child to bed with him one night, strangling him, and hanging the corpse on the wall before eating it. Keseberg, in his defense, claimed the children had died naturally. When the rescuers left the lake the next day to return to California, they left Keseberg behind with just four others: the elderly Lavina Murphy, the badly in-

Manifest of a Tragic Journey

DONNER FAMILY

Jacob Donner	M	65	died in Nov. in winter camp
George Donner	M	62	died in Apr. in winter camp
Elizabeth Donner	F	45	died in Mar. in winter camp
Tamsen Donner	F	45	died in Apr. in winter camp
Elitha Donner	F	14	
Solomon Hook	M	14	
William Hook	M	12	died Feb. 28 with first rescue team
Leanna Donner	F	12	
George Donner	M	9	
Mary Donner	F	7	
Frances Donner	F	6	
Isaac Donner	M	5	died Mar. 7 with second rescue team
Georgia Donner	F	4	
Samuel Donner	M	4	died in Apr. in winter camp
Lewis Donner	M	3	died Mar. 7 or 8 in winter camp
Eliza Donner	F	3	

MURPHY-FOSTER-PIKE FAMILY

Lavina Murphy	F	50	died around Mar. 19 in winter camp
William Foster	M	28	
William Pike	M	25	died Oct. 20 by gunshot
Sara Foster	F	23	
Harriet Pike	F	21	
John Landrum Murphy	M	15	died Jan. 31 in winter camp
Mary Murphy	F	13	
Lemuel Murphy	M	12	died Dec. 27 with snowshoers
William Murphy	M	11	
Simon Murphy	M	10	
George Foster	M	4	died in early Mar. in winter camp
Naomi Pike	F	3	
Catherine Pike	F	1	died Feb. 20 in winter camp

GRAVES-FOSDICK FAMILY

Franklin Graves	M	57	died Dec. 24 with snowshoers
Elizabeth Graves	F	47	died Mar. 8 with second rescue team
Jay Fosdick	M	23	died Jan. 5 with snowshoers
Sarah Fosdick	F	22	
Mary Graves	F	20	
William Graves	M	18	
Eleanor Graves	F	15	
Lavina Graves	F	13	
Nancy Graves	F	9	
Jonathan Graves	M	7	
Franklin Graves Jr.	M	5	died Mar. 8 with second rescue team
Elizabeth Graves	F	1	died soon after rescue by second team

BREEN FAMILY

Patrick Breen	M	40	
Mary Breen	F	40	
John Breen	M	14	
Edward Breen	M	13	
Patrick Breen Jr.	M	11	
Simon Breen	M	9	
Peter Breen	M	7	
James Breen	M	4	
Isabella Breen	F	1	

REED FAMILY

James Reed	M	46	
Margaret Reed	F	32	
Virginia Reed	F	12	
Patty Reed	F	8	
James Reed Jr.	M	5	
Thomas Reed	M	3	

EDDY FAMILY

William Eddy	M	28	
Eleanor Eddy	F	25	died Feb. 7 in winter camp
James Eddy	M	3	died in early Mar. in winter camp
Margaret Eddy	F	1	died Feb. 4 in winter camp

KESEBERG FAMILY

Lewis Keseberg	M	32	
Phillipine Keseberg	F	32	
Ada Keseberg	F	3	died Feb. 24 with first rescue team
Lewis Keseberg Jr.	M	1	died Jan. 24 in winter camp

MCCUTCHEN FAMILY

William McCutchen	M	30	
Amanda McCutchen	F	24	
Harriet McCutchen	F	1	died Feb. 2 in winter camp

WILLIAMS FAMILY

Eliza Williams	F	25	
Baylis Williams	M	24	died Dec. 16 in winter camp

WOLFINGER FAMILY

Mr. Wolfinger	M	?	killed around Oct. 13 by Reinhardt and Spitzer
Mrs. Wolfinger	F	?	

UNRELATED INDIVIDUALS

Mr. Hardkoop	M	60	died around Oct. 8, abandoned by Lewis Keseberg
Patrick Dolan	M	40	died Dec. 25 with snowshoers
Charles Stanton	M	35	died around Dec. 21 with snowshoers
Charles Burger	M	30	died Dec. 29 in winter camp
Joseph Reinhardt	M	30	died in Nov. or early Dec. in winter camp
Augustus Spitzer	M	30	died Feb. 7 in winter camp
John Denton	M	28	died Feb. 24 with first rescue team
Milton Elliot	M	28	died Feb. 9 in winter camp
Luke Halloran	M	25	died Aug. 29 of consumption
William Herron	M	25	
Samuel Shoemaker	M	25	died in Nov. or early Dec. in winter camp
James Smith	M	25	died in Nov. or early Dec. in winter camp
John Snyder	M	25	killed Oct. 5 by James Reed
Jean Baptiste Trubode	M	23	
Antoine	M	23	died Dec. 24 with snowshoers
Noah James	M	20	

jured George Donner, his 4-year-old nephew Samuel and his healthy wife Tamsen, who could have traveled but insisted on staying with her dying husband.

The fourth and last rescue team reached the lake on April 17 to find Keseberg alone, surrounded by indescribable filth and mutilated corpses. George Donner's body lay with his skull split open to permit the extraction of his brains. Three frozen ox legs lay in plain view almost uneaten beside a kettle of cut-up human flesh. Near Keseberg sat two kettles of blood and a large pan full of fresh human liver and lungs. He alleged that his four companions had died natural deaths, but he was frank about having eaten them. As to why he had not eaten ox leg instead, he explained that it was too dry: human liver and lungs tasted better, and human brains made a good soup. As for Tamsen Donner, Keseberg noted that she tasted the best, being well endowed with fat. In a bundle held by Keseberg the rescuers found silk, jewelry, pistols, and money that had belonged to George Donner.

After returning to Sutter's Fort, one of the rescuers accused Keseberg of having murdered his companions, prompting Keseberg to sue for defamation of character. In the absence of legal proof of murder the court verdict was equivocal, and the issue of Keseberg's guilt remains disputed to this day. However, Tamsen Donner's death is especially suspicious since she had been in strong physical condition when last seen by the third rescue team.

Thus, out of 87 Donner Party members, 40 died: 5 before reaching Donner Lake, 22 in their winter camp at the lake, and 13 (plus the two Indians) during or just after efforts to leave the lake. Why those particular 40? From the facts given in the roster, can you draw conclusions, as Grayson did, as to who was in fact the most likely to die?

As a simple first test, compare the fates of Donner Party males and females irrespective of age. Most of the males (30 out of 53) died; most of the females (24 out of 34) survived. The 57 percent death rate among males was nearly double the 29 percent death rate among females.

Next, consider the effect of age irrespective of sex. The worst toll was among the young and the old. Without exception, everyone over the age of 50 died, as did most of the children below the age of 5. Surprisingly, children and teenagers between the ages of 5 and 19 fared better than did adults in their prime (age 20 to 39): half the latter, but less than one-fifth of the former, died.

By looking at the effects of age and sex simultaneously, the advantage the women had over the men becomes even more striking. Most of the female deaths were among the youngest and oldest, who were already doomed by their age. Among those party members aged 5 to 39—the ones whose ages left them some reasonable chance of survival—half the men but only 5 percent of the women died.

The dates of death provide deeper insight. Of the 35 unfortunates who died after reaching the lake, 14 men but not a single woman had died by the end of January. Only in February did women begin to buckle under. From February onward the death toll was essentially equal by sex—11 men, 10 women. The differences in dates of death simply underscore the lesson of the death rates themselves: the Donner Party women were far hardier than the men.

Thus, sex and age considered together account for much of the luck of the survivors. Most of those who died (39 of the 40 victims) had the misfortune to be of the wrong sex, or the wrong age, or both.

Experience has taught us that the youngest and oldest people are the most vulnerable even under normal conditions, and their vulnerability increases under stress. In many natural disasters, those under 10 or over 50 suffered the highest mortality. For instance, children under 10 accounted for over half the 240,000 deaths in the 1970 Bangladesh cyclone, though they constituted only one-third of the exposed population.

Much of the vulnerability of the old and young under stress is simply a matter of insufficient physical strength: these people are less able to walk out through deep snow (in the case of the Donner Party) or to cling to trees above the height of flood waters (in the case of the Bangladesh cyclone). Babies have special problems. Per pound of body weight a baby has twice an adult's surface area, which means double the area across which body heat can escape. To maintain body temperature, babies have to increase their metabolic rate when air temperature drops only a few degrees below body temperature, whereas adults don't have to do so until a drop of 20 to 35 degrees. At cold temperatures the factor by which babies must increase their metabolism to stay warm is several times that for adults. These considerations place even well-fed babies at risk under cold conditions. And the Donner Party babies were at a crippling further disadvantage because they had so little food to fuel their metabolism. They literally froze to death.

But what gave the women such an edge over the men? Were the pioneers practicing the noble motto "women and children first" when it came to dividing food? Unfortunately, "women and children last" is a more accurate description of how most men behave under stress. As the *Titanic* sank, male crew members took many places in lifeboats while leaving women and children of steerage class below decks to drown. Much grosser male behavior emerged when the steamship *Atlantic* sank in 1879: the death toll included 294 of the 295 women and children on board, but only 187 of the 636 men. In the Biafran famine of the late 1960s, when relief agencies tried to distribute food to youngsters under 10 and to pregnant and nursing women, Biafran men gave a brutally frank response: "Stop all this rubbish, it is we men who shall have the food, let the children die, we will make new children after the war." Similarly, accounts by Donner Party members yield no evidence of hungry men deferring to women, and babies fared especially poorly.

Instead, we must seek some cause other than male self-sacrifice to account for the survival of Donner Party women. One contributing factor is that the men were busy killing each other. Four of the five deaths before the pioneers reached the lake, plus the deaths of the two Indians, involved male victims of male violence, a pattern that fits widespread human experience.

However, invoking male violence still leaves 26 of 30 Donner Party male deaths unexplained. It also fails to explain why men began starving and freezing to death nearly two months before women did. Evidently the women had a big physiological advantage. This could be an extreme expression of the fact that, at every age and for all leading causes of death—from cancer and car accidents to heart disease and suicide—the death rate is far higher for men than for women. While the reasons for this ubiquitous male vulnerability remain debated, there are several compelling reasons why men are more likely than women to die under the extreme conditions the Donner Party faced.

First, men are bigger than women. Typical body weights for the world as a whole are about 140 pounds for men and only 120 pounds for women. Hence, even while lying down and doing nothing, men need more food to support their basal metabolism. They also need more energy than women do for equivalent physical activity. Even for sedentary people, the typical metabolic rate for an average-size woman is 25 percent lower than an average-size man's. Under conditions of cold temperatures and heavy physical activity, such as were faced by the Donner Party men when doing the backbreaking work of cutting the wagon road or hunting for food, men's metabolic rates can be double those of women.

To top it all off, women have more fat reserves than men: fat makes up 22 percent of the body weight of an average nonobese, well-nourished woman, but only 16 percent of a similar man. More of the man's weight is instead

made up of muscle, which gets burned up much more quickly than does fat. Thus, when there simply was no more food left, the Donner Party men burned up their body reserves much faster than did the women. Furthermore, much of women's fat is distributed under the skin and acts as heat insulation, so that they can withstand cold temperatures better than men can. Women don't have to raise their metabolic rate to stay warm as soon as men do.

These physiological factors easily surpass male murderousness in accounting for all those extra male deaths in the Donner Party. Indeed, a microcosm of the whole disaster was the escape attempt by 15 people on snowshoes, lasting 33 days in midwinter. Of the ten men who set out, two were murdered by another man, six starved or froze to death, and only two survived. Not a single one of the five women with them died.

Even with all these explanations, there is still one puzzling finding to consider: the unexpectedly high death toll of people in their prime, age 20 to 39. That toll proves to be almost entirely of the men: 67 percent of the men in that age range (14 out of 21) died, a much higher proportion than among the teenage boys (only 20 percent). Closer scrutiny shows why most of those men were so unlucky.

Most of the Donner Party consisted of large families, but there were also 16 individuals traveling without any relatives. All those 16 happened to be men, and all but two were between 20 and 39. Those 16 unfortunates bore the brunt of the prime-age mortality. Thirteen of them died, and most of them died long before any of the women. Of the survivors, one—William Herron—reached California in October, so in reality only 2 survived the winter at the lake.

Of the 7 men in their prime who survived, 4 were family men. Only 3 of the 14 dead were. The prime-age women fared similarly: the 8 survivors belonged to families with an average

size of 12 people, while Eleanor Eddy, the only woman to die in this age group, had no adult support. Her husband had escaped with the snowshoers, leaving her alone with their two small children.

The Donner Party records make it vividly clear that family members stuck together and helped one another at the expense of the others. A notorious example was the Breen family of nine, every one of whom (even two small children) survived through the luck of retaining their wagons and some pack animals much longer than the others, and through their considerable selfishness toward others. Compare this with the old bachelor Hardkoop, who was ordered out of the Keseberg family wagon and abandoned to die, or the fate of the young bachelor Antoine, whom none of the hungry snowshoers bothered to awaken when his hand fell into the fire.

Family ties can be a matter of life and death even under normal conditions. Married people, it turns out, have lower death rates than single, widowed, or divorced people. And marriage's life-promoting benefits have been found to be shared by all sorts of social ties, such as friendships and membership in social groups. Regardless of age or sex or initial health status, socially isolated individuals have well over twice the death rate of socially connected people.

For reasons about which we can only speculate, the lethal effects of social isolation are more marked for men than for women. It's clear, though, why social contacts are important for both sexes. They provide concrete help in case of need. They're our source of advice and shared information. They provide a sense of belonging and self-worth, and the courage to face tomorrow. They make stress more bearable.

All those benefits of social contact applied as well to the Donner Party members, who differed only in that their risk of death was much greater and their likely circumstances of death more grotesque than yours and mine. In that sense too, the harrowing story of the Donner Party grips us because it was ordinary life writ large.

The New Politics of Archaeology: A Trowel for Your Thoughts

"Good morning, ladies and gentlemen. Welcome to the first annual convention of WARP, the World Archaeological Research Project. I am Dr. Derk Digger. As we all know, from the very beginning archaeology was an underground science fraught with a lot of just plain dirt flying around. By the end of the nineteenth century, disagreement within the rank and file had elevated to mud slinging.

"During the 1960s in the historical period known as the 'New Archaeology,' infighting among archaeologists reached new intellectual lows. A whole decade was spent arguing about the true meaning of mousterian points. Heavies like 'Louie the Blade' and 'François the Flake' perpetuated pointed discussions ignoring core materials.

"When push came to shove in the 1970's, some archaeologists viciously attacked vending machines at professional meetings. Whole dynasties of stellar archaeological families fought others for sites and National Geographic funding, sometimes misplacing whole sites or taking over small nations. Rulers of sites rose and fell as espionage and counterespionage tossed reputations around like so much falling backdirt.

"There was much splitting and lumping of heads during these fluctuating dates and not much was salvaged. This pugnacious pattern of archaeological antics continued to worsen during the decades of the 1980s and 1990s until archaeology was in ruins. The garbage finally hit the pits and archaeologists surrendered on July 4, 1999, at Point Clovis in New Mexico. The Marshalltowns hitting the ground made a sound the likes of which had not been heard since Howard Carter opened King Tut's tomb.

"Ah, but this is all history, or maybe proto-history. At any rate, calibrated, of course, we remaining archaeologists hope to form a hypothetical agreement on the issues that concern all of us here today. That is, of course, the future of archaeological sites. Remember, as you sit here today, we are about to create TRASH (The Ruling Archaeological Sites Hierarchy). During this morning's session we can consider about six demands from our various special interest groups. Please put your shards on the table before you speak.

"I would like to introduce our first speaker, Mr. Peter Potlooter of TPL, Inc. You all know of the impact on archaeology that this worldwide organization representing thieves, pothunters, and looters has had. We welcome our fellow enthusiasts and hope to convert a great deal of their views into TRASH. As archaeologists we are eager to make up for the past two hundred years of tyranny when we tried to keep archaeological sites for ourselves.

"What was that? I can't hear you! Oh yes, certainly, Mr. Sharp Arrow, this afternoon we will get to your proposal to bury the Smithsonian, artifacts and all!"

And the tale above goes on, somewhere in someone's dust-clogged brain. In this unit the real state of the health of the science of archaeology is examined.

In any science, there is good deal of infighting that goes on. But it seems like there is something about archaeologists that makes them carry on with an exquisite pugnaciousness that impresses even the most hardened veterans of other disciplines. Much speculation has been spent on the eccentric stereotype of archaeologists. If there is an answer, it probably is to be found in the nature of the subject matter and its closeness to ultimate concerns such as the nature of human beings and their very origins. So far geneticists have not come up with a defective gene that causes people to become archaeologists.

In this unit, articles address the concerns that archaeology faces in terms of a whole new set of politics. There are other serious contenders for the rights to archaeological sites.

As long as there has been property, there have been thieves. As long as there have been archaeological sites, there have been looters. And what of the native or descendant generations who feel a continuity with their past, either in a specific area or in a generalized sense? North American archaeology has been revolutionized by recent laws designating ownership of all archaeological sites to those who claim to be of the native descendant generation. This leads to the question of repatriation of what are now archaeological materials, as well as the rightful ownership of antiquities by museums, collectors, or whole nations.

Thus, archaeologists must walk an ethical and legal tightrope on all of these issues. It's a very hard thing to do when our shared human past, and all the wisdom it can offer us, is at stake. Our species has always had an insatiable need to know. This is what we are: human beings, searching into the depths of our past to define *who* we are.*

Looking Ahead: Challenge Questions

There are many antiquity laws in the United States. Are they ever enforced?

What is meant by the term *native descendant generation* as used in archaeology?

What arguments would an archaeologist use who feels natives have no claim to sites?

What arguments would a native use?

What compromise might the archaeologist and the native reach?

What is meant by repatriation of archaeological finds? Specifically, how can repatriation be accomplished?

Give several examples of human activities that destroy archaeological sites.

*Any resemblance to real persons or events in this fictional story are purely coincidental, with the exception of Howard Carter and King Tut's tomb.

The Antiquities Market

DAVID P. STALEY

David P. Staley (M.A. 1990, Washington State University) is a research associate at the University of Alaska Anchorage's Environment and Natural Resources Institute. He has 10 years' cultural-resource management experience in Alaska. Mailing address: University of Alaska Anchorage, Environment and Natural Resources Institute, 707A Street, Anchorage, Alaska 99501.

INTRODUCTION

The market in ancient human artifacts has always had a supply problem. Apart from the resale of objects in the possession of collectors—objects, that is, already in slow circulation—maintaining a profitable market tempo has left dealers with two major options. One possibility is to attempt to create new categories of objects deemed worthy of sale, purchase, and collection; this obviously involves the manipulation of tastes and perceptions so as to imbue previously disdained or ignored objects with new value. The other possibility is far more notorious: the encouragement of continued mining of known sources for objects of established saleability. The connection, overt or covert, between dealers and those non-archaeologists who dig for artifacts is well known.

Far less understood are the diggers themselves. These people, usually called looters, are strangely anonymous in the literature on the illicit market in antiquities. Their names are not known,

or, if known, not published. Usually only the empty trenches and gaping holes they leave behind are all that is left to mark their progress. For the most part, discussions of why the past is put up for sale conclude (without more than cursory investigation) that the economic straits in which these suppliers find themselves are so dire that looting is an attractive solution.

The following article by David P. Staley seeks to develop a better understanding of the market's supply side through a look at the lives of a group of Bering Sea natives who engage in what Staley calls "subsistence digging." Certain inhabitants of St. Lawrence Island spend some time every year excavating and selling ancient ivory and other artifacts, an activity which brings them some profit. These objects command high prices when they reach the centers of the art market. Recently, a New York dealer was asking $17,500 for an ivory anthropomorphic drum handle, with inlaid metal eyes, said to date to A.C. 600 and to have been excavated on St. Lawrence Island. The dealer, Jeffrey R. Myers, apparently makes a point of spending a part of his summers on St. Lawrence, which is when subsistence digging is done.

Staley's article will also be of interest to those who enjoy the ethical dilemma of who owns the past. Since St. Lawrence is owned by its natives, their excavations are not illegal. Since they are unearthing the possessions of their own ancestors, can any outsider object?

Timothy Kaiser
Editor

ST. LAWRENCE ISLAND'S SUBSISTENCE DIGGERS: A NEW PERSPECTIVE ON HUMAN EFFECTS ON ARCHAEOLOGICAL SITES

The problem of archaeological site destruction is receiving much deserved attention from the archaeological profession and from the public. Native subsistence diggers are significant agents of destruction in Alaska and their situation is representative of third world conditions. A case study, featuring the St. Lawrence Island community of Gambell, Alaska, describes the subsistence diggers' attitudes and motivations. This study provides insight into behavioral aspects of archaeological looting, causal factors underlying site destruction, and the internal workings of the artifact market. The Gambell case illustrates an ethical dilemma that needs to be addressed, since newly adopted policies to curtail site destruction may cause significant harm to a Native population that is compelled by economic forces to cannibalize its own heritage. The introduction of alternate sources of cash income through sensible economic development offers a possible solution.

Introduction

Archaeologists are shaping public policy through lobbying efforts in the area of cultural resource legislation and through their involvement in the U.S. public education campaign. The international archaeological community has been very much concerned with site looting, artifact trafficking, and the ethics of collecting (Messenger 1989; Neumann 1989; Smith and Ehrenhard

Figure 1. Map showing the location of the study areas. (By Ray Norman)

1991; Vitelli 1984). Major educational campaigns, supported by government agencies and professional organizations, have been launched to enlighten the public regarding the importance of heritage preservation (Hoffman and Lerner 1988; McManamon 1990; Rogge 1988). This is now the archaeologist's primary weapon against the destruction and degradation of historical and archaeological sites. While archaeologists are actively attempting to influence public attitudes and policies, we know very little about the people involved in site destruction. With few exceptions (Gramann and Vander Stoep 1986; Nickens, Larralde, and Tucker 1981; McAllister 1991), the behavioral aspects of looting and trafficking and the factors underlying the destruction of sites have not been evaluated.

Native subsistence diggers are significant agents in site looting in Alaska (Crowell 1985; King 1991; Morton 1989: 2; Staley 1990: 22–23). I opt for the term "digger" since both "looter" and "pothunter" have negative connotations and do not apply well in this situation. In this article, the subsistence digger is defined as a person who uses the proceeds from artifact sales to support his or her traditional subsistence lifestyle. My usage of "traditional subsistence" follows that of

Wenzel, who described the notion as having " . . . little to do with the technology used but much to do with internal relations . . ." of a culture (1991: 180). The term subsistence includes "cultural values that socially integrate the economic relations of a hunting peoples into their daily lives" (Wenzel 1991: 57). For the most part, subsistence diggers have been either overlooked by investigators of the problem or considered a limited regional phenomenon (Christensen et al. 1988; Nickens 1991; McAllister 1991). In contrast with other destructive agents, very little is known of the subsistence digger's situation, attitudes, or motivations.

On St. Lawrence Island, Eskimos are mining their ancestral archaeological sites (Scott 1984; Wardell 1986). The case study presented here, focusing on the community of Gambell, Alaska, contributes to an understanding of human impact on archaeological sites and highlights the Native subsistence digger. A brief summary of conditions and factors illustrates the extreme nature of the situation in Gambell. Economic conditions in the community are bleak (Little and Robbins 1984), yet St. Lawrence Island ivory artifacts are world renowned, and delicately carved pieces command high prices (Wardell 1986). Unlike raw or

fresh ivory, trade in old or fossil ivory is not restricted by the Marine Mammal Protection Act. St. Lawrence is one of the few sources for bulk ancient or fossil ivory sold to artisans and manufacturers. Unrestricted, fee simple title to the island is held by the Gambell and Savoonga village corporations established under the Alaska Native Claims Settlement Act (ANCSA) of 1971. Thus, since the entire island is privately owned, its lands are not covered under existing laws such as the Archaeological Resources Protection Act. Site access is relatively easy, as three sites are located in Gambell or within a short walking distance. Destruction of sites around Gambell has been so severe that the sites have lost their National Historic Landmark status (Morton 1989: 2).

During July and August of 1991, I monitored a municipal construction project in Gambell. In my "off" hours, I wandered about the sites, observed work in progress, and visited with local diggers and traders. Much of the information presented in this case study was personally observed or learned through these conversations.

The Setting

Gambell is a Yupik community located at the NW end of St. Lawrence Island (FIG. 1). Only one other community, Savoonga, is located on the 160 km-long island, which is situated less than 65 km from Siberia and 200 km from the Alaskan mainland. In 1990, Gambell had a total population of 525 people. At that time, 317 adults lived in the community and the median age was 24.2 years. There were 120 houses in Gambell with 4.38 persons per household (U.S. Department of Commerce, Bureau of the Census 1991: 33).

The people of Gambell are engaged in a mixed cash and subsistence economy, with the latter being more important (Little and Robbins 1984: 64; John Muir Institute, Inc. 1984: 112). A considerable amount of cash income is required for subsistence pursuits (Nowak 1977; VanStone 1960; Wenzel 1991: 106–133). A decade ago, a family would spend an average of $6700 each year on transportation, weapons, ammunition, and fishing equipment used in subsistence pursuits and an additional $1700 per year on gasoline. In 1984, the average family paid out $3800 for goods and food. This included primarily cereals, tea, coffee, sugar, pilot bread, soda, and cigarettes (John Muir Institute, Inc. 1984: 121). Of course, prices have increased over the last decade. For example, in 1991, a household of seven persons spent between $200 and $300 a month on food alone. A delayed barge delivery during the summer temporarily drove gasoline prices to $5.00 per gallon, although eventually prices returned to $2.50. Other monthly expenses included $74 for water and sewer services, $72 for cable television, $70 for electric service, and a heating fuel bill around $345 a month during winter.

Jobs are relatively scarce and extremely dependent upon State and Federal appropriations. Based on a community survey of Gambell conducted by the Norton Sound Health Corporation during 1990, 51% of 95 household respondents were unemployed. Only 22% of these households included a member with full time employment (Don Smith, Bering Strait Economic Development Corporation, personal communication, 1991). Monthly wage income in Gambell averaged $85 per person (Alaska Department of Labor, personal communication, 1991). This income was supplemented by food stamps, Aid to Families with Dependent Children, Energy Assistance, Longevity Bonus, and Permanent Fund Dividend programs. The production and sale of crafts, particularly ivory carvings, is a large source of locally generated income on the island. During the 1980s, ivory-carving sales volumes were estimated at approximately $100,000 per year (Little and Robbins 1984: 68). Between September, 1983, and October, 1984, sales of bulk ivory mined from sites netted more than $100,000. Sales of artifacts totalled around $40,000 in 1983 (Crowell 1985: 20). An analysis of average household income and expenses during 1991 demonstrated the critical importance of both the subsistence oriented economy, and

48% of the expenses, and cash influx from ivory and artifacts, 13% of the income. Sales of ivory and artifacts are especially important because household budgets appear to be operating in a break-even or deficit mode.

Since 1983, Sivuqaq, Inc., Gambell's village corporation established under ANCSA, has been actively involved in the sale of bulk ivory (Crowell 1985: 21–22). The corporation acts as a middleman in the trade, providing a consistent, accessible market for the ivory diggers and attempting to maximize economic returns to the resident shareholders. The village corporation's perception of archaeological sites as economic resources is contrary to the perspective of most Native groups in the United States. Native groups generally advocate protection and conservation of historical and prehistoric sites (Nichols, Klesert, and Anyon 1989; Anyon 1991). Sivuqaq, Inc. sees archaeological sites as the source of extractable commodities, whereas other Native groups perceive cultural resources as a means to economic development but through a combined strategy of preservation and tourism (Parker 1990: 67).

Gambell's Subsistence Diggers
The entire demographic spectrum of the community participates in the excavation of Gambell's archaeological sites. Young and old, male and female, single individuals and entire families mine sites for old ivory and artifacts. Children brought to the site may help, but often bring toys to entertain themselves while the adults work. Both employed and unemployed residents work at the sites, although the latter have more time to devote to this activity.

Digging is limited to the summer season while permafrost sediments are thawing. Ardent diggers tend to work between four and 10 hours a day, while casual diggers are more likely to spend a few hours at a site one evening a week. Although digging may take place at any time, it seems to be predominantly an evening affair. The work is typically cold, wet, and arduous.

A variety of tools and apparatus is used at the sites including simple hand tools such as shovels, mattocks, picks, and buckets. Ice axes, manufactured for mountaineers, are preferred by both serious and casual diggers. This may be related to their easy access through mail-order catalogs. Wheelbarrows are in short supply; a village entrepreneur was recently renting one for $20 per day. At times, gasoline-powered portable pumps are used to drain pooled water from excavations. Hydraulic excavation occurs at some sites but not at those adjacent to Gambell. Many people leave their tools and equipment at the site between digging sessions.

The focus of excavation shifts around on the sites based on other diggers' findings or rumored findings. Rumored success of diggers under one of the few road beds in town caused substantial sections of the road to be torn up in a matter of days. Word of the recovery of potentially valuable pieces travels fast through the community and often stimulates others to get out and dig.

Excavation intensity and technique vary considerably. Men tend to excavate larger and deeper holes. When working by themselves, women and children dig numerous small shallow holes and never invest much time in any one location; but they tend to do more prospecting than the men, who concentrate on mining. Patterns of permafrost thawing also tend to influence excavation strategies and techniques. At present, diggers go to great lengths to find rare, undisturbed sections of the sites. The digging undercuts paths and roads and exposes various pipes, and phone and power lines. At times, diggers are forced to move tremendous piles of backdirt and disturbed sediments extending to depths of 4 m. Plastic covers surprisingly deep limits of previous mining efforts. Once undisturbed deposits are located, excavations proceed horizontally into the face, sometimes undercutting large blocks of sediments. These blocks frequently give way and negate the time and effort used to clear the area as well as burying equipment and diggers alike. Curious passersby are sharply warned not to walk above these excavations. Diggers often follow house wall logs, as whole walrus tusks are known to have been used to support vertical posts. Other structural elements are often chopped out of the way before they are completely exposed, and rock slab flooring is often torn up as the excavation proceeds.

Some of the techniques used by diggers in Gambell were learned directly from archaeologists who have worked in the area. In the late 1920s, Otto Geist experimented with boilers and steam thawing as well as using pumps, hoses, pressure nozzles, and screens to hydraulically excavate sites and water screen artifacts (Geist and Rainey 1976: 35, 42). The use of steel rod probes to differentiate subsurface bone and ivory was adopted from Hans-Georg Bandi, who used the technique to locate human burials. One digger stated she had been shown by archaeologists how small artifacts on the surface are more easily observed after a rain storm. Gambell diggers often toss faunal remains into a separate pile as they dig. This behavior may have been adopted from Otto Geist, who also segregated bone into large piles (Geist and Raney 1976: 246).

Artifacts
The relative importance of various artifact classes to the people of Gambell is expressed in the way they sort, accumulate, and conserve artifacts. Artifacts with certain monetary values are piled separately while digging and bagged at the end of the session. These include complete or fragmentary ivory artifacts with or without incised decoration, ivory scrap, walrus tusk and teeth, large sea mammal teeth, and walrus penis bones. Artifacts of marginal value or interest, such as seal teeth, groundstone ulus and endblades, palettes, chipped stone scrapers, points or blades, baleen bucket parts, scapula shovel blades, and various whole or broken wood and bone tools, are consistently sorted from the dirt and piled near the pit. Some of these artifacts are composite tool parts that are kept sep-

arately until the digger is certain that other components are lost. Artifacts are often shown to children, visitors, and other diggers and are the main topic of discussion. Artifacts of marginal value are often displayed on a whale or walrus scapula in or on the margins of the pit. Structural elements, faunal remains, flaking debitage, and small fragments of stone artifacts are either tossed into the backdirt or segregated into piles.

Valuable artifacts are typically amassed until sold to village visitors, professional artifact dealers or, if unmarketable as art or curio, eventually sold as scrap ivory. Diggers are anxious to show their artifacts even without any potential for sale. People will invite you into their houses to see their collections. In one home, I saw composite fish hooks, harpoon heads, buttons, and a wrist-guard fragment made of ivory and decorated with Punuk design elements. Most collections, however, included large varieties of mundane, undecorated artifacts. Although most household collections are awaiting sale, there are several families that keep groups of interesting artifacts in their homes with no intention of selling them.

Old ivory begins to crack, split, and peel after it is removed from the ground. Diggers attempt to conserve ivory artifacts using a variety of techniques and substances. Most understand that the problems are caused by too-rapid drying. Therefore, many try to control temperatures and humidity by drying specimens in a cool place inside sealed plastic bags. Others attempt to replace the water in the artifacts by soaking them in baby or gun oils.

Staking Claims and Territoriality
The passage of ANCSA legally made the natural resources on St. Lawrence Island common property and essentially gave all residents access to these resources. Control over the island's natural resources is shared by the village corporations of Gambell and Savoonga. This is the latest step in the liberalization of natural-resource use

rights. Prior to ANCSA, each community claimed control over a portion of the island's resources (Burgess 1974: 78). Preceding the consolidation of the population into these communities, territories were controlled by clans (Little and Robbins 1984: 82–83). Even at present, however, clans do maintain use rights over specific camping, hunting, and fishing locations.

The archaeological sites on St. Lawrence Island are also considered a common natural resource. There appear to be some differences in use rights, however, depending on the distance between the site and the main village. At sites close to Gambell, diggers who begin an excavation or adopt an abandoned, existing pit have use rights contingent on their consistent and continuous work in the location. Claimed areas are often shared between brothers who may work together or in staggered shifts. These rights may be traded or passed to other individuals, and permission is requested to dig in areas that are not clearly abandoned.

During the summer, many families leave Gambell to stay at subsistence camps, which are positioned within larger clan territories at prime subsistence-resource locations (Little and Robbins 1984: 184–205; Crowell 1985: 18). These same resources have drawn people to these locations for millennia. As clan members have use rights for the location, they also have exclusive control over any nearby archaeological resources. Unlike the Gambell sites, there is no requirement for consistent and continuous digging at these sites to maintain use rights.

Claims on digging areas at subsistence camps follow the historical, kinship-based pattern of use rights. Closer to Gambell, no clan can claim exclusive rights to an area, therefore, a different system has developed to define digging territories within sites. This system is a reflection of the liberalization of natural-resource use rights but only at the community scale. Future research on this subject may find even further communal ownership, with Savoonga residents freely digging at Gambell and vice versa.

Use rights to digging territories are generally respected although there are interlopers. It seems likely that incidents of encroachment are more common near Gambell than at subsistence camps. Diggers complain about trespassers more for their sloppy technique than for the potential loss of ivory and artifacts. Some diggers have threatened to place booby traps in their pits to discourage poaching by their fellow villagers.

Attitudes
The people of Gambell are very friendly, generous, and kind. Their attitudes toward the profession of archaeology are generally negative, however. Early archaeological investigations on the island were sophisticated for their time, although by today's standards the methods were coarse, and the large scale trenches through mounds would appear to the uninitiated as uncontrolled massive disturbances. Other than the excavation techniques described above, one can safely assume that little effort was expended toward explaining archaeological method and theory to the residents of Gambell.

Before the early archaeological investigations on the island by Otto Geist and Henry Collins, various superstitions and fears of the dead made most residents very reluctant to dig at the sites (Keim 1969: 114, 218). Archaeologists had a hand in changing this attitude by purchasing artifacts and hiring local assistants (Collins 1975: 25, 31, 35; Geist and Rainey 1976: 25, 31–32; Keim 1969: 150; Scott 1984: 48). Due to a lack of funds, Geist could not pay his assistants an hourly or daily wage. He paid the "volunteers" according to the amount of ivory they uncovered (Geist and Rainey 1976: 32). Geist soon realized the mistake of paying for unprovenienced artifacts, as residents became uncontrollable diggers. In his biography of Geist, Keim (1969: 115) describes the result: "The car Otto had oiled, greased, and carefully cranked was running away with him and there was not much he could do until it ran out of gas."

People frequently complain about archaeologists digging up their sites and, justifiably, about the removal of the artifacts from the island. Historically, collecting artifacts for museums was a primary reason for doing archaeology. At present, the lack of an appropriate facility prevents curation on the island. The excavation of artifacts by archaeologists is variously presented as a cultural or a financial loss. Crowell (1985: 26–27) has found that buyers and collectors tend to support or encourage the notion of the archaeologist as resource competitor. Portions of the population wish the artifacts returned, and some would like to profit from the sale of these returned items. Others have proposed placing the artifacts in a local museum to be used for educational purposes and also for generating tourist revenues.

Many Gambell residents disagree with the position that only archaeologists can extract worthwhile information through controlled excavation of the sites. Local diggers contend that they have learned much about their heritage through their excavations. Traditional craftsmanship, innovations, architecture, and natural history are all learned from digging. Although not written in reports, heritage learned from digging at the site has been expressed orally to other villagers. In contrast, few, if any, archaeologists have presented their findings to the people of Gambell.

Some diggers see their work at archaeological sites as a form of recycling, realizing that previous residents gleaned materials from the sites to be reused or remade into needed tools. Similar attitudes have been expressed to other researchers (Little and Robbins 1984: 194; Crowell 1985: 25).

The Gambell diggers do not want to intensify their extraction of artifacts. Intensification would merely cause the resource to be consumed too quickly and, thus, a slower pace is preferred. A slow pace maintains prices at current levels and also extends the financial gain into the future. The diggers fear that a sudden, large influx of money would be squandered. In this instance, people do not favor strict conservation

to preserve their heritage for posterity, but rather a conservative management style to provide a steady source of cash.

Motivations
Digging on St. Lawrence Island is fueled by a combination of motives including economic requirements, education, tradition, and recreation. Economic conditions provide the primary motive for digging at the sites, and the earlier overview of the Gambell economy and the cash requirements of modern subsistence practices provides a partial context for this discussion. A description of the Gambell ivory market, including rates, prices, and structure is critical for understanding residents' motivations.

The return for scrap ivory and artifacts is an important source of the community's cash income. Most of the return comes from the slow, steady recovery and sale of scrap ivory. The purchase price for this commodity varies depending upon the size and condition of the pieces, as well as seasonal supply and demand factors. During August, 1991, the prevailing rate for small ivory scrap was $20 per pound.

Prices for artifacts destined for the curio or native art markets vary considerably. Mundane utilitarian objects are sometimes sold for a few dollars to a tourist or visitor. More often, these same items are of more value if sold as scrap ivory. Those bound for the art market bring the greatest prices. These pieces include decorated ivory figurines, winged objects, tridents, and utilitarian objects of the Old Bering Sea and Punuk periods (Wardwell 1986). It is difficult to get an accurate estimate of sale prices in Gambell as these have become clouded by myth and legend. Gambell residents spoke of an ivory ulu handle in the form of a polar bear that was recently sold by a digger for $10,000. Other legendary prices paid to finders range from $45,000 up to as high as $60,000. These prices are most often mentioned in relation to the winged objects or "butterflies." Such large monetary returns, whether real and rare or purely imaginary, are a major driving force in the system.

Diggers have several avenues for converting scrap ivory and artifacts into cash. Scrap ivory is purchased by the Native store, the Native corporation, and various visiting private buyers. Visiting buyers may also buy ivory carvings and artifacts. These individuals advertise their upcoming visits through posters and flyers. It was said that in 1991 there was only one buyer, down from the annual average of three buyers, who tended to bid against each other.

Several recent developments may now be acting to preclude the necessity of actual buying trips on the part of brokers and/or collectors. A Gambell entrepreneur, particularly adept at negotiating and facilitating business deals, has established himself as a middleman between diggers and a New York City buyer. The middleman describes the find to his contact by telephone. If the buyer is interested in a piece, he asks for it to be sent along for viewing. A price is agreed upon and the middleman gets 10% of the sale price. This same middleman has sold a number of pieces for a group of diggers directly through Sotheby's auction house in New York City. He said Sotheby's gets a 5% commission on any of these sales. Many other diggers have the capability to sell directly to auction houses, brokers, and collectors. The names and telephone numbers of New York collectors are casually traded among allied diggers. Many have arrangements to call dealers collect or via toll-free numbers.

The participants in digging activities are not exclusively those in need of cash. Successful individuals and families, with economic, social, and political power, also dig at the sites. These people often have steady, full-time employment, are whaling captains and boat owners, and may hold or have held political office. Factors other than economic necessity, such as recreation, education, and tradition, apparently prompt these people. Excavation at the sites is often seen as family recreation that provides educational opportunities. Artifacts are shown to children and are placed in a context of modern and traditional lifeways. They are also used to substantiate legends and local oral history. Tradition is also cited as a factor, since people have now been digging in these sites for over 50 years; it has been a socially acceptable activity for several generations.

The casual nature of some digging at least partially reflects recreational motivations. The activity provides opportunities to leave the household, enjoy the outdoors, socialize or find solitude, and get exercise. Digging, as a form of gambling or treasure hunting, provides a recreational thrill. The popularity of this type of recreation is manifested by frequent participation in sweepstakes, lotteries, bingo, and card playing. In Gambell, many games of chance are well established; community bingo and pull-tabs are especially popular. Expended pull-tabs, also known as "rippies" or "ripoffs," are often found in backdirt piles at the sites. Extremely worn, small bills commonly observed in circulation are attributed by locals to heavy use during card games. The largest potential payoffs, however, are found in another popular game of chance: digging.

Finally, the sites are common property, and all people in Gambell have the right to dig. Perhaps families with no economic pressures are motivated to dig in order to maintain their rights to this resource or to guarantee a share of the resource before it is gone. Whatever the non-economic motives, the economic gains from digging are an added bonus.

The Ethical Dilemma

Current strategies for curtailing the looting problem in the United States include legislation, law enforcement, education, and public involvement. Legislation and law enforcement alone have not been effective. Education and public involvement are the newest approaches to the problem and may eventually have a significant effect, although doubts remain (King 1991). All of these strategies or policies have been advocated by individual archae-ologists and archaeological organizations. If these policies succeed in shutting down the demand for artifacts, quenching or deflecting collectors' desires to possess Native American artifacts, and protecting archaeological sites from looting, what will be the effect on the Native subsistence digger? Should archaeologists, as anthropologists, ignore the potentially substantial effects of archaeologist-influenced public policies regarding site looting on a group of Native Americans? How will they continue their "traditional" lifestyles which now include technology purchased and maintained by cash? Parallel dilemmas exist in Canada where policies have been generated by animal rights activists (Wenzel 1991: 175); native communities that once had their economic basis in seal hunting have been significantly disrupted by the seal fur ban. At present, there are no clear and easy solutions to the subsistence digger dilemma.

The introduction of alternate sources of cash income combined with present anti-looting strategies could stop site destruction and ameliorate any economic effects on Native groups. The Eskimos of St. Lawrence are extremely wary of large-scale natural resource development. They fear the land will be lost through sales to corporations or individuals who will become majority shareholders in the corporations (John Muir Institute, Inc. 1984: 125; Crowell 1985: 23). Elsewhere in the Arctic, non-indigenous development plans have not meshed with traditional subsistence pursuits and have not been productive (Wenzel 1991: 183). The people of St. Lawrence must have input into any development schemes if they are to be successful.

The two villages on St. Lawrence have joined together in a non-profit venture named St. Lawrence Economic Development Corporation (SLEDCO). Appointments to the 12 member board are evenly divided between the villages and represent Indian Reorganization Act (IRA) councils, City governments, and at-large members from both Gambell and Savoonga. The organization is intended to address all development issues (Don Smith, personal communication, 1991).

Several economic development plans currently are being considered for St. Lawrence Island, and short-term projects should continue to provide money to the local economy. The clean-up of World War II debris, airport runway expansions, and other government-sponsored public works projects will provide some employment, but not permanent, full-time jobs. Exploitation of other island-based resources might have more long-term effects. The feasibility of harvesting various seaweeds for sale to the health food and medical industries is actively being researched. The reindeer industry is being revived through herd expansions that may increase sales of meat and antler products to Asian markets. The expansion of eco-tourism, particularly bird-watching, is another possible development for the future (Don Smith, personal communication, 1991).

Alternatives must be found that will contribute cash to the local economy, decrease demands for ancient artworks and curios, promote conservation, and increase reverence for the island's antiquities. Hopi and Zuni artisans of the American Southwest use designs from ancient potsherds for inspiration (Stanislawski 1969: 13, 1978: 221–222), and St. Lawrence Island craftspeople could incorporate some of the aesthetic features of earlier works and use their own cultural heritage in a similar fashion. In this way, their traditional art and heritage would be continually revived and reinforced as something important and meaningful.

Summary

This case study reveals some of the behavioral aspects of looting, examines causal factors underlying site destruction, and illuminates the shadowy world of artifact trafficking. Mainly, however, this study has focused on Native subsistence diggers: their situation, attitudes, and motivations. As a group, subsistence diggers add a unique level of complexity to the site looting problem in Alaska and elsewhere in the world. The information presented here contributes to a better understanding of the looting-trafficking/local economy dichotomy and may ultimately lead to appropriate solutions to the problem. As pointed out by Cheek (1991), what is lacking are Native perspectives on the subject. Further investigations in Gambell would doubtless identify a greater range of concerns and attitudes than those presented here and would more accurately represent the Native perspective. This study presents a complicated problem but does not provide solutions. Perhaps, however, it will stimulate professionals to apply some thought to this dilemma.

Acknowledgments

The anonymous Gambell diggers must be thanked for their candor in discussing this emotionally-charged issue. A number of scholars contributed useful comments, ideas, and information. In particular, I would like to thank Robert Ackerman, Stephen Braund, Aron Crowell, Steven Loring, Ken Pratt, and George Wenzel. Figure 1 is by Ray Norman.

REFERENCES

Anyon, Roger, 1991. "Protecting the Past, Protecting the Present: Cultural Resources and American Indians," in George Smith and John Ehrenhard, eds., *Protecting the Past.* Boca Raton: CRC Press, 215–222.

Burgess, Stephan, 1974. *The St. Lawrence Islanders of Northwest Cape: Patterns of Resource Utilization.* Ph.D. dissertation, University of Alaska Fairbanks. Ann Arbor: University Microfilms.

Cheek, Annetta, 1991. Review of Phyllis Messenger, ed., *The Ethics of Collecting Cultural Property: Whose Culture? Whose Property? American Antiquity* 56: 557–558.

Christensen, H., K. Maberry, M. McAllister, and D. McCormick, 1988. "Cultural Resource Protection: A Predictive Framework for Identifying Site Vulnerability, Protection Priorities, and Effective Protection Strategies," in J. Tainter and R. Hamre, eds., *Tools to Manage the Past: Research Priorities for Cultural Resource Management in the Southwest.* U.S. Forest Service, Southwestern Region and Rocky Mountain Forest and Range Experimentation Station, 62–67.

Collins, Henry, 1975. *Archaeology of St. Lawrence Island, Alaska.* (Originally published in 1937 as *Smithsonian Miscellaneous Collections* Vol. 96, No. 1.) Ann Arbor: University Microfilms.

Crowell, Aron, 1985. *Archeological Survey and Site Condition Assessment of Saint Lawrence Island, Alaska, 1984.* Report submitted to Department of Anthropology, Smithsonian Institution, Washington, D.C., and Sivuqaq, Incorporated, Gambell, Alaska.

Geist, Otto, and Froelich Rainey, 1976. *Archaeological Investigations at Kukulik, St. Lawrence Island, Alaska.* (Originally published in 1936 as Vol. 2 of *Miscellaneous Publications of the University of Alaska* by the U.S. Government Printing Office, Washington, D.C.). New York: AMS Press.

Gramann, J., and G. Vander Stoep, 1986. "Reducing Depreciative Behavior at Shiloh National Military Park," *Technical Report* No. 2. College Station: National Park Service Cooperative Park Studies Unit, Texas A&M University.

Hoffman, Teresa, and Shereen Lerner, 1988. "Arizona Archaeology Week: Promoting the Past to the Public," *Archaeological Assistance Program Technical Brief* No. 2. Washington, D.C.: U.S. Department of the Interior, National Park Service, Archaeological Assistance Division.

John Muir Institute, Inc., 1984. "A Description of the Socioeconomics of Norton Sound," *Technical Report* No. 99, Contract No. AA851-CT2-38. Prepared for the Minerals Management Service, Alaska Outer Continental Shelf Region, Leasing and Environmental Office, Social and Economic Studies Unit.

Keim, Charles, 1969. *Ahgvook, White Eskimo: Otto Geist and Alaskan Archaeology.* College: University of Alaska Press.

King, Thomas, 1991. "Some Dimensions of the Pothunting Problem," in George Smith and John Ehrenhard, eds., *Protecting the Past.* Boca Raton: CRC Press, 83–92.

Little, Ronald, and Lynn Robbins, 1984. "Effects of Renewable Resource Harvest Disruptions on Socioeconomic and Sociocultural Systems: St. Lawrence Island," *Contract No. AA851-CT1-59.* Prepared for The John Muir Institute, Napa, California, and Alaska Outer Continental Shelf Office, Socioeconomic Studies Program, Minerals Management Service, Anchorage, Alaska.

McAllister, Martin, 1991. "Looting and Vandalism of Archaeological Resources on Federal and Indian Lands in the United States," in George Smith and John Ehrenhard, eds., *Protecting the Past.* Boca Raton: CRC Press, 93–99.

McManamon, Francis, 1990. "A National Strategy for Federal Archaeology," *Federal Archeology Report* 3(1): 1, 13, 23. Washington, D.C.: U.S. Department of the Interior, National Park Service, Archaeological Assistance Division.

Messenger, Phyllis, ed., 1989. *The Ethics of Collecting Cultural Property? Whose Culture? Whose Property?* Albuquerque: University of New Mexico Press.

Morton, Susan, 1989. "The Archaeological Resources Protection Act and Alaska," *Federal Archeology Report* 2(3): 1–2. Washington, D.C.: U.S. Department of the Interior, National Park Service, Archaeological Assistance Division.

Neumann, Loretta, 1989. "Saving the Past for the Future: SAA Embarks on a Project to Prevent Looting," *Bulletin of the Society for American Archaeology* 6(1).

Nickens, Paul, 1991. "The Destruction of Archaeological Sites and Data," in George

Smith and John Ehrenhard, eds., *Protecting the Past*. Boca Raton: CRC Press, 73–81.

Nickens, Paul, S. Larralde, and G. Tucker, Jr., 1981. *A Survey of Vandalism to Archaeological Resources in Southwestern Colorado. Cultural Resources Series* No. 11. Denver: Bureau of Land Management, Colorado State Office.

Nichols, Deborah, Anthony Klesert, and Roger Anyon, 1989. "Ancestral Sites, Shrines, and Graves: Native American Perspectives on the Ethics of Collecting Cultural Properties," in Phyllis Messenger, ed., *The Ethics of Collecting Cultural Property: Whose Culture? Whose Property?* Albuquerque: University of New Mexico Press, 27–38.

Nowak, Michael, 1977. "The Economies of Native Subsistence Activities in a Village of Southwestern Alaska," *Arctic* 30: 225–233.

Parker, Patricia, 1990. *Keepers of the Treasures: Protecting Historic Properties and Cultural Traditions on Indian Lands*. A Report on Tribal Preservation Funding Needs Submitted to Congress by the United States Department of the Interior, National Park Service, Interagency Resources Division, Branch of Preservation Planning, Washington, D.C.

Rogge, A. E., ed., 1988. "Fighting Indiana Jones in Arizona," *American Society for Conservation Archaeology Proceedings 1988*.

Scott, Stuart, 1984. "St. Lawrence: Archaeology of a Bering Sea Island," *Archaeology* 37(1): 46–52.

Smith, George, and John Ehrenhard, eds., 1991. *Protecting the Past*. Boca Raton: CRC Press.

Staley, David, 1990. "Wait's Modest Proposal and Cultural Resource Reality in Alaska," *American Society for Conservation Archaeology Report* 17(1): 19–24.

Stanislawski, Michael, 1969. "What Good is a Broken Pot?" *Southwestern Lore* 35: 11–18.

———, 1978. "If Pots Were Mortal," in Richard Gould, ed., *Explorations in Ethnoarchaeology*. Albuquerque: University of New Mexico Press, 201–227.

U.S. Department of Commerce, Bureau of the Census, 1991. *1990 Census of Population and Housing. Summary: Population and Housing Characteristics, Alaska*. Washington, D.C.: Economics and Statistics Administration.

VanStone, James, 1960. "A Successful Combination of Subsistence and Wage Economies on the Village Level," *Economic Development and Cultural Change* 8: 174–191.

Vitelli, K., 1984. "The International Traffic in Antiquities: Archaeological Ethics and the Archaeologist's Responsibility," in E. L. Green, ed., *Ethics and Values in Archaeology*. New York: The Free Press, 143–155.

Wardwell, A., 1986. *Ancient Eskimo Ivories of the Bering Strait*. New York: Hudson Hills Press.

Wenzel, G., 1991. *Animal Rights, Human Rights: Ecology, Economy, and Ideology in the Canadian Arctic*. Toronto: University of Toronto Press.

Who Owns the Spoils of War?

As Germany and Russia spar over the return of wartime booty, historians and legal scholars take a fresh look at what really happened 50 years ago.

Karl E. Meyer

Karl E. Meyer is a member of the editorial board of The New York Times *and the author of* The Plundered Past *and* The Pleasures of Archaeology.

What Byron called the "fatal gift of beauty" is again sowing international discord, as it has since the Trojans abducted Helen. The latest dispute concerns a dazzling collection of Old Master and Impressionist paintings, recently exhibited for the first time in half a century in Moscow and St. Petersburg. It also concerns a royal ransom in the decorative arts; several million books, including two or perhaps three Gutenberg Bibles; whole storerooms of manuscripts and archival records; and the celebrated Treasure of Priam, the Bronze Age artifacts unearthed at Troy in 1873 by Heinrich Schliemann, a symbol and metaphor of the entire dispute (see ARCHAEL-OGY, November/December 1993).

Germany claims ownership of most of these prizes, all of which were removed by Russian forces in 1945. At first glance the German case seems airtight. The Soviet Union and Germany agreed in 1990 to exchange all works uprooted from either country during World War II, an agreement confirmed two years later by President Boris Yeltsin of the new Russian Federation. A joint commission was estab-lished to compile lists of missing works and to preside over exchanges. But it soon became apparent that un-der such an agreement far more art would flow from Russia back to Ger-many than vice versa.

Hesitantly at first, then more boldly, the Russian government took up the refrain of militant nationalists and mu-seum directors such as Irina Antonova of the Pushkin State Museum of Fine Arts in Moscow, whose vaults had hidden the Trojan treasure since 1945. Do not give back a thing, they argued, noting that Russia was still owed repa-rations for 20 million war dead and 400 looted museums. That Russia had approved a repatriation agreement with Germany, not to mention succes-sive Hague conventions that bar use of cultural treasures as reparations, went unmentioned.

Hence the buzz of anticipation in New York early this year when a dozen Russians turned up at a confer-ence on "The Spoils of War." The three-day event, sponsored by the Bard Graduate Center for Studies in the Decorative Arts, was literally an eye-opener. Delegates from Germany, France, Poland, Hungary, and else-where gaped at Russian slides of long-missing Old Master paintings, prints, and drawings seized by Soviet forces. And for the first time at a public forum, Russian cultural officials de-veloped their case for keeping every-thing. Mark M. Boguslavsky of the Institute of State and Law of the Rus-sian Academy of Science, a legal ad-viser to the Russian Ministry of Culture, claimed that all art removed from Soviet soil during World War II was taken illegally. "On that we all agree," he said, but as for the art removed from Germany by the Red Army, "we cannot agree it was ille-gal." He reasoned that with Hitler's defeat there was no German state, and since the Soviet Union was the legiti-mate governing authority in its occu-pation zone, it had every right to remove cultural property. Besides, in vaguely defined wartime declarations the Allies had accepted the idea of "restitution in kind," and Russia was merely applying that principle to Ger-many. It had indeed pledged to return what had been illegally removed from Germany, but, since everything was legally removed, Russia was not obliged to return anything.

This demarche was reminiscent of earlier times when Soviet diplomacy consisted of a thump on the table and a tirade in *Pravda*. What was different at the Bard conference, the Cold War being over, was the absence of una-nimity among the Russian delegates. Not only did they differ with each other on the need for compromise and an end to secrecy, they differed openly and passionately. Resistance among younger scholars to official orthodoxy was borne home by the presence of Konstantin Akinsha, an art historian and journalist, and Grigorii Kozlov, a former inspector for Russia's Department of Museums and former curator of the Museum of Private Collections affiliated with the Pushkin Museum. Akinsha and Kozlov were the first to disclose, in a 1991 *ARTnews* article, that the Schliemann treasure, along with countless other works missing from German and European collections, had been hidden for decades in Soviet "special depositories." Their report encouraged similar exposés by other young researchers, notably Alexei Rastorgouev, an art historian at Moscow University, whose specialty is the "displaced" art of World War II. Thanks to their combined work, which appeared in Russian and international art journals, it is possible for the first time to piece together what really happened 50 years ago.

Russian passions concerning captured German artworks cannot be understood without recalling the rape of European cultural treasures during the Third Reich. A failed artist himself, Hitler dreamed of building a vast art museum in Linz, near his Austrian birthplace. He recruited a Dresden museum director, Hans Posse, to gather a collection by whatever means necessary and ordered the Wehrmacht to assist a special trophy unit commanded by Nazi ideologist Alfred Rosenberg. Posse and Rosenberg competed for spoils with the sybaritic Hermann Goering, with Himmler's SS, and with thousands of officers billeted in foreign castles and estates.

In France and the Low Countries art was harvested by seizing works from Jewish collections and state museums, or by forced sales, such as the "purchase" of superb Old Master drawings from Dutch collector Franz Koenigs. In the East, Polish museums were stripped and royal palaces destroyed. Slavs were deemed *Untermenschen,* their history worthless. In his first tour of the Royal Palace in Warsaw, Governor-General Hans Frank set the example by tearing silver eagles from the canopy covering the royal throne and pocketing them.

Poland's fate foreshadowed the devastation of the Soviet Union. Within weeks of Hitler's blitzkrieg of June 1941, German forces occupied czarist palaces on the outskirts of Leningrad. At the palace of Catherine the Great at Tsarskoye Selo, they dismantled the Amber Room, a great chamber whose walls were lined with precious amber, which had been given to Peter the Great by Frederick-William II of Prussia. The walls of the room were taken to Koenigsberg in East Prussia, where they disappeared, removed and hidden by the Germans or unknowingly destroyed in the Russian assault on the city. German depredations over a three-year period are graphically described in Lynn Nicholas' account of World War II plunder, *The Rape of Europa:* "They took anything they could pry loose from the myriad palaces and pavilions around Leningrad, right down to the parquet floors. They opened packed crates and helped themselves to the contents. Mirrors were smashed or machine gunned, brocades and silks ripped from the walls. At Peterhof . . . the gilded bronze statues of Neptune and Samson upon which the waters played were hauled off to the smelting furnace in full view of the distraught townspeople." Not since the Goths and Vandals had Europe witnessed so spiteful an assault on other people's cultural treasures. The ancient cathedral at Novgorod was ravaged, Pushkin's house ransacked, Tolstoy's manuscripts burned, and elsewhere museums, churches, libraries, universities, and scientific institutes were robbed and destroyed. Most of the Nazi plunder has never been recovered.

Small wonder that, as the battlefront shifted toward Germany, Soviet retribution was swift and all encompassing. In November 1943 an edict of an Emergency State Committee authorized the removal of state and private libraries and art collections to Russia. A Trophy Commission was formed to comb castles, bunkers, salt mines, and caves in which Germans had hidden their own treasures as well as looted foreign art. In Dresden the Russians removed everything portable, including the jeweled contents of the famous Green Vault in the royal castle and more than 500 drawings from the Koenigs collection, which Hitler's agents had brought from Holland. By then a new vision had taken hold in Moscow: the postwar creation of a great Museum of World Art to be filled with works seized as compensation for Nazi vandalism. In January 1945 Stalin signed a directive authorizing massive removal of cultural property of all kinds, ostensibly for the supermuseum.

Four months later the trophy unit arrived in Berlin, where it seized the Pergamon Altar, with its celebrated Hellenistic frieze depicting the battle of the gods and giants, originally acquired by Germany in Turkish Asia Minor. From a bomb-proof bunker near the Berlin Zoo, it confiscated cases of Trojan gold that Schliemann had found at Hisarlik and presented to his native Germany in 1881. Romantically if erroneously dubbed by its finder the Treasure of Priam, the collection consists of hundreds of gold and silver objects, including a gold-beaded headdress once proudly modeled by Schliemann's young Greek wife, Sophia. The cases were flown to the Pushkin Museum, where a receipt was signed by 28-year-old curator Irina Antonova, a tiny woman with blazing eyes who had grown up in Berlin, where her father had been a Soviet trade official. Antonova has survived six Soviet leadership upheavals and the collapse of communism, and still reigns as Pushkin director and guardian of wartime spoils.

Soviet soldiers needed little encouragement in following the Trophy Commission's lead. General Vassily Chuikoff, having settled in the estate of Otto Krebs outside Weimar, saw to it that 98 Impressionist paintings in the Krebs collection were removed to Leningrad, where they were hidden until this year. Other commanders filled railroad cars with the contents of Prussian estates. At Schloss Karnzow, Lieutenant Victor Baldin came upon soldiers in the cellar shuffling through hundreds of Old Master drawings, placed there for safekeeping by curators of the Bremen Kunsthalle. Baldin crammed into his suitcase 364 drawings, including a Dürer that he acquired in a swap for a pair of boots. Baldin, an art historian, preserved the drawings, and years later tried vainly to have them returned to Bremen.

By all these routes, a flood of art reached Russia. Soviet plans for a supermuseum, however, were stalled in good part by the long-forgotten work of a handful of soldiers in the West known as "monuments men." That archaeologists, with an interest in ruins and their preservation, might play a useful military role was not at first obvious to the British War Office. Italy unwittingly caused a change of mind in 1941 when it accused British troops of vandalizing the classical ruins of Leptis Magna, Cyrene, and Sabratha in Libya. Lieutenant Colonel Mortimer Wheeler, the breezily self-assured excavator of Mohenjodaro, who happened to be serving in North Africa, was given the job of safeguarding the sites, which he did with éclat. Wheeler was supported in London by Sir Leonard Woolley, excavator of Ur, who headed the army's Archaeological Adviser's office (consisting of Sir Leonard, Lady Woolley, and a clerk).

When the United States entered the war, influential scholars soon began lobbying for a more ambitious American counterpart to Woolley's office. William Dinsmoor, then president of the Archaeological Institute of America, was among those who met with, and apparently convinced, Chief Justice Harlan Fiske Stone, an ex-officio trustee of the newly formed National Gallery of Art, that an art and monuments unit be formed. Stone sent his recommendations to the White House on December 8, 1942. What probably tipped the scales in favor of the recommendation was Roosevelt and Churchill's decision in January 1943 to invade Sicily, with its vulnerable Greek and Roman ruins and its famous Byzantine churches.

Months later in Sicily, Captain Mason Hammond, a Harvard classics professor acting as art adviser to the Supreme Allied Commander, appropriated a battered vehicle, organized rescue groups, posted off-limits signs,

and courted the annoyance of generals. Hammond was the first of several score monuments officers, men and women, most of them scholars and museum curators, who accompanied Allied armies through Italy, France, and Germany. There was little they could do about wartime devastation: Monte Cassino was destroyed; Pompeii was bombed, as was a church in Padua with frescoes by Mantegna. There were devastating aerial assaults on Dresden, Nürnberg, and other old German cities. Nor could they be held responsible for thousands of soldiers who pocketed spoils of war. In one memorable heist, a U.S. Army artillery officer from Texas, Lieutenant Joe Tom Meador, "liberated" the cathedral treasures of Quedlinburg in the Harz mountains of north-central Germany. He mailed home rock-crystal reliquaries, a jewel-encrusted silver casket, and the priceless *Samuhel Gospels,* written in gold ink and bound in a jeweled cover, part of a treasure associated with Henry I of Saxony, who is sometimes described as the founder of Germany. After Meador's death in 1980, his heirs tried to sell his booty, which to their astonishment was appraised at tens of millions of dollars. An enterprising *New York Times* reporter, William H. Honan, picked up rumors of the attempted sale, identified Meador, and helped bring about the repatriation of the Quedlinburg treasures, with the lubrication of a $3.75 million "finder's fee" to the heirs from the German Cultural Foundation.

The monuments officers were far more successful protecting the quantities of German art and Nazi booty hidden in castles, caves, and mines. At war's end they learned that senior American officials, abetted by covetous museum directors, had proposed sequestering German art as war reparations. The idea was opposed by General Lucius Clay, commander of U.S. forces in Germany, who favored the swiftest possible return of all booty to its rightful owners, though he did suggest that some German masterpieces might be exhibited temporarily in America.

To monuments officers, even that

was all too reminiscent of the Nazi policy of "temporary" removals, purportedly to "protect" other people's art. They drew up what became known as the Wiesbaden Manifesto, which soberly warned, "no historical grievance will rankle so long, or be the cause of so much justified bitterness, as the removal, for any reason, of a part of the heritage of any nation, even if that heritage may be interpreted as a prize of war." Signed in November 1945 by 25 officers and supported by five others not present, the manifesto came to the attention of Janet Flanner, whose account in *The New Yorker* was immediately cited by officials opposing any use of art as reparations.

President Truman rejected the reparation idea but did approve an exhibition of 202 masterpieces from Berlin museums. The National Gallery's first blockbuster show, it drew a million visitors in 1948, then traveled to New York and St. Louis. By then Europe was dividing into East and West, and General Clay was mounting an airlift to encircled West Berlin. Returned in 1955, the Berlin paintings were placed in the new Dahiem Museum in what was then the American sector, and there they remain today. Meanwhile, thanks to the monuments officers, some 500,000 cultural items looted by Nazis in Slavic countries and found in western Germany were repatriated, an unreciprocated restitution that is invariably ignored in Russian reckoning.

All this had its effect on Moscow. Nothing more was said about establishing a Museum of World Art, with its embarrassing resemblance to Hitler's plans for Linz. In 1945, Soviet prosecutors at Nürnberg agreed with Western victors in defining the plunder of art as a war crime. The Soviet Foreign Minister, Vyacheslav Molotov, even joined with Britain in censuring America's temporary removal of German art. But what truly complicated Soviet cultural diplomacy was the division of Germany and the emergence of a comradely ally, the German Democratic Republic. In 1958, as a goodwill gesture and to buttress the legitimacy of the new East German regime, Nikita

Khrushchev returned the Pergamon Altar to its old home in East Berlin and gave back to Dresden most of its Old Masters and the bejeweled objets d'art from the Green Vault. This wise and realistic gesture was opposed by museum officials such as Irina Antonova, who at the Bard conference in New York was still deploring a decision "dictated by politics." Curators come to believe they own what is in their care. Commenting on the fate of Priam's Treasure in an interview in ARCHAEOLOGY (November/December 1993), Valery Kulishov, a member of the Russian State Commission on Restitution, noted: "You must understand the feelings of the Pushkin Museum officials. If you have it, it's part of you. Psychologically, you're so much attached and bound to what you had, even secretly, in your repository. It's very hard now to give it back, regardless of any kind of agreements."

Trophy art, however, is not exhibited or cataloged. Anybody with access to storerooms can steal and sell it. Leakage has been considerable. Of 562 drawings in the Dutch Koenigs collection seized in Dresden, 33 remained in Germany. But in 1957, the Pushkin Museum's unpublished records listed only "337 sheets," and the total today is said to be 308. A similar attrition has taken place in the Krebs collection, which for five decades has been hidden in the Hermitage in St. Petersburg. At the Bard conference, Alexei Rastorgouev showed slides of drawings from Dresden now owned by unidentified Russian private collectors. Dealers in Europe and America routinely check the Koenigs catalog when offered drawings of suspiciously high quality.

Hence the urgent need to display and catalog all of Russia's wartime booty as soon as possible. It was this consideration that prompted the Hermitage director, Mikhail Piotrovski, to arrange the showing this past March of Impressionist and Post-Impressionist paintings from the Krebs and other private collections. A few weeks earlier Irina Antonova, not to be outdone, had quickly organized a comparable show of Old Masters from German and Hungarian collections at the Pushkin. One hopes such competition will be contagious. In Piotrovski's sensible view, it is up to the courts to decide legal title, and up to the museums to make public what they hold. In a wider sense, though, the courts can only settle claims of heirs and museums when and if Russia and Germany reach a political settlement.

As for Russia . . . even those sympathetic to its cause will wonder whether five decades of concealment attest a confident claim of ownership.

In the early 1970s, I delved into the secretive antiquities market and its links with collectors and curators. The results were serialized in *The New Yorker* and published as The *Plundered Past.* If I learned any lesson, it was that on matters of acquiring cultural treasures, no art-consuming nation has truly clean hands. Consider the United States. As Lynn Nicholas recounts in *The Rape of Europa,* in 1939 the Nazis staged a scandalous auction at the Fischer Gallery in Lucerne at which allegedly "degenerate" art by Braque, Picasso, Van Gogh, and others was sold at derisory prices. The pictures had been taken from leading German museums. Among the bidders was a refugee German dealer, Curt Valentin of the Bucholz Gallery in New York, who acquired paintings by Derain, Kirchner, Klee, Lehmbruck, and Matisse. He was bidding on behalf of the Museum of Modern Art, whose director, Alfred Barr, exhibited the five works with no hint of their true provenance. No doubt the sale was legal, but it speaks volumes that the entire transaction was secret. By the same token, Harvard's acquisition of a major work by Max Beckmann, sold at the same auction, was also legal. But both institutions were extracting an advantage from a political calamity that befell German museums, a fact not advertised in accession labels.

As for Germany, everyone repudiates the cultural barbarities and wholesale brigandage that marked the Third Reich. There will be no such unanimity on Germany's legal title to the Schliemann treasure, which was spirited from Ottoman Turkey in murky circumstances, provoking a criminal suit and cash settlement at the time, and leading to a formal claim by the present Republic of Turkey. Nor is anyone talking about the controversy surrounding the bust of Queen Nefertiti, Germany's single most celebrated antiquity. Acquired in a division of finds at Amarna in 1914, the statue was hidden for a decade; Egyptians cried foul from the moment it was finally put on display in Berlin. Like other European art-importing countries, Germany has yet to ratify the UNESCO convention barring the illegal importation of cultural property. Purchase of unprovenanced antiquities, many of them clearly smuggled from their country of origin, is widespread, as visitors to German museums can readily see.

As for Russia, it can indeed point to a traumatic past, but even those sympathetic to its cause will wonder whether five decades of concealment attest a confident claim of ownership. Certainly neither Poland nor Holland, Ukraine nor Hungary, ever invaded the Soviet Union, yet their claims for restitution have also gone unanswered. Ironically the Yeltsin government is seeking restitution of real estate and other properties owned by the czarist regime and its subjects in France, Italy, and Israel, appealing to the very norms of law and equity it declines to apply to its own wartime booty.

How sensible if Russia broke the ice by returning a set of rare books taken from Gotha in 1945, an act of restitution urged by a Moscow librarian speaking at the Bard conference. This gesture might be coupled with an offer to submit claims to the Trojan gold to the World Court for binding adjudication (as Germany has proposed) with the proviso that Turkey's claim also be given a full hearing. And how wise if Germany promoted an international

Limits of World Law

LIEBER

ROERICH

Two remarkable people helped write the laws meant to bar warring nations from destroying or looting each other's cultural treasures. One was the German American soldier and philosopher, Francis Lieber, author of a military code promulgated by Lincoln during the Civil War. The other was Nicholas Roerich, a Russian painter and mystic, who in 1935 persuaded the United States and 20 other countries to approve a treaty asserting the inherent neutrality of works of art in wartime.

The belief that cultural treasures need special treatment was expressed as early as 1758 by Emheric de Vattel, a legal scholar during the Enlightenment, whose treatise *The Law of Nations* spoke to the future: "For whatever cause a country is ravaged, we ought to spare those edifices which do honor to human society, and do not contribute to increase the enemy's strength—such as temples, tombs, public buildings and all works of remarkable beauty. . . . It is declaring one's self to be an enemy of mankind, thus wantonly to deprive them of these wonders of art." Napoleon, nonetheless, crammed the Louvre with wagonloads of conquered art. At the Congress of Vienna in 1815, the Allies ordered France to return the art, since looting, in the words of the Duke of Wellington, was "contrary to the principles of justice and the rules of modern law."

Yet those laws were unwritten. By chance, this was rectified by Francis Lieber, a Prussian-born soldier who in 1827 emigrated to America. He taught legal philosophy at Columbia College in New York and during the Civil War President Lincoln asked him to draft a military code. Issued as General Order 100 in 1863, it called among other things for the protection during wartime of "classical works of art, libraries, scientific collections or precious instruments, such as astronomical telescopes."

The Lieber code inspired a similar declaration in 1874 at the Conference of Brussels that was endorsed by the German kaiser. This declaration in turn inspired the Russian czar to promote a more ambitious conference at the Hague. In 1907, some 40 nations approved a series of conventions that expressly forbade the seizure or destruction in wartime of cultural treasures. The Hague codes proved of limited value during World War I, so in 1935 a fresh attempt was made. This was the work of Nicholas Roerich (1874–1947), a Russian artist who designed the sets for Stravinsky's ballet *Le Sacre du Printemps*. As an explorer, he had led a five-year expedition to central Asia, and had also served as vice-president of the Archaeological Institute of America. A friend of Secretary of Agriculture Henry Wallace, Roerich persuaded the Roosevelt Administration to support a new treaty to protect artistic works, scientific instruments, and historic monuments. He devised a special flag, with three globes in a mystic triad, to mark protected cultural treasures.

Since World War II, insurgents have targeted the great Khmer ruins at Angkor, the walled medieval city of Dubrovnik, and the Ottoman bridges of Bosnia, as well as thousands of churches, mosques, synagogues, temples, palaces, libraries, and memorials of every kind. Nobody has yet found a way of enforcing civilized aspirations; the worst enemy of humanity's noblest works is still humanity itself.—K.E.M.

effort to restore Russian museums and churches. Initiatives like these must be taken quickly, for it takes only a modicum of historical memory to know that it is later than the two governments think.

The Russian parliament has already given preliminary approval to legislation that would give Russia full title to all wartime booty. If that legislation is adopted, there will certainly be repercussions. German aid to Russia is reckoned at more than $73 billion since 1990, including $40 billion in loans and $14 billion in direct grants. If Bonn cuts or conditions its aid to Moscow, a likely next move, there will be a Russian outcry over German bullying and a clamor for reprisals in the Russian parliament.

Back in 1945 American monuments officers, in their Wiesbaden declaration, warned that disputes over captured spoils can sow enduring acrimony. That indeed is the theme of Homer's *Iliad,* which begins with Achilles' fury at the prizes of war that Agamemnon greedily bestows on himself. If no progress is made this year toward resolving the quarrel over Russia's wartime booty, positions will harden, and taking a modest step forward will be even more difficult. As evidence, consult the *Iliad.*

Politics and Archaeology

Amos Elon

A story is told of some early Zionist pioneers of Beit Alpha, a communal settlement in the Esdraelon Valley. The settlement was founded in the early Twenties by young men and women belong to the socialist youth movement *Hashomer Hatzair* (Young Guard). They subscribed to a bizarre combination of utopian Marxism, Freudian psychoanalysis, and the then fashionable German *Jugendkultur,* with its Romantic worship of nature, cult of eroticism, and disdain for bourgeois values. In December 1928, some of them were digging an irrigation channel and suddenly struck the brilliantly colored mosaic of a sixth-century Jewish synagogue. Their first reaction was to keep the discovery secret, and possibly cover it up again—a natural impulse, perhaps, that field archaeologists often encounter. The main concern, after all, had been to dig an irrigation channel. The unexpected discovery complicated this task and threatened to hold it up, perhaps indefinitely.

But there was more to it: an anti-religion attitude. The young kibbutzniks, full of the fervor of Russian radicalism, had only a year or two earlier come out of Eastern Europe with—as the saying went at the time—"no clothes, but with copies of *Das Kapital* and Freud's *Interpretation of Dreams* in their knapsacks." A few were still teen-agers. Others were in open rebellion against their Orthodox religious fathers. Some had actually run away from home to help build socialism and create the "new Jew" in the historic land of his forefathers; a utopian community not unlike those of the late 1960s in which their identity would be redefined and based on socialism and love. Religion was the opium of the people. For this reason alone, it might be best if the synagogue mosaic were covered up again. Others argued that the mosaic was not necessarily religious but rather political, a Zionist monument. It was important, so the argument went, to uphold every archaeological remnant that testified to the Jewish presence in the land, and confirm the legitimacy of the Zionist claim. A debate took place. The conservationist view prevailed over the iconoclastic.

The story may be apocryphal but it sums up, as such stories sometimes do, the central facts of the case. A Jewish archaeologist, Eliezer Lipa Sukenik (the father of Yigael Yadin), was consulted. He proposed to conduct a scientific excavation of the site. It would be his first. Sukenik, formerly a high school teacher of mathematics and geography in Jerusalem, had spent a year studying archaeology at the University of Berlin at a time when the leading archaeologists and ethnologists at that university were obsessed with *Volk* and other ethnocentric prejudice. He never graduated in Berlin. His great ambition was the creation of a "Jewish archaeology." His view of history was narrowly Zionist, or, if you like, Hegelian. He thought he recognized its spirit in Jewish longings for Zion throughout the ages. In his view, Jewish history during the past eighteen centuries was only an insignificant interval between national independence lost in the first century and national independence to be regained in the twentieth. Sukenik lectured the young kibbutznks on Jewish history, modern archaeology, and memory. Jews were a community of memory. In his enthusiasm for digging up remnants and relics of the glorious Jewish past, he won over most of the kibbutzniks who until that moment had been less interested in digging up the past than in building a utopian future. This site was solemnly excavated to much acclaim throughout the Jewish world. A story in *The New York Times* reported that Jewish workers in Palestine were excavating Jewish history—in the holy land.

It was probably no accident that this first recorded outbreak of a popular passion for Jewish archaeology occurred at a time of relatively low morale among the settlers, owing to the economic crisis and the mounting Arab opposition to Jewish settlement. Among the more sensitive pioneers there might even have been something like nagging guilt at being intruders in a country populated by another people that bitterly resented their arrival. For them, Sukenik's Jewish archaeology had a kind of cathartic effect. Word of Sukenik's dig at Beit Alpha spread quickly. Volunteers streamed to Beit Alpha to work on the dig. The richly colored mosaic was uncovered in a remarkably good state of preservation. It included not only Hebrew inscriptions and common Jewish religious symbols but also a surprising representation of Helios, the pagan Greek sun god—highlighting the eclectic nature of Jewish religious worship at that time.

Contemporary reports stress the festive atmosphere among the participants at the dig. Reading these accounts today you get the feeling they were participating in a kind of communion. By

Reprinted with permission from *The New York Review of Books*, September 22, 1994, pp. 14-18. © 1994 by Nyrev, Inc.

digging up the hard ground they were retrieving memory—one is tempted to say—as though they were recovering checked baggage from a storage room.

Sukenik later recalled the event in glowing terms.

> Suddenly people could see things that had never been so tangible before. . . . There was a feeling that this piece of ground, for which people had suffered so much, wasn't just any plot of land but a piece of earth where their forefathers had lived fifteen hundred to two thousand years ago. Their work in the present was cast in a different light. Their history was revealed to them and they saw it with their own eyes.

The enthusiasm at Beit Alpha, from all we know, was unprecedented in the history of the Zionist enterprise. Earlier pioneers—in the first and second wave of immigration—had barely been moved by the charm of antique sites or objects. They felt little need for buried proofs of the past to uphold their claims of the present. Self-conscious about their historic roles, many of them were men of letters, inveterate diarists, polemicists, endlessly writing editorials, manifestoes, essays, and pamphlets. It was said of the men and women of the second wave that never was so much written about so many subjects by so few in so short a time. Yet even though their first years in Israel coincided with the first great excavations of important biblical sites by leading Protestant archaeologists, including Sir William Sellin, Sir Flinders Petrie, and R. A. S. Macalister, in their extensive writings there is hardly a word to suggest that any discoveries touched them even peripherally. The sudden outbreak of enthusiasm for Jewish archaeology at Beit Alpha in 1928 was unique. It anticipated the fervor of future years, and the political uses of archaeology in what was later hailed— or decried—as a "national syndrome": a popular craze for archaeology, a *bulmus* in Hebrew. *Bulmus* is an old Talmudic term. It denotes a fit, a rage, a craze, a mania, a ravenous hunger resulting from prolonged fasting.

Archaeology often converged with nationalism in the new nation states created in Europe after the great war, but perhaps nowhere else did archaeology loom so large, or for so long, as in Israeli life until the early Seventies. In Czechoslovakia, Turkey, Finland, Poland, and the Baltic states archaeology was used politically to provide and occasionally fabricate material evidence of unbroken historical continuity. And let us not forget the Byzantine Queen Helena. I remember the late Yigael Yadin once calling her, a little wistfully perhaps, "the most successful archaeologist in history." Whatever she looked for she promptly found hundreds of years after the event: the stable where Mary had given birth to Christ, the twelve stations of the cross, Calvary, the true cross, the nails, the lancet, the Holy Sepulchre and so on and on. In our own time we have seen elaborate celebrations at Persepolis staged by the Shah, a few years before his fall, to commemorate the 2,500th anniversary of "his" empire. In Iraq, Saddam Hussein proclaims himself a worthy successor of the ancient Babylonians. The Serbs venerate Kosovo, which, like Masada, is not the site of a victory but of a defeat.

Archaeological finds have inspired nearly all Israeli national symbols, from the State Seal to medals and coins and postage stamps. (Walter Benjamin claimed that postage stamps were the visiting cards left by governments in children's playrooms.) Since independence, Israeli coins have been stamped with motifs copied from first century Jewish silver shekels. (Many years ago I remember seeing in the shop window of an antique dealer on Allenby Road in Tel-Aviv a display that attracted some attention: a few modern Israeli coins were placed there in a row next to the ancient Jewish coins that had inspired them. It was obvious to anyone looking that the ancient coins were considerably more accomplished and more beautiful in design, more aesthetic generally, than those of the modern.) And I remember a television interview with Prime Minister Menachem Begin at the peak point of hyper-inflation in Israel in 1980 when a pack of cigarettes cost in the thousands, and cash registers could no longer cope with so many digits, and the economy was grinding to a halt because of a sudden drop in investments. Begin was expected to announce cuts in public spending, a wage-and-price freeze, and other anti-inflation measures. He didn't. He only proclaimed that the name of the monetary unit would be changed from the foreign name *lira* (i.e., "pound") to shekel, a Hebrew name of ancient renown which by its historic weight alone, as Begin put it, would make it one of the world's hard currencies at par with the American dollar.

How did all this come about? In the years of struggle leading up to the establishment of the new state and during its first two decades of so, the cult of archaeological relics did much to determine the direction of Israeli culture. It was widely thought to provide an immigrant society with a common culture. There was, of course, also a calculated effort at public relations aimed at Bible-minded gentile customers abroad. In a deeper sense, however, the apparent obsession with ancient Jewish sites and artifacts grew out of the feverish search for identity—a secular identity—which was characteristic of that period. The Dead Sea scrolls thrilled *secular* Israelis; most Orthodox Jews were and still are indifferent to them. In the ethnocentric atmosphere of these early years there was a rush to identify Jewish sites, an overemphasis on digging them up, and a tendency to expose to public view the Jewish strata of a site even where other layers may have been historically or artistically more significant or revealing. The task of archaeology was to prove a point about Jews in the Holy Land and not always, as it probably should have been, to explore material remains in order to determine the circumstances of ancient cultures and civilizations in a country where they have been so varied and so many. There was even a somewhat comic attempt, fortunately short-lived, by the then director of antiquities to impose a nationalistic nomenclature. He asked that the Iron Age be referred to henceforth as the Israelite Period, the Hellenistic as Hasmonean, the Roman as the

Mishnaic and the Byzantine as the Talmudic periods.

In our own time, a new post-Zionist generation of younger archaeologists has come to question the patriotic oversell and single-mindedness of their predecessors, their arbitrary choice of terms and subject of study, their seeming haste, occasionally, to identify this or that site as unfailingly Jewish on the basis of partial or insufficient evidence. There is even a movement to discard the very term "Biblical archaeology" as a misleading and ethnocentric term. This is, perhaps, as it should be. And yet mistakes in attribution are common in art, too. The big question we must always ask is: Was the mistake caused by ideology? Excessive claims are also made in physics and in all other exact sciences. They are often made in order to raise money to support further research. In the philosophy of science it is common to distinguish between contexts of discovery and justification. We all have the right to pursue what we want to pursue, and to explore the buried past and eventually dig it up—the discovery. That we do so may be a personal or even a nationalistic choice or prejudice. But making a choice as a result of personal interest or ideology is common and natural in every field and as such is not objectionable. The problem arises when the justification or proof of our discovery is prompted not by evidence but by ideology. I may decide to study the history of my own family rather than that of someone else. But I may present my grandmother as a Balkan princess only if I can provide exact and irrefutable proof.

To judge them on this basis, I should say, most Israeli archaeologists, even of the early period, come out rather well. They were digging not only for knowledge but for the reassurance of roots, which they found in the Israelite ruins scattered throughout the country. They may have been prejudiced in their choice of study but not, in most cases, in their analysis of the results. They oversold their discoveries as other scientists do. The difference lay in the effects of their work on the culture as a whole, and in the manner its results were heralded in the press and on television, adopted by patriotic fan clubs, and popularized by eager schoolteachers, nationalist historians, tour guides, Bible nuts, youth leaders, and politicians. I am not saying that the archaeologists themselves had nothing to do with this manipulation. I am suggesting that their role in it was minor in comparison to say, the powerful lobby of elementary- and high-school Bible teachers.

There were political and, I assume, psychological reasons why Israeli archaeology has at that time a distinctive, even chauvinistic, air. Several amateur archaeologists among the generals and the politicians imbued archaeological discoveries with a current "meaning." Moses Finley, reviewing Yadin's book on Masada in 1966, suggested that there was "a large and interesting book to be written about the politics of modern archaeology in which Masada will be a centerpiece." This has now been done by Neal Silberman in his very revealing biography of Yadin, *'A Prophet From Amongst You'—The Life of Yigael Yadin: Soldier, Scholar and Mythmaker of Modern Israel.**

As Silberman puts it, very succinctly I think, under Yadin archaeology in Israel was not strictly an academic activity but "a tangible means of communion between the people and the land." The religious term communion is very well chosen here. Yadin himself often suggested that for young Israelis a "faith" in history and archaeology was a kind of "religion." Its high priests were schoolteachers, youth leaders, army education officers. They and the mass media combined to give archaeology—a certain kind of archaeology—a cultic aspect, and a prominence it never had, as far as I know, in another culture.

As Silberman writes, archaeological discoveries of ancient Jewish sites offered "poetic validation for modern Jewish settlement. Artifacts came to possess the power of sacred relics in a new cult of veneration for the ancestors." Now Yadin was certainly a very serious scientist. I am told that in his archaeological digs he followed the strictest scientific rules. And he kept insisting that archaeology and politics must be scrupulously kept apart. Yet, as Silberman shows, there was always an extra-scientific message afterward, in the oversell.

He notes Yadin's reluctance or inability to define precisely the modern significance of Masada, if there was one. This is only partly true. Yadin initiated the practice of swearing-in troops on the top of Masada. He attended these bizarre ceremonies himself. In one often quoted speech he told the young recruits during the ceremony:

> When Napoleon and his troops stood by the pyramids of Egypt he told them that four thousand years of history were looking down on them. What would he not have given to be able to say: Four thousand years of *your own* history look down on you. . . . The echo of your oath this night will resound throughout the encampments of our foes. Its significance is not less powerful than that of all our defensive armaments.

In his 1957 book *The Message of the Scrolls* Yadin gave a special symbolic meaning to the date on which his late father had purchased the first of the Dead Sea scrolls:

> . . . at the (very) moment of the creation of the state of Israel. It is as if these manuscripts had been waiting in caves for two thousand years, ever since the destruction of Israel's independence until the people of Israel returned to their home and regained their freedom. The symbolism is heightened by the fact that the first three scrolls were brought to my father for Israel on 29 November 1947, the very day the United Nations voted for the re-creation of a Jewish state in Israel after two thousand years.

He had, when he spoke, the rare knack for drama that allows some men to endow dumb stones with the quality of speech. Speak they did in his hands, on his lecture tours through five continents, where he did more for Israel than all its hack government propogandists put together; and, in Israel, on a highly successful TV quiz program on archaeology which he hosted

*Addison-Wesley, 1993.

for two years every fortnight. After finding a series of ancient paryri in a Judean desert cave, including dispatches from Bar Kokhba, the fabled leader of the last Jewish uprising against the Romans in 120 AD, he arranged for the entire government to assemble at president Ben Zvi's residence without, however, giving them notice of what he had unearthed. At one point he turned to the President and announced: "Excellency, Mr. President of the State of Israel. I have the honor to present to you letters dispatched by the last president of the state of Israel: Bar Kokhba." The event, if I remember correctly, was broadcast live on radio.

I remember hearing Yadin argue, on one private occasion, that he could not be held responsible for the immense publicity emanating from his digs; or for the popular message of Masada which had registered so powerfully and on occasion incorrectly in the public mind ("the Masada complex"). It is also true that he never conducted excavation in the occupied territories: or even in East Jerusalem, as he might have done after 1967. Moreover, after 1967 he publicly decried the spreading worship of national and religious relics as an "idolatrous" practice. Judaism was an abstract religion, he claimed, not given to the worship of saints and dead stones. And he ridiculed those who in 1968 had forced their way into the Muslim mosque within the cave of the Makhpela at Hebron, where Abraham, Isaac, Jacob, and their spouses are supposed to be buried, and had turned parts of the mosque into a Jewish synagogue. (The awful massacre took place there earlier this year.) He mocked the entire idea and the worshipers too, and claimed he did not see why they were making so much fuss over the tombs of a couple of Arab sheiks.

He demonstratively refused to attend the bizarre state funeral Prime Minister Begin staged before television cameras for some obscure bones that had been found twenty years earlier in a Judean desert cave and were said to be the remains of Bar Kokhba's heroic soldiers, who had died in battle

for Israel. By then Yadin was Begin's deputy prime minister. Begin insisted on staging the event as one of great contemporary relevance. The coffin containing the bones (several were of women and children) was draped in flags and carried to a tomb on the shoulders of four generals. Yadin's protests against this kind of political theater were in vain. The images he had helped to imprint on the nation's mind had taken on a life of their own.

In the 1950s, thousands of Israelis became ardent amateur archaeologists. Archaeology—by now a national cult—became a popular movement, as well as a sport of kings: politicians, socialites, top civil servants, famous army generals were known as ardent collectors. It was a cult quite unknown in this form in other countries: a national sport, almost—not a spectator sport but an active pastime. It turned into a movement that included tens of thousands of people, as perhaps fishing or hunting or bowling does elsewhere. In many a suburban private garden, flowerpots appeared on florid ancient marble pedestals. In middle-class houses one could see sizable archaeological collections assembled in bookshelves and glass cages through purchase or illicit digging by enthusiastic amateurs.

Government attempts to curtail illegal digging in the interest of science and the public museums were halfhearted and generally futile. The best known amateur archaeologist was General Moshe Dayan. His lifelong pursuit of archaeology nearly cost him his life in 1968 when a tunnel he was digging through a wet Philistine mound near Tel Aviv collapsed and he broke several of his ribs. He was asked in an interview what exactly he had been looking for underground. His answer was: "The ancient Land of Israel. Everything that ancient Israel was. Those who lived here then . . . I sometimes feel I can literally enter their presence."

Dayan was a man of great personal magnetism. Apart from his military victories, he had an enormous collection of ancient artifacts, fast cars, numerous mistresses, and a highly developed business sense. His fame vastly contributed to the popular macho appeal

of archaeology as a bloodless field sport. His private collection included one of the world's largest hoards of ancient Near Eastern artifacts, some of them dug up with his own hands. The most dramatic items were sarcophagi and burial urns. Here was a man, the darling of the local and foreign electronic news, the favorite guest star of all the Barbara Walterses of the world, who in the eyes of millions had come to symbolize the sabra, the new Jew, an ancient people's newly found vitality in modern times. Yet at home he lived in a morbid decor, among his burial urns, funeral plaques, death offerings, and sarcophagi.

In the Fifties and Sixties, the annual conventions of the Israel Exploration Society—a get-together of patriotic Bible and geography-of-Israel teachers—were regularly attended by more than a thousand spectators. This was almost one per thousand of the total Jewish population at that time. (Imagine about 150,000 people attending a similar seminar in the United States.) Long before the cable car to the top of Masada was built, scout leaders regularly led their young followers up the steep serpentine path to spend the night there. Lit by blazing torches, the dramatic nocturnal setting on Masada—much like Barbarossa's mountain—invited mythic interpretations. Gathering around camp fires the youngsters recited the grisly tale of the mass suicide and intoned the well-known refrain of Lamdan's poem "Masada Shall Not Fall Again." Masada, Hatzor, and Megiddo—all excavated by Yadin and popularized thanks to this marvelous gift of communication—were part of a young person's political education at that time.

So were the Dead Sea scrolls, displayed in the specially built "Shrine of the Book" on the grounds of the Israel Museum in Jerusalem. Archaeology and nationalism were perfectly matched in the "Shrine of the Book," shaped like a chapel over a round altar where the main scroll was displayed like the relic of a saint. A ten-year-old schoolboy or girl could easily read it—as guides did not fail to point out. (Can a ten-year-old in Athens or Rome read ancient Greek or Latin inscriptions? In Greece and Italy, the language is no longer the same. In Jerusalem it is.) In an immigrant country, among a hybrid people from over a hundred countries of origin, the cult or archaeology reflected an obsessive search for common roots. It also promoted a kind of historical amnesia which assured that events that had taken place two thousand years ago were grasped more vividly than anything since, until the present. Joshua Kenez, one of Israel's foremost novelists, vividly portrayed this in his fine novel *Hitganvut Yekhidim* ("Individual Stealth"). Here is the monologue of Alon, a training sergeant haranguing a couple of *nebbish* recruits in an army auxiliary unit:

Imagine a shepherd of kibbutz Megiddo with his flock of sheep on the slope of an ancient mound. He suddenly discovers a tablet. It's inscribed in cuneiform letters. He passes this on to the archaeologists. They decipher it. They discover it's part of the epic of Gilgamesh. Someone wrote it 3500 years ago. . . . D'you understand? . . . Here's a tale from ancient Babylon. It's suddenly discovered here. In the Land of Israel. Next to your house. In the yard outside they discover Herod's palace. In Hahal Hever near Ein Gedi they find a cave. Close to the remains of the Roman encampments there. A cave full of skeletons. Women's and children's bones. They all starved to death during the siege. Next to them shoes. Rags of clothes. Remains of foodstuff. And the big shard of a jar with Hebrew letters. As though waiting for us. For us to come and discover it. And now it all overflows and explodes. As the earth has saved it all just for us. As our roots. . . . It's amazing. It's not like reading about it in the Bible. . . . These men . . . they were like Arik Sharon's guys . . . men who know every wadi and don't know what fear is. . . .

But it wasn't all politics, of course. Archaeology was more than politics, roots, or romantic yearnings for a distant barbaric past. There was an easy attraction in archaeology: unlike other outdoor sports, it combines fresh air with bookish toil and adventure. In Tel Aviv, where I grew up, we were never more than fifteen minutes away from

three or four known but not yet fully excavated sites—Roman, Jewish or Hellenistic—each of them so rich in all kinds of fantastic finds that we rarely returned from an outing without a nice coin, or a shining piece of wonderful blue Phoenician glass, or an oil-lamp or the interesting fragment of one, or a potsherd or a lump of sculptured marble.

As we grew older, we occasionally had a sense in Israel of living inside a time machine. The mixture of ancient and modern history, the relentless intensity of daily life coupled with a notion, perhaps not always quite conscious, of a national legitimacy widely contested and by our nearest neighbors in the region—all that was likely to reinforce a lifelong fascination with antiquities of all kinds. You did not have to be an Israeli to share in it. Edmund Wilson who by inclination was a shrinker of myths succumbed to it very willingly, as his recently published diaries, *The Sixties,* clearly show.

Later on when the Old City of Jerusalem became accessible, the forces and physical presence of the past were so palpable that it sometimes seems the city failed to have a present. The ancient past and the present intersected but almost never met. Everything was tight, crowded, old, ruined and intertwined. Under a stone parapet placed there by a British engineer after the First World War lies a Mamluk doorway built over a Hasmonean tower standing on foundations from the time of the Judean kings. A Roman arch of the first century spans an early Jewish pavement that connects the apses of a Byzantine church with the top of a Muslim mosque. The Western Wall, the Church of the Holy Sepulchre, the mosques on the ancient Temple Mount are within a stone's throw of each other—no pun is intended here—I simply wish to emphasize the oppressive proximity of things, the way they overhang and overlap.

A young person growing up in this milieu would frequently hear it said that the present in Israel reflected the distant past (and vice versa). Ben Gurion himself drew the analogy between Yoshua, conqueror of Canaan "in

storm" (to quote Tshernichovsky's famous poem), and General Yadin himself. Such rhetoric highlighted the mirroring of past and present. It stressed myths and symbols. We all turn history into myth and ritual and into symbols that give meaning to life. This is why we celebrate birth, and have mourning rites and funerals. The rhetoric was convoluted at times, but it had its appeal and sometimes it almost caused the time zones to overlap, as in those historic paintings in Italy or France where one sees Dante holding hands with Virgil, or Charlemagne in animated conversation with Napoleon.

Today, more than a century since the beginning of the Zionist settlement, Israel is often said to be the most excavated country in the world. Last year, according to official figures, some 250 excavations took place within Israel proper (plus over fifty in the occupied territories). And yet archaeology seems no longer so large an enterprise as it was in years past. It is no longer the popular field sport of two or three decades ago. The trend has been noticeable for some years. The great stars are gone too. There has been a dramatic decline in public interest in archaeology. The army, for reasons of economy, I am told, no longer stages spectacular swearing-in ceremonies on Masada. Native Israelis—they are the large majority now—appear to have less need to search for roots; those who do turn rather to religion. The secular majority appears self-assured enough to accept a historical compromise with the Palestinians in a pragmatic mood of post-Zionist open-mindedness.

During the past decade a younger generation of archaeologists and historians has deconstructed the Masadan myth of patriotic suicide into what might have been, at best, the calculated invention of the first-century historian Josephus Flavius, and, at worst, a senseless mass hysteria, a kind of Jewish Jamestown. (Oddly enough, this may well have been the view at the time of the Jewish religious establishment. If indeed the mass suicide had taken place at Masada, as Josephus claimed, the Rabbis must have preferred to suppress all memory of it. In the vast body of Rabbinic literature there isn't a word about Masada.)

In a population almost six times larger than it was in 1952 the number of those attending the annual conventions of the Israel Exploration Society is still roughly the same as it was then. University statistics indicate a parallel drop, relatively speaking, in the number of archaeology students and a truly dramatic decline in Jewish and Hebrew studies generally, from Talmud to Jewish history and Hebrew literature and language. At the Hebrew University—in the Fifties the center of Jewish, Land of Israel, and related studies—504 students registered this year in the department of Japanese and Chinese studies. Only nineteen are in the Department of Talmud (one of them is a Japanese).

Peace, if it comes, will accelerate this openness. It may not necessarily bring an end to the political uses of archaeology. Following the Oslo agreement between Israel and the PLO a first exchange of views on "archaeology" last spring was marked by intransigence on both sides. Israel was ready to grant the Palestinians control only over "Muslim" or "Arab" archaeological sites on the West Bank; PLO representatives insisted on con-

trol of all sites, including Jewish ones, and furthermore demanded the restitution, among others, of the Dead Sea Scrolls (which were bought by Israelis in New York and elsewhere or seized during the 1967 war). They argued that the authors of the Dead Sea Scrolls, the Essenes, had been an "ancient Palestinian sect." Jesus Christ too is being claimed nowadays by Palestinian intellectuals as an "ancient Palestinian." Palestinian nationalism which has so often in the past taken cues from Zionism seems nowadays to be in need of archaeology to assist in nation building.

It may well be that both Israeli and Palestinian claims on archaeological sites are merely opening positions in what is bound to be a long-lasting negotiation. Except when it comes to Jerusalem, which is a hypersensitive subject for everyone, those claims are not likely to jeopardize a future settlement in the name of the past, however evocative or important the sites may be for the sense of identity on both sides.

We have all heard the old saying that archaeology thrives on ruins and war. There are more known ancient sites per square mile in Israel than in any other country. In Jerusalem alone we know of some fifty major sieges, sacks, captures, and destructions dur-

ing the past thirty centuries (three in this century alone), and of at least ten more or less violent changes in the ruling religion. Jerusalem is a veritable outdoor Louvre of the history of warfare. A short time before his death W. H. Auden visited Jerusalem. I saw him standing one afternoon on the terrace of Mishkenot Saanim, the municipal guest house, admiring the magnificent view of the Old City. The mayor, Teddy Kollek, was standing there, too. They were both looking out across the valley of Hinnom, at the battlements and the tombs, and the mayor said in a laconic tone that Jerusalem would be a beautiful place if it weren't for the wars, and the orthodox of all faiths, and their squabbles and their riots. He said this, Auden recalled later, as one would say in London that it would be a lovely place except for the weather. Shortly after this Auden wrote the following lines, in one of his poems before he died in 1973:

From Archaeology
one moral, at least, may be drawn
to wit, that all

our school text-books lie.
What they call History
is nothing to vaunt of,

being made, as it is
by the criminal in us:
goodness is timeless.

An Anthropological Culture Shift

A federal law that puts Native American rights and religion ahead of scientific curiosity is reshaping North American anthropology and archeology.

Museums, universities, and federal agencies are beginning to clean skeletons out of their closets all across the United States. They're clearing out other objects important to Native Americans as well, such as sacred shields and medicine bundles. This flurry of housecleaning is prompted not by a shortage of storage space, but by a law that recognizes Native Americans' claims to their past.

The Native American Graves Protection and Repatriation Act (NAGPRA) requires some 5000 federally funded institutions and government agencies to return Native American skeletons, funerary and sacred objects, and items of profound cultural importance to American Indian tribes and Native Hawaiians. Although NAGPRA was passed 4 years ago, it didn't really start to bite until last November, when facilities had to notify the tribes about the sacred and cultural items in their collections. That was just the first step in a process that will see tens of thousands of scientifically valuable items handed over, many of them for reburial, over the next few years. Hundreds of scientists who depend upon this material will be cut off from their research data, and North American anthropology and archeology will be changed forever.

"The reality is there's been a shift in the equation," says Dan Monroe, executive director of the Peabody Essex Museum in Salem, Massachusetts. "It's a matter of basic human rights versus scientific rights, and in this new equation in many instances those scientific rights have been constrained, no doubt about it." But NAGPRA isn't just placing skeletons and artifacts out of reach of scientific study. It's also giving Native Americans influence over what research is conducted and published. Scientists who were once accustomed to "doing as they damned well-pleased," as one anthropologist put it, must now involve Native Americans in almost every phase of their research—from requesting research permits to study collections to, in some cases, passing completed studies to tribal councils for prepublication review. "The shocking thing is that we really haven't spent time talking to the Indians," admits Thomas J. Green, director of the Arkansas Archeological Survey. "NAGPRA is forcing us to do that, and maybe once we get through these issues, we'll see that there's actually a natural alliance between the archeological and Indian communities."

But this bridge-building doesn't mean that the bitter debate that preceded passage of NAGPRA 4 years ago has died down. Many scientists still decry the repatriation as an improper melding of church and state, and they are particularly upset that the law provides Native Americans very broad ancestral claims—even on items that scientists say predate the origins of the tribes themselves.

From the Indians' perspective, however, the return of sacred items is long overdue. "The reality is, it's our stuff," says John Pretty On Top, cultural director for the Crow. "We made it and we know best how to use it and care for it. . . . And now because of the law, we're going to get it back." Leigh Jenkins, the director of the Hopi Cultural Preservation Office, notes that graves and religious icons of all other peoples in America were never treated the way Indian material was treated. "Every tribe has sad stories about graves being pillaged, the offerings and skeletons taken, and ritual objects removed," he says. "Scientists always had one standard for themselves and another for Indians."

A shift of power

Now that museums have notified tribes that they possess sacred and culturally important Indian material, the next step will be to determine exactly what will be returned. By 1995, the museums must provide detailed inventories of all skeletal remains and funerary goods, and the tribes can then request that the material be shipped back to them. NAGPRA provides a set of guidelines to help Native Americans and museums sort out what can and cannot be returned, but both sides anticipate disagreements—particularly over prehistoric remains and burial goods. "Those are emerging as the flash point," says Jonathan Haas, McArthur Curator of North American anthropology and archeology at Chicago's Field Museum of Natural History.

No anthropologist interviewed by Science objected to reburial when the

State Laws Provide a Glimpse of the Future

As researchers and museum officials begin to implement a new law requiring repatriation of Native American skeletons and artifacts, some clues to what lies ahead may be found in the operation of similar state laws already on the books. One of those laws in Idaho sent "Buhla," a 10,675-year-old female skeleton, back into the ground in 1992. Idaho state archeologists had recovered the bones from a gravel pit operation near the town of Buhl just 3 years earlier. During this time the remains had only been studied for 3 days, by a single physical anthropologist—research that was delayed because of technical problems in obtaining a radiocarbon date.

The remains and the artifacts found with the skeleton were reburied on the Shoshone-Bannock reservation, 100 miles from where it was found—although archeologists doubt any Shoshone-Bannock inhabited the region 10,000 years ago. In the tradition of the Shoshone-Bannock, the woman is perceived as "our Mother; the Mother of us all," explains Diana K. Yupe, a Shoshone-Bannock anthropologist. "To us, she is our ancestor, and hers is not just a decomposed body; she is alive."

"There are about 25 skeletons in North America older than 8500 [before present]," says Thomas J. Green, the former Idaho state archeologist and now director of the Arkansas Archeological Survey. "And of these, she was one of the oldest and certainly one of the best preserved. Now, probably the most signifi-

Reinterred. Skull of 10,675-year-old skeleton reburied under Idaho state law.

cant thing about Buhla is that she's reburied."

Archeologists expect to see a similar fate befall many of the funerary goods now stored in museums. A 1991 Arizona case, in which archeologists were complying with state law, suggests what might be in store on a broad scale. When a new highway in Phoenix was going to destroy a portion of a known, large Hohokam settlement called Pueblo Grande that dated from 900 to 1450 years ago, the state called in an archeological consulting firm to salvage and record what was found. Eventually, 2000 funerary vessels and 800 skeletons were recovered—the largest such collection of Hohokam pottery and individuals ever found. "It was the best collection of its kind," says Cory Breternitz, president of Soil Systems

Inc., the archeological firm that handled the dig. "And we'd worked out an agreement about the study of this material with the tribes ahead of time." But in the spring of 1991, the tribal council objected to the study of the human remains, and a few months later every item was reburied on the Ak-Chin Reservation.

Also destined for reburial is the Grasshopper Collection, skeletal and funerary material dating from 1300 to 1400 years ago that was recovered from a large Mogollan complex on the White Mountain Apache Reservation over the past 30 years. Consisting of more than 700 skeletons and thousands of artifacts, including arrow points, stone and bone tools, beads, shells, pottery, and hair ornaments, it is now housed in the Arizona State Museum. According to University of Arizona archeologist William A. Longacre, who oversaw much of the excavation, it is "the best documented and largest collection from a single Native American community that's been occupied consistently for 100 years.

But the collection is going back into the ground. Although the excavations took place on White Mountain Apache land, the material is culturally linked to the Zuni and Hopi—and the three tribes have decided they want all the skeletons and grave goods repatriated and reburied. "It's an incredible resource that we are going to lose," Longacre says. "From our perspective, it is a terrible loss. But from theirs [the Indians], it's a terrible thing that we've done."   —V.M.

remains were those of a known individual—in fact, scientists expressed dismay that such items should have found their way to a museum in the first place. But the return and reburial of skeletal material several hundreds or thousands of years old, where ancestral relationships are not always clear, has researchers groaning—especially since these materials are often scientifically the most interesting. To American Indians, however, a skeleton's age

is immaterial. "We don't accept any artificial cutoff date set by scientists to separate us from our ancestors," says Walter R. Echo-Hawk, the attorney for the Native American Rights Fund, one of the groups that fought for NAGPRA. "What Europeans want do with their dead is their business," he says. "We have different values."

NAGPRA, in fact, places those values on an equal footing with scientific evidence. "The law explicitly says

that their oral traditions have standing in this process," explains C. Timothy McKeown, an ethnographer and program leader for the implementation of NAGPRA at the National Park Service, the federal agency charged with overseeing the law. Thus, a tribe can claim prehistoric remains if tribal tradition says that its people were created in the same region where the remains were found—a claim that has already led to reburial of some collections under existing state laws (see box). (If a museum objects to these claims, then a special NAGPRA review committee will make the final determination, weighing both the scientific and tribal evidence.)

Many museums, in order to maintain good relations with the tribes and salvage some material for study, have already handed over, or are in the process of doing so, large collections of skeletons. The Field Museum, where more than 300 scholars a year come to use the extensive Native American materials, has given back 62 of its 2000 remains, and expects to return the rest. At the Smithsonian Institution's physical anthropological collections, 2000 skeletons have been returned for reburial, with the remaining 14,000 skeletons set to follow.

Many scientists are troubled by the prospect of massive reburials of prehistoric materials because they shut the door on studies using new techniques. "Once the material is gone, it is no longer available for restudy or for future studies using new techniques, nor can anyone check the original data for observer error—something that is fundamental to science," says Jane Buikstra, a physical anthropologist at the University of Chicago. Douglas Owsley, a physical and forensic anthropologist at the Smithsonian, points out that "we can do studies now—on health and disease, demographic rates, settlement patterns—that we simply had no inkling of when I was in graduate school [in the 1970s]. To say that we have learned all we can from these skeletons is a serious mistake."

Take the case of Ethne Barnes, a physical anthropologist at Witchita State University, who recently developed a new method for identifying developmental defects in adult skeletons. "The data collected in the past on these skeletons has very little value to my work," says Barnes, "because I'm looking at them from a completely new perspective and scaling the growth patterns differently than others have done." Barnes began her study shortly before NAGPRA, using skeletal material housed in the Smithsonian and other museums. Initially, she needed

only the museums' permission to study the collections, but now she must also seek each tribe's permission, which is not always forthcoming. "The Cochiti Pueblo flat-out said no, while the Hopi were very interested," she says. However, the Hopi want to see her research results before she publishes. "It is a kind of censorship," she agrees, "but I also think we should be collaborating with the Indians."

So far, most of the attention has been focused on NAGPRA's impact on archeology and physical anthropology, but some scientists think it will eventually have a major effect on cultural anthropology as well. Lynne Goldstein, a mortuary archeologist at the University of Wisconsin, Milwaukee, says Native Americans aren't going to be satisfied with the return of bones and artifacts: "They'll ask next for field notes, tapes, photographs; and they'll insist that you have their permission before you publish." Goldstein's concern is more than hypothetical: The Hopi Tribe, in its response to the museums' inventory letters, asked museums to declare a moratorium on the study of any archival material pertaining to the Hopi people—a request that has stunned the museum community, although to the Hopi it seems a logical extension of NAGPRA. "We feel very strongly that there is a connection between the intellectual knowledge and the sacred objects that were collected from our religious altars: The knowledge and the object are one," says Leigh Jenkins. "The Hopi people want that esoteric knowledge protected right now."

An alliance out of adversity?

Despite all the turmoil NAGPRA has caused, scientists and Indians alike agree that the law has started to bring them together. Scientists, says Goldstein, "have to look at this situation pragmatically because the reality is, we lost. . . . [F]or those of us doing excavations, we're going to have to be a lot more responsible collecting information and sharing it with the people we're studying."

Not sharing information appears to be at the root of much of the distrust

now afflicting academic researchers. Archeologists, for example, excavated homes and burials of the Pawnee people for more than a half-century before they ever contacted the tribe, says Roger Echo-Hawk, a Pawnee graduate student studying the relationship between oral history and archeology at the University of Colorado, Boulder. Indeed, scientists admit they made little effort in the past to involve Native Americans. "We've had to move from the ethics of conquest to the ethics of collaboration," says Martin Sullivan, director of Phoenix, Arizona's Heard Museum.

Still, scientists should "not look at collaboration through rose-colored glasses," says Goldstein, who points to her excavation last summer of a cemetery in California's Fort Ross State Park as an example. It took her 18 months to acquire all the necessary permissions—from state agencies, California and Alaskan tribes, the Russian Orthodox Church, and the local coroner's office—and then she went out of her way to keep all parties informed as the dig progressed. "Was it the easiest way to do archeology?" she asks. "Hell, no. But it was effective. Everybody felt they were a part of it."

Similar alliances, if they take shape, will probably coalesce around a new series of tribal museums. Not every tribe is planning to rebury all returned material; many have opened or are planning to open museums of their own, as the Confederated Tribes of the Warm Springs Reservation did last summer in Oregon. Some 120 such institutions now exist, and although some are little more than cultural centers, others maintain small research centers, which are staffed with Indian scientists.

The museums will have the material, and much of it (aside from sacred objects) will be made available to academic researchers, who are willing to work with tribal councils. "We do have common ground," says Roger Echo-Hawk. "If we build on that, we may create a new science of North American archeology."

-Virginia Morell

When My Grandmother
is Your Database:
Reactions to Repatriation

Nathalie F S Woodbury

Certainly nothing concerning the past is more present than the issue of repatriation. Establishing federal and state policies of skeletal and artifact return (see January, March, April 1991 *AN*s) was not the result of a swift Indian raid on American museums, but of a long, steady campaign in the '70s and '80s by concerned Native Americans using communication, consultation and the legal system at both state and national levels. Confrontation, a form of communication, has been present, as has resentment, on the part of both Indians and anthropologists—among the latter, especially the archeologists, who dig literally into the past to reconstruct it, and the biological anthropologists, who use skeletal material to study such areas as disease, diet and genetic relationships.

The reaction of a senior archeologist to restraints on dealing with Indian remains is printed below. This letter from *The Teocentli* (January 1991) represents an extreme view.

Sixty-five years ago, when I began my archaeological career, I never dreamed that I would live to see the death of archaeology in the Northern Hemisphere. Fortunately, during the 46 years of my activities, I spent much of my time in the field, excavating some 100 major prehistoric sites in the northeast, and putting together a veritable jigsaw puzzle of data into a comprehensive picture of aboriginal occupations.

No longer is it possible to carry on such researches. It seems that everywhere there is an Indian waiting to look over one's shoulder and demand a halt to the work and the confiscation of one's discoveries. A classic example is going on right now (December 1990) at Wenatchee, Washington, where perhaps the most striking Paleo-Indian find on record is being closed down, unfinished, by the Colville Indians, whose possible ancestral relationship to the site is nil.

With only oral traditions, the actual history of the Indians rests almost entirely on the work of archaeologists, physical anthropologists, and ethnohistorians, a fact apparently completely lost on most Indians. They would have us believe in a pan-Indian religion, philosophy, and set of traditions, largely at variance with the findings of science.

Just as the archeologist quoted above is not altogether accurate in his appraisal of the situation, so neither is Vine Deloria Jr, a Standing Rock Sioux who is a professor of political science at Arizona and holds a JD and a theology degree. Deloria wrote "A Simple Question of Humanity: The Moral Dimensions of the Reburial Issue" in the *Legal Review* of the Native American Rights Fund (Fall 1989). The article includes a section, "How valuable are Indian remains for science?" from which I quote:

When Indian tribes approach museums and other institutions to seek return of human remains, they are often told that it is necessary to keep the Indian human remains because of their great value to science. Allegedly profound and sophisticated experiments are being conducted with these remains which promise great things for all of humanity. But what are these profound studies? In spite of the repeated attempts by American Indians to get a bibliography of the studies being done by these so-called scientists, scholars have yet to produce any significant materials which would justify their claims. Scientific arguments should therefore not be given credence unless and until a clear and concise statement is made explaining the urgency and hysteria behind the scientific opposition to the reburial of Indian human remains. At the present time the arguments used by museum directors and scientists appear to be merely a crude appeal to the authority status of science and little else.

Assuming, for the moment, that American Indian human remains are critical to scientific knowledge, no explanation has been given regarding the peculiar characteristics which make Indian remains more valuable than the remains of other races. What could possibly be learned exclusively from Indian bones which could not also be learned from the bones of other races? The answers that Indians generally receive to this question are superficial and unsatisfactory. Diet? The annual reports of the Commissioner of Indian Affairs, particularly the reports of the Indian agents, can provide much more accurate information on the diets of these people in historical times. For periods of time earlier than modern recorded history, it is a matter of such tenuous speculation that scientific tests would not reveal much of anything. It is a fact, recorded in the agents' reports, that many Indians starved to death on the reservations when Congress failed to appropriate funds for rations which were due Indians. To conduct tests to see whether or not Indians starved is superfluous and would be comparable to testing the bones of holocaust victims to see if they had died of malnutrition.

Some representatives of science claim that the prevalence of disease can be recorded using human remains in specific tests. But most of the diseases afflicting Indians in historical times are well recorded in government reports; discovering diseases of earlier Indians would produce information only mildly interesting and, in any case, speculative in the extreme. It is also suggested that by testing bones and other materials it is possible to demonstrate that American Indians actually came from Asia. But why should this proposition need to be supported by tests? It is absolute doctrine for most scientists in spite of the massive evidence in the oral traditions of the tribes that they had their origin elsewhere. In any case, tests on human remains cannot tell which way the footprints were heading and it may well be that Asia was populated from the western hemisphere, but no present test could confirm or deny that proposition.

Let us suppose for the moment that a great deal of information about disease can be elicited from human remains. Why use Indians remains when there are so many other, easily identified remains that would yield an incredible body of important and vitally needed information? In the 19th century the southern coastal cities were periodically ravaged by epidemics of typhoid fever and cholera. What actually caused these epidemics? Did they strike only the slaves, the free whites, or the slave-owning families? We have records and graveyards available. We can run precise tests on the remains of people who died of these diseases and those who survived them. Why isn't the Smithsonian Institution digging up the family graveyards of the first families of Savannah, Charleston, and New Orleans, perhaps even Mobile, in an effort to obtain this data?

It is a known fact that human beings in America are growing in average size and stature of skeletal structure. Soldiers who served in the American Rev-

olution were a bit smaller than those who were engaged in military service in the Civil War. The First and Second World Wars also saw a rise in the average size of the men in the military. What caused this increase in size? Was it the benefits of democracy, since most of these wars were waged to establish and protect democracy? Was it the rations or the military training? Did the size and capability of the weapons influence the growth of body size? These questions are important because we intend to continue waging wars and we should be at work now doing everything we can to produce future armies that are bigger and better than what we have historically fielded in our wars.

Douglas Ubelaker, a biological anthropologist at the National Museum of Natural History, and Lauryn Guttenplan Grant, Office of General Counsel, Smithsonian, published "Human Skeletal Remains: Preservation or Reburial?" in the 1989 Yearbook of Physical Anthropology; the abstract, included below, summarizes the article's coverage. It provides a balance to Deloria's. Incidentally, the literature cited is a good start on "a bibliography of studies being done," which Deloria claims American Indians are unable to procure.

> Recent years have witnessed a surge of scientific interest in the biocultural analysis of mortuary sites and human remains. Concurrently, members of the American Indian community and others have questioned the merit of scientific study and argued for reburial of Indian human remains and associated artifacts. Strong differences of opinion have led to varied responses among museums, professional organizations, federal and state organizations, and individuals. This article addresses the scientific, ethical, religious, political, and legal issues raised by this debate.

Although archeologists (and physical anthropologists) grumble about "loss of the database," recognition of "traditional interests in human remains among a diversity of interests" is included in the formal statement on reburial of the Society for American Archaeology (Bulletin 1986). The American Association of Physical Anthropologists passed a resolution on the reburial of skeletal remains at its 1982 annual meeting. Both organizations urged

case-by-case consideration. More recently the SAA has published in the April 1990 Bulletin "A Perspective on Reburial and Repatriation," by Keith Kintigh, chair of the SAA Task Force.

The Yearbook of Physical Anthropology article includes a state-by-state summary of reburial legislation (p 275) and also provides a short section on international repatriation developments. The past decade has brought increasing activity in Australia where "the [1984] Archaeological and Aboriginal Relics Preservation Act of the state of Victoria was amended to make it unlawful for any person to hold aboriginal remains without government consent" (p 279). In 1988 a London auction house-sale of a tattooed Maori head was halted by court action brought by the Maori Tribal Council. Ubelaker and Grant write, "An open question now is the fate of the remaining 150 Maori heads extant around the world, including 30 at the American Museum of Natural History in New York" (p 279).

Anthropology Today, the bimonthly publication of the royal Anthropological Institute, reports on repatriation of Australian Aborigine remains in the February 1991 issue; the claims, attitudes and arguments are familiar.

> The move to repatriate Aboriginal relics from the UK is reviewed in the Financial Times (8/12/90). Since the 1820s museums have collected Aboriginal skeletons, and Tasmanian and Australian Aborigines have increasingly campaigned for the return of these. "The campaign for repatriation of human remains makes the issue of returning the Elgin Marbles look like a genteel sideshow." Why? Curators who return the Marbles will know these will not be destroyed when handed back, but when the human remains are handed over these will almost certainly be cremated or buried. Aboriginal activists claim that Britain's institutions hold about 2000 items "which must be returned if the spirits of their land are to cease crying for them." The debate is a difficult one for members of both sides. Great steps have recently been made in the methods of analysis of human remains, but Bob Weatherall, a barrister who is leading the campaign, points out that it should be decided by the Aboriginal community what is "significant research." It looks as if the Aboriginal

community is winning. The Australian government has announced in October that it will be asking overseas institutions to hand back human remains, and in March Irish premier Charles Haughey intervened directly to force the Royal College of Surgeons in Dublin to give up the skull of "Shiney," to which the surgeons were bitterly opposed. In June the Pitt-Rivers Museum returned five skulls and a penis, and in October the Kelvin Grove Museum in Glasgow returned remains of three individuals. Items were returned also from Bradford University and Peterborough City Museum. The campaigners are lobbying the Royal College of Surgeons in London for the remains of 53 unnamed individuals, the National Museum of Scotland with 160 items, and collections in France and Germany. The main criterion by which the remains are returned is whether the person issuing the request can be shown to be related, but it is exactly these well-documented remains which are considered by scientists to have the "best" scientific value. Scientists are now able to identify sex, kinship, racial affinities and medical history of 5000-year-old bones, and are able to detect information about diet, health and maturation from the sectioning of teeth. Archaeologists such as Don Brothwell hope that Aborigines too, as American Indians have increasingly done, take responsibility as custodians of irreplaceable evidence of their past; *FT* comment to this is that "the idea of educating Aborigines to take a different view of their past can have the ring of intellectual colonialism."

Archeology Division

Patricia A. McAnany

Contributing Editor

A few years ago, the *AN* ran a series of articles on Repatriation—the issues and the process. Since that time, many anthropologists working in museums, within the federal government and within the academy, have been involved in "operationalizing" the repatriation mandate as set forth by NAGPRA (Native American Graves Protection Act) and earlier by the National Museum of the American Indian Act. It can be said that nothing has so profoundly changed the practice of North American anthropology as have these pieces of legislation. The change has been all-pervasive and, in many cases, painful for all involved. I thought that archaeologists might want to read about repatriation as an ongoing effort and as a movement toward collaborative research between anthropologists and Native Americans. With this thought in mind, I interviewed Thomas W. Killion, who heads the Repatriation Program at the National Museum of Natural History at the Smithsonian Institution. Often dubbed "America's attic," the NMNH has initiated a comprehensive inventory of human remains and cultural materials: this inventory is repatriation-driven. Through the Repatriation Program, protocols for handling repatriation requests have been established and a program developed to host representatives from Native American communities who want to conduct research at the NMNH in order to better understand the nature and content of the collections. Before beginning the interview, I would like to take this time to thank Carina Pech of Trial Farm, Belize, who transcribed this interview and entered the bulk of it into the computer. Without her assistance, I could not have finished this column while running a field research project and a Boston U. field school at K'axob, Belize.

Tom, you are heading up the Repatriation effort at one of the focal museum institutions of our country—what is the size of your staff and how secure is your funding base?

There are presently 20 people on board in the Repatriation Program at the Natural History Museum. They are divided into several groups: one is located in the physical anthropology laboratory, where we do the documentation of skeletal remains. Another section of our operation includes people who are working on responses to ongoing cases and are writing reports. We also have support staff who assist those individuals writing case reports and there is administrative staff as well. We are funded directly from Congress on an annual basis. The language of the law indicates that we be renewed on a yearly basis until the work is done.

How many Native Americans have been involved as employees, contractors or interns in the repatriation effort conducted by your office?

We have a fair number of native peoples working in the office: perhaps the largest number have come through the intern program that is coordinated within the Smithsonian itself. We've had student participants from universities and tribes across the country. They have assisted in case work: that is, they work directly with our case officers or with the person responding to a request for the return of materials. Other times they assist in developing an inventory for the tribes with which we are working. In other words, Native American interns and students have been research assistants, pulling together records, summarizing information and helping to get the case reports completed. They learn how repatriation works here and, in many cases, keep their tribal groups informed as to procedures at the Natural History Museum. In addition to interns, we've also had Native American contractors work for us. Two contractors from Zuni Pueblo assisted in the documentation of cultural materials, as opposed to human remains. Working full time for us now is Phillip Minthorn, who is Cayuse-Nez Perce. Phillip is working on documentation of archaeological objects that are part of a large collection from the River Basin surveys conducted in the 1960s and 1950s.

Well, it sounds as if you have been very successful in integrating the Native American community into the repatriation process. In terms of policy, how has your office responded to the repatriation mandate?

Most immediately, what we have done is to prioritize our activities parallel to the law we are following, which is a bit different from NAGPRA. Our law indicates only that we document and, if indicated, offer for repatriation human remains and the objects with which they were buried.

NAGPRA, on the other hand, is a much broader mandate to return or to evaluate for return human remains as well as other sensitive kinds of cultural objects.

But why is there a difference between NAGPRA and the law that you are following?

The law that we are following is called the National Museum of the American Indian Act, and within that there are repatriation provisions. The National Museum of the American Indian Act was passed primarily to establish a museum devoted to Native Americans on the mall in Washington, DC. As part of that, the prototype repatriation legislation was included so the collections that are to become part of the National Museum of the American Indian would first be evaluated for repatriation. This law was passed in 1989 and served as the prototype for NAGPRA, but NAGPRA was broadened to deal with issues beyond the collections in the museums and to include additional objects not part of the original National Museum of the American Indian Act.

Does your office receive requests from Native American tribes for the return of materials? In other words, how is the procedure initiated?

The law mandates that we initiate an inventory of all potential remains and funerary objects included in the museum collections. At the same time that the law was passed, a lot of groups across the country began making specific requests. Some of them were very broad requests for all materials that may fit under the mandate of repatriation and a lot of groups don't distinguish between our more limited mandate and NAGPRA. On the other hand, some of the groups have very specific knowledge of materials or remains that are in the museum and specifically request those. So much of our work is request-driven. We ask people to initiate a request with a letter indicating the kinds of materials and human remains they are interested in getting information about or actually recovering. The requests could be for the return as indicated under the law or simply for information so that a group can make a decision about requesting a return. We ask for background information on geographical region and time period in order to focus our research more specifically and to help us determine whether the relevant materials or human remains may be culturally affiliated with the tribe requesting their return.

On a broader level, as a piece of legislation, NAGPRA is an example of what Republicans are now calling an "unfunded mandate." That is, museums—apart from the Smithsonian—are told to do something but are not given any resources with which to do it. I have heard from anthropologists working in small museums who are trying to work with the NAGPRA legislation and are hard put to follow the letter and the spirit of the law. Do you have any advice for smaller institutions as to how they might comply with the law and seek out funding?

There is a difference between our operation and other museums and organizations affected by this law. There was no real funding provided to museums, or to tribes for that matter. This is a problem encountered not only by museums but also by the tribes who must muster resources to put forth requests. There is a small amount of funding provided for repatriation that is distributed by the Archaeological Assistance Division of the National Park Service. It's a pool of about $2 million for grants to museums and tribes. Proposals are evaluated by the Park Service. As you may well imagine, that money is quickly used up by the large number of museums and tribes in the US, and competition for that money is stiff. The actual amounts, once they are distributed, are not that large. Essentially, that is the only funding source of which I am aware, unless small museums and tribes approach other funding agencies for support of repatriation activities. In the Park Service's granting program, the successful funding requests are collaborative efforts on the part of a museum working with tribes to identify sensitive materials or human remains and also include a plan of consultation between an institution and a tribe or tribes to determine the best way to proceed with either repatriation or some other alternative to repatriation.

I understand that many of the cases you have been handling—and in which returns of human remains have occurred—were not actually part of archaeological collections. Can you tell us about some of the cases that your office has handled?

We have made it a priority to deal first with those collections in this museum that came to the museum through the activities of the US military on the Plains in the second half of the 19th century. These human remains were sent to the Army Medical Museum from forts and military posts in the western areas and were the result of the wars between Native Americans and the military at that time. So a lot of the remains are recent, sometimes only 4 or 5 generations removed from people living today. In many cases, the remains were from historic incidents that are well understood and the individuals were related to descendant groups that are still living on or off reservations throughout the country. Priority was given to those remains that were in the Army Medical Museum collection which, through a series of transfers, ended up in the Museum of Natural History. They are really a different sort of case than the archaeological remains that come from distant time periods and for which cultural affiliation is much more difficult to establish.

It sounds as if you face some rather difficult issues here especially in trying to ascribe ethnic affiliation to some very old archaeological materials in the Museum. What, to your mind, are the greatest challenges to carrying out the repatriation mandate?

I think the greatest challenge is to establish relationships with the Native American communities most concerned with repatriation. Obviously, these are the communities and representatives of these communities that worked on the Hill to get the legislation passed. These people believed that the curation of human remains and sensitive objects were problematic and needed to be dealt with on a national level. How do we move from meeting that mandate to establishing forward-looking relationships with these communities? We would like a relationship that would allow us to grow in terms of anthropological understanding of the diversity of Native American groups that live in this country today. Also, how do we go about developing a collaborative effort to understand their heritage with participation by them in the inquiry into their past, their cultural heritage and reflecting their concerns about their culture and what relationship they have to the past? I think that the greatest challenge will come during that period after repatriation—and there is life after repatriation. I think that we should strive to establish relationships with groups which will reflect an understanding of their culture, not only where it came from but how it is changing today. It is important to incorporate into an anthropological perspective what Native groups think are the most important ways of presenting their culture at the national level. In other words, bringing them to the table as fully enfranchised participants in an endeavor that has been ongoing here at the Museum for 100 years—namely, the understanding of cultural diversity that exists in North America and throughout the world.

There seems to be a limited understanding of repatriation within our discipline and little effort to integrate issues of repatriation into graduate training programs. Why do you think that this is the case and what could be done to change it?

Repatriation has been a real challenge to the normative practice of anthropology or to anthropology as business as usual. It certainly has been a challenge to that part of anthropology that exists within the museum community because repatriation means that business as usual is not something that can continue. I think that the first step is to understand repatriation as a cultural process rather than an onerous task. Repatriation is a potential area of growth in anthropological understanding, as opposed to a threat to the prerogative of anthropology. I think

that anthropologists normally think of themselves as the "voice of native people" around the world. An anthropologist goes into a community and brings information about that community back to museums and the academy and, hopefully, that information is disseminated widely. Repatriation turns that relationship upside down. We are no longer the advocates of Native cultures, but are on the other side of the fence as a group or an institution against which Native peoples are struggling. In this case, Native groups want respect for their human remains and for their objects on their own terms regardless of what the anthropological community might desire. We are looking a mirror and seeing ourselves in a much different light—not as advocates but as adversaries. I think that this altered perspective certainly is one of the largest difficulties of repatriation although one would think that we have moved beyond that point. Unfortunately, in the general mainstream of anthropology repatriation is still seen as a threat to the prerogative of anthropologists to conduct their inquiry; but, the threat is really to a type of anthropology that does not integrate inquiry with the sensitivities and rights of the living descendants of the materials with which archaeologists work or with the contemporary peoples from whom the objects that are held in museums were collected.

This situation is exacerbated by the very difficult economic conditions that most Native American groups face and their real separation from the anthropologists who have been interested either in their past or in their contemporary culture. The potential is here, however, to reconnect with these communities—to do an anthropology that not only includes a consideration of the past but also of contemporary groups and their relationship, as they see it, to their material culture and to their past. In other words, enfranchising Native groups as decision makers in inquiry, in presentation of their culture and ultimately in the disposition of the remains and materials that are held in the museums. I think there is a great potential here for anthropological learning and for understanding cul-

tural process and transformation. Certainly, we have the opportunity to establish relationships that will go beyond repatriation to ensure the active expression of Native American voices and, for that matter, ethnic voices in anthropological inquiry at museums throughout the world.

We have been discussing the dialectical relationship between Native Americans and anthropologists. This dynamic reminds me of another emerging dialectic within anthropology—one that is being played out in the pages of American Anthropologist. *Specifically, I refer to the dialogue between our colleagues who see anthropology as a more humanistic kind of endeavor and those who see it as primarily a scientific discipline. I want to ask you how repatriation relates to this debate?*

One clear way in which I see that it relates is in the real gap between many Native American communities and the biomedical and physical studies of the remains of their ancestors. This gap reflects a rejection by Native Americans of science as practiced within the academy and a rejection of technical approaches in general. More narrowly expressed, it is a disinterest in those approaches that don't take into consideration cognitive or humanistic questions. This rebuff of the science of archaeology partly may be a result of the failure of some scientists within anthropology to establish links between human values and social issues and the "hard" science they practice. I think these links can be made but, for the most part, Native Americans do share a rejection of science for the sake of fact-building and of the perspective that understanding can come only from a very empirical approach. Frankly, much anthropological research is not at all related to the kinds of social issues that Native peoples are facing on a regular basis. So there is a rejection of empiricism and, within many Native communities, a move toward appreciating the importance of non-science-based forms of knowledge. As I see it, this reaction parallels that within part of the academy as well. I think that the rejection of science within the Native community also comes from a more fundamental rejection of Western approaches to their culture. Such approaches have had very little positive feedback into their lives in terms of preserving their heritage, improving their economic standing and upgrading the quality of life for Native peoples. In my opinion, there is very little that has come from archaeology and from physical anthropology that can be directly related to improvements on that level.

Now, there is potential in working to make more generally understood the value of biomedical approaches to the human body, particularly what we can learn from more ancient human remains n terms of the history of diseases and health conditions under which earlier populations of Native Americans existed on this continent. There is also a great deal of value in exploring archaeology in terms of documenting Native American presence on this continent and the territories across which Native American polities coalesced. I think that there is a mutual interest on the part of archaeologists and Native Americans to understand boundaries and territories and, in a general sense, how human social organization evolved and functioned. Native Americans have demonstrated a great interest in documenting their presence here, asserting their claim to lands and, potentially, achieving a return of some of the sovereignty they once had over these lands. I see good possibilities in the future for collaborative work between archaeologists and Native Americans.

Your perspective is fairly optimistic and suggests that the paths of archaeologists and Native Americans may yet prove to be compatible. Thank you for giving us some very thoughtful answers to the questions and issues swirling around repatriation.

Indians, Archaeologists, and the Future

Vine Deloria, Jr.

Vine Deloria, Jr., Department of History, Center for Studies of Ethnicity and Race in America, Campus Box 234, University of Colorado, Denver, CO 80309-0234

The most recent encounter between American Indians and archaeologists, over the Native American Graves Protection and Repatriation Act (P.L. 101-601), has left hard feelings on both sides. From the Indian point of view, conflict will be inevitable so long as archaeologists maintain a stance that privileges their interests as scientists over all other human considerations. Nonetheless there are some areas where American Indians and archaeologists might develop cooperative ventures, for example, in the investigation of Precolumbian contact and diffusion, and in clarifying the status of sacred sites.

I realize that there is still considerable emotional baggage connected with the reburial issue that has been the most recent encounter between American Indians and archaeologists, and while I do not wish to reverse the progress made to date, I do feel a responsibility to represent some of the residual feelings that we see present in Indian minds across the country.

The Society for American Archaeology (SAA) did finally come to a compromise position that supported the Indian efforts to get the Native American Graves Protection and Repatriation Act (Public Law 101-601) passed, although not without some doing. Some representatives of the SAA feel that their final efforts of support should thereby mask what were some dreadfully arrogant attitudes earlier in the struggle. It may well be that we should simply move forward and make the best of the present situation, but we should also recognize that it will take more than a few representatives gathering together in civil conversations to erase the hard feelings on both sides of the issue.

Some of what I can gather as hard feelings from the Indian point of view stem back to the position that the scholarly community has enjoyed for the past century, i.e., that only scholars have the credentials to define and explain American Indians and that their word should be regarded as definitive and conclusive. Indians reject that attitude out of hand, and therefore when the reburial issue was first raised and we heard cries of "Science" and its sanctity given as the excuse for not considering the repatriation of Indian human remains and funerary objects, Indians naturally got their backs arched and resentments built quickly. We have been the objects of scientific investigations and publications for far too long, and it is our intent to become people once again, not specimens.

Science today has the edge in establishing itself as the primary source of truth because of the spectacular success of technology which, in the minds of the general public, is devised by people in white lab smocks busily providing us with more gadgets. Some scholars, particularly people in California, adopted the attitude that the Indian interest in human remains was purely political and had no emotional or religious substance while they, as scientists, were impartial and stood above the battle. Nothing could be further from the truth of course. Considering the vast financial and status rewards that the academic community bestows on its members, the chances are that scientists would lie, cheat, and steal in order to advance their personal careers. But the implication of crying out "Science" whenever reburial was mentioned was just the opposite—Indians were made to appear as if they were looting the scientific heritage instead of receiving back the remains of loved ones who had been illegally and immorally taken from them a century or more ago.

Conflicts will always arise, and increasingly so, as long as a substantial number of people in the academic establishment insist that their careers and research come before all other human considerations. This conflict is probably inherent in the nature of the academic enterprise itself. We have a society so wealthy that we can pay people outrageous salaries to become experts on butterfly wings, verb tenses of obscure Indian languages, and custodians of fragments of old pottery abandoned by earlier people. But in the extreme example, only the National Socialist German Workers' party of the 1930s and 1940s in Germany insisted they had the absolute right to use and dispose of human beings and human remains without giving any other people a voice in the proceedings.

I wish some of you could hear the descriptions of the medicine men who conducted the reburial ceremonies for some of the tribes. In these ceremonies the spirits of the people whose remains were being returned appeared. They asked surprisingly practical questions for spirits. Some wanted to know if it was possible to get the indelible ink removed from their bones. Others said their remains had no feet or no head and they wondered at the kind of people who would remove these parts of the body and what they thought human life was. I don't much care whether any of you believe in spirits or a life hereafter. I think it is foolish to pretend on the basis of a wholly materialistic science (which can only measure quantities) that there is nothing spiritual and nonmaterial in our universe. It is this attitude, as much as anything, that distinguishes Indians from the rest of American society and most certainly from the scientific endeavor. Whether there is sufficient proof of the Indian beliefs and experiences or not, it is a hazardous thing to assume without good cause that the Indians are lying or simply superstitious. Indeed, large numbers of non-Indians are now embracing the Indian beliefs in increasing numbers, so in some sense materialists are on the

losing side of this crest of the historical/emotional wave of sensitivities.

Archaeology has been a suspicious science for Indians from the very beginning. People who spend their lives writing tomes on the garbage of other people are not regarded as quite mentally sound in many Indian communities. And to define Indian civilizations by watching the change of pottery styles as archaeology once did is not exactly a process of compiling irrefutable knowledge; it is mere White man speculation and fiction and should be regarded as such. We all of us still carry the baggage of former days, and it should be a task in the days ahead for archaeologists who truly want cooperative ventures with American Indians to begin to communicate about some of the new techniques that are being used and the changes in dogmas and doctrines that are occurring as a result of the new instruments and processes available to you.

In this respect I wonder at the isolation of archaeologists today. I have in the neighborhood of 80 books dealing in one way or another with Precolumbian expeditions to the Western Hemisphere. These books range from utter nonsense to rather sophisticated and careful review of your own archaeological reports and the addition of new interpretations and efforts to interpret the anomalies that you seemed unable to understand at the time. I began to take this expanding body of literature seriously when I happened to mention Barry Fell's writing to people in the Smithsonian. Before I could even say whether I agreed with Fell or not, William Sturtevant and Ives Goddard got exceedingly heated and began to argue with me about Lybian verb tenses and some translation, or purported translation, of an inscription that Fell had made.

My rule of thumb is that the Smithsonian is the last bastion of nineteenth-century science, so if people there are against any new theory, the chances are they are dead wrong. Thus I have maintained a lively interest in the possibility of proving that some of the theories embraced by lay people regarding Precolumbian America will

someday be demonstrated. I will willingly grant that we have nothing in the way of small artifacts at some of these sites and that seems puzzling if the other aspects of the site seem to hold. But the "official" explanation I have received about the stone chambers in New England and the ogam inscriptions which seem to abound in other places is simply ludicrous.

Without even examining some of these sites, scholars have told me that they are root cellars or simply marks made by colonists' plows or Indians sharpening their arrows. Now some of the locations where these alleged ogam inscriptions are found are on inaccessible cliffs, and I have great difficulty imagining colonists hitching up their teams and suspending their plows over some abyss in order to make these marks. Additionally, there seems to be an abundance of old coins found in various parts of the country but most noticeably in the eastern United States. If I were to accept the usual scholarly explanation I would come to believe that the ships that brought immigrants from Europe were stuffed with British, German, and French coin collectors who brought hoards of old coins to this continent and then casually scattered them all over Ohio as a joke. In fact so many of these sites have been declared to be hoaxes that American society seems to have been filled with practical jokers during most of the 300 years of European occupation. Looking at the presidential candidates every four years is almost irrefutable evidence for your present interpretation of the alleged Precolumbian sites but I am still uncomfortable with the idea that NO contacts were made between Europe and North America before Columbus.

As a side note to this problem, I have been told that there is great debate between diffusionists and others over the interpretation of some digs and that many people feel they cannot advocate Precolumbian contact for to do so would mean demeaning the Indians and suggesting that they could not have made discoveries on their own. Strangely this debate also rages in Indian circles, and a few of my best friends are adamant about maintaining the theory of isolation in order to enhance the achievements of our ancestors. Here I part company with other Indians and urge you to take a good look at all possible theories of Precolumbian contacts and even the transmission of every cultural trait that is found elsewhere. Samuel Eliot Morrison is now dead, and we need no longer cringe in fear that he will discredit us for believing that someone besides Columbus visited these shores.

Unpleasant though it may be to some Indians, we need to know the truth about North American prehistory, and indeed that of the Western Hemisphere. I personally feel that unless and until we are in some way connected with world history as early peoples, perhaps even as refugees from Old World turmoils and persecutions, we will never be accorded full humanity. We cannot be primitive peoples who were suddenly discovered half a millenium ago. The image and interpretation are all wrong, and we are regarded as freaks outside historical time. During the Wounded Knee trials I was forced to go along with Bering Strait advocates and argue that Indians had come across from Siberia, during one of those times that you people manipulate by increasing or decreasing the amount of water tied up in the glaciers, and bringing along a very sophisticated culture and a protoscientific technology.

Standing in the hall of the courtroom one day, a non-Indian approached me and said "I am very interested in this Bering Strait theory. It proves we are all natives." I said that being here perhaps 40,000 or even 100,000 years is a little more than having arrived in third-class steerage in 1920. I don't think he got the point since he was a Nebraska intellectual, and we all know that the "N" on Nebraska football helmets represents "Knowledge." But

the point I wish to make is that this migration from Siberia is regarded as doctrine, but basically it is a fictional doctrine that places American Indians outside the realm of planetary human experiences. So I hope you will stop being so staid and respectable and begin an era of courageous speculation and openness and try to give Precolumbian expeditions serious consideration.

Finally, in recent months I have been working hard with the coalition of American Indians seeking to get federal legislation clarifying the status of sacred sites, and naturally archaeology is involved or eventually will become involved in this problem. I must honestly report to you that many Indians are looking to your discipline for specific technical assistance in this struggle. One problem is the requirement of courts, at the present time, to insist that the location be a longstanding sacred site, and so it will make a big difference whether or not continuous or at least consistent use of the site is demonstrated by scholarly means as well as by traditional religious leaders. Some locations have very little evidence of use because they were considered of sufficient spiritual power that few individuals were allowed to go there. Consequently the locations show very little evidence of Indian use. It's not as if annual Methodist picnics and camp revivals were held at these locations.

You will be pleased to know that some very powerful Indian spiritual leaders have decided to find a reliable archaeologist or group of archaeologists who can help them completely cover and record what is present at some of these sacred sites. These people are very worried that if the site is declared sacred it will be invaded by hundreds of New Agers looking for a spiritual experience. So there is concern that plants, paths, shrines, rocks, and other aspects of the site be care-

fully and accurately recorded in case the place is desecrated by the curious in the years to come.

We can look forward, therefore, to creating a more constructive relationship between scholars and the people they study if we look at the present and future and make an effort to leave the past behind us. One difficulty in making this transition is that we already have a large body of data which represents the efforts of the previous century, and we are stuck with these writings and with the language they represent, which is often derogatory and demeaning to American Indians. Students continue to have access to these materials and consequently old attitudes and stereotypes are perpetuated even in spite of our best efforts. Archaeologists might well consider what the field of law has done in a comparable situation. In law we have what basically amounts to modernization of concepts through the device of scholars and practicing attorneys working to create "restatements" of the law.

One project that might be considered in the decades ahead would be a cooperative effort between archaeologists and interested Indians to rework and restate the findings of major importance in terms and language that eliminates cultural bias and attempts to give an accurate summary of what is known. That task seems formidable, but with some few exceptions is not only manageable but probably an effort that is easily funded. We may not be able to promote such a project on a national scale, but we can certainly consider the beneficial impact such a recasting would create with respect to specific tribes and scholars and perhaps come up with a solution or alternative way of establishing good relations for the future.

Contemporary Archaeology

The origins of contemporary archaeology may be traced back to the nineteenth century. Several currents of thought and belief coalesced in this unique century. Some say it started with a Frenchman named Boucher de Perthes, who found odd-shaped stones on his property, stones that could be held comfortably by a human hand. Undoubtedly, thousands of other people made such finds throughout history. But to Monsieur de Perthes these stones suggested a novel meaning. He wondered if these odd rocks might not have been *tools* made by long-ago humans lost in the mists before history.

Other exciting changes were occurring in the epistemology of the nineteenth century that soon lent credibility to this hypothesis. There was the publication of *On the Origin of Species* by Charles Darwin in 1859. In this book, which, by the way, never mentioned humans or any implied relationship that they might have to contemporary apes, Darwin suggested a general process which became known as *natural selection,* wherein species could change gradually through time. This was a revolutionary idea because then even biologists believed that species were immutable. Now if species could change, the implication was that maybe even human beings (who were considered above nature) could change.

In addition, there was the concurrent emergence of the idea of *uniformitarianism,* which indicated that the Earth was old, very old, perhaps hundreds of thousands of years old. (It is in fact about five billion years old.) With this idea, the revolutionary possibility that human beings could have existed before history became more plausible. Such a serious challenge to the established wisdom that Earth was about 6,000 years old gave rise to a new age of speculation on the very nature of human beings. The newly emerging science of paleontology and the discovery and recognition of fossilized, extinct, forms of animal life further challenged the elevated status of human beings. Nineteenth-century (and earlier) philosophers challenged the very nature of being human. Among the intellectuals of the Western world, the long-held position of the anthropocentricism of the Christian view quickly shifted to a secular view of humans as part and parcel with nature and, thus, subject to the rules of nature and natural events without reference to theology.

It was within the juxtaposition of these new philosophies and sciences in the nineteenth century that Boucher de Perthes let his hypothesis on the antiquity of his stone tools be known. Throughout the world, others answered that they, too, had found these same odd-shaped stones and had thought similar thoughts. The study of archaeology had begun.

As a science evolves, it naturally diversifies. In the case of archaeology, there is some concern now that, as archaeologists continue toward greater diversity, they will specialize themselves right out of the mainstream of archaeology. However, as discussed in the overview of unit 1, archaeology is a subfield of cultural anthropology, and the shared cultural concept keeps the field of archaeology united. That is not to say that mainstream archaeology at this time is not being pulled in many different directions. However, these different directions might best be viewed as an expansion of traditional archaeological pursuits.

In this unit, articles deal with the interest in the preservation, conservation, reconstruction, and transformation of archaeological sites in the present and for the value of the sites themselves. Such is the direction of contemporary archaeology. This must be understood in terms of the new politicalization of archaeology. Serious attention must be directed toward the practical aspects of the financing of archaeology and alternate sources of labor for archaeological endeavors.

For example, wherein do archaeologists make moral judgments? What of the rights of developers, dam builders, and road builders? It is their livelihood to do these things even if it means destroying archaeological sites. In a sense, archaeologists may be the most potentially serious threat to archaeological sites. An archaeological site is a *nonrenewable* resource. Archaeological excavation is the systematic destruction of sites, or regions, and their total ecological context. Anything overlooked, mislaid, not measured or in some way not acknowledged is a lost piece of the past But worse, if the information is never shared (published), it is a complete loss. But unlike dam builders or those who construct roads, the goal of archaeology is the recovery and understanding of extinct cultures in terms of understanding ourselves as human beings, and for the preservation of these sites for their own sake.

From the time human beings picked up stones and made them into tools, we were holding microchips in our hands. And we've only just begun.

Looking Ahead: Challenge Questions

Discuss salvage archaeology. Give an example.

How do dams destroy archaeological sites and their ecological context?

Should dam building be stopped? Why or why not?

What is the current status on U.S. federal government funding of archaeological pursuits?

Should spectacular archaeological sites be preserved? Why or why not?

Should we preserve/destroy historical monuments of the cold war era?

What is transformation in an archaeological sense? Give an example.

Discuss public archaeology. What causes people to volunteer for archaeology digs?

What is conservation archaeology? Give several examples.

Tales from a Peruvian Crypt

The looting of a prehistoric pyramid stimulates an operation in salvage archeology, with unexpected scientific dividends

Walter Alva and Christopher B. Donnan

Walter Alva, a native of Peru, has participated in numerous excavations on that country's north coast and is the director of the Museo Brüning at Lambayeque. Coauthor Christopher B. Donnan is a professor of anthropology and director of the Fowler Museum of Cultural History at the University of California, Los Angeles. They are the coauthors of Royal Tombs of Sipán *(Los Angeles: Fowler Museum of Cultural History, University of California, 1993).*

In the fertile river valleys that relieve Peru's arid coastal plain, mud-brick pyramids stand as the most visible evidence of the prehistoric Moche civilization, which flourished between the first and eighth centuries A.D. Rising out of agricultural fields in the Moche River valley, the massive Pyramid of the Sun was the largest structure ever built in South America. With a ramp that led up to small buildings on its flat summit, it stood about 135 feet high and sprawled over 12.5 acres at its base. It once contained more than 130 million sun-dried bricks. Some of it has eroded away naturally, while part was demolished in the seventeenth century by Spanish entrepreneurs in search of rich burials or other treasures.

About ninety-five miles north of the Pyramid of the Sun, in the Lambayeque River valley, the Moche cemeteries and three pyramids near the village of Sipán have long been the target of looters. Over the years they have dug many deep holes with picks and shovels in hopes of locating intact tombs containing ceramic vessels, shell and stone beads, and rarer ornaments of silver and gold. By November 1986, they had nearly exhausted the cemeteries, and one group of treasure seekers decided to focus on the smallest pyramid. Working at night to avoid police detection, they dug a series of holes, but found little of value. Then, on the night of February 16, 1987, at a depth of about twenty-three feet, they suddenly broke into one of the richest funerary chambers ever looted, the tomb of an ancient Moche ruler.

The looters removed several sacks of gold, silver, and gilded copper artifacts. They also took some ceramic vessels, but they broke and scattered many others in their haste. Almost immediately, the looters quarreled over the division of the spoils, and one of them tipped off the police. The authorities were able to seize some of the plundered artifacts, but only a pitiful amount was salvaged from the find. The rest disappeared into the hands of Peruvian collectors or was illegally exported for sale in Europe, Japan, and the United States.

Building on civilizations that preceded them in coastal Peru, the Moche developed their own elaborate society, based on the cultivation of such crops as corn and beans, the harvesting of fish and shellfish, and the exploitation of other wild and domestic resources. They had a dense, socially stratified population, with large numbers of workers devoted to the construction and maintenance of irrigation canals, pyramids, palaces, and temples. Their lords apparently received food and commodities from their subjects and distributed them to lesser nobles and to the potters, weavers, metalworkers, and other artisans who created luxury objects for the elite. In sculptures, decorated ceramics, and murals, archeologists have glimpsed many complex scenes of Moche life, including hunting, combat, and ceremonial practices.

The luxury items from Sipán that were confiscated by the police, including hollow gold beads of various shapes and sizes, hinted at the magnificence of the plundered burial, which must have belonged to one of the Moche elite. More fortune-hunters descended on the site in search of overlooked valuables. They hacked at the tomb walls and sifted through the excavated dirt. By the time the police secured the area, little was left except a boot-shaped hole. Nevertheless, with armed guards stationed around the clock, we hastily organized an archeological survey to learn everything possible of scientific value (author Walter Alva directed the project; coauthor Christopher B. Donnan was one of the many participants.)

We began by making a contour map of the three pyramids and what remained of their ramps and adjacent plazas. The small pyramid, where the

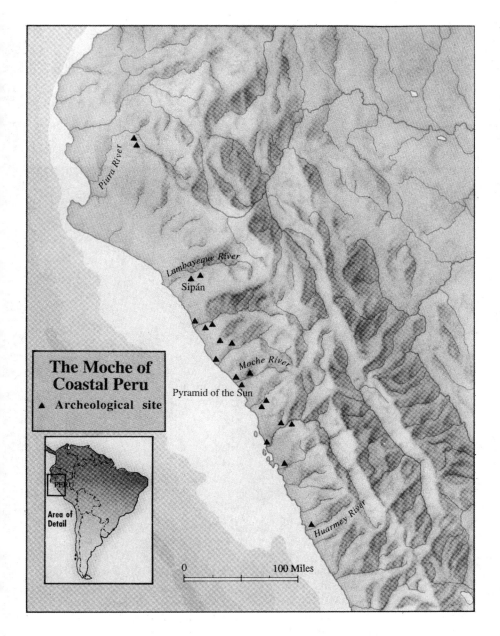

The Moche of Coastal Peru

▲ **Archeological site**

PERU

Area of Detail

0   100 Miles

platform with a balustrade, surrounding an open-front building with one back wall and a peaked roof supported by posts. Seventeen double-faced human heads decorated the roof ridge, while depicted in relief on the wall was a supernatural creature, half feline and half reptile, copulating with a woman on a crescent moon.

Knowing that the pyramid would be further plundered once we left, we decided to open up a new section to methodical excavation, choosing a ten-by-ten meter (1,076-square-foot) area near the summit. Here we came upon a place where the mud brick had been carved out and refilled in ancient times. Digging down, we found eight decomposed wood beams, similar to those that had roofed the looted burial chamber. Buried beneath these, in the debris of what had been a small rectagular chamber, we found 1,137 ceramic bowls, jars, and bottles. They portrayed a variety of human figures: warriors holding war clubs and shields, nude prisoners with leashlike ropes around their necks, musicians with drums, and seated figures wearing beaded pectorals (biblike coverings). Some were arranged in symbolic tableaux, for example, musicians and prisoners ringing and facing noble personages.

As we removed the ceramics, we found several pieces of copper and, finally, a man's skeleton lying jack-knifed on its back, with chin, knees, and arms pulled in toward the torso. Since the Moche customarily buried their dead in a fully extended position, we interpreted this individual to be a sacrificial victim, whose body had been shoved into the small chamber as part of the ritual offering.

Even as these offerings were being excavated, we discovered a second, larger rectangular area that appeared to have been carved into the pyramid and refilled. As we carefully excavated this, we found, about thirteen feet below the original surface of the pyramid, the skeleton of a man wrapped in a cotton shroud. He lay stretched out on his back and wore a gilded copper helmet. Over the right forearm, which rested on his chest, was a round copper shield. A little below we found the

tomb had been found, was riddled with looters' tunnels, but in some places, the piles of dirt they had excavated helped preserve the original contours. The tunnels also enabled us to examine the internal construction. The pyramid and the rest of the complex evidently had been built and rebuilt over a long period of time, undergoing many changes as the various parts were enlarged. The small pyramid seems to have gone through six phases, beginning in the first century A.D. and ending about 300.

Although the burial chamber had been gouged out of shape, we were able to determine that it had originally

been roofed with large wood beams, which had decomposed. To our great surprise, we were able to uncover some of the tomb's contents that had been missed by the original looters and the subsequent gleaners. Clearing along one side of the chamber, we found the remains of a large, gilded copper crown decorated with metal disks; four ceramic jars modeled in the shape of human figures; and a copper mask with inlaid turquoise eyes. In excavating these, we also discovered a heavy copper scepter forty inches long, pointed at one end and bearing a three-dimensional architectural model on the other. The model depicted a remains of seventeen parallel beams that, we dared hope, lay over a major, undisturbed burial chamber.

The discoveries that subsequently emerged surpassed our dreams. Buried in the chamber were the remains of a wood coffin that contained the richest grave offerings ever to be excavated scientifically in the Western Hemisphere. The body of a man between thirty-five and forty-five years of age had been laid to rest with a feathered headdress, banners of cloth with gilded copper decorations, beaded pectorals, nose ornaments and necklaces of gold and silver, ear ornaments of gold and turquoise, face coverings of gold, a gold backflap and a silver backflap that would have been hung from the belt, and countless other precious objects. In his right hand the deceased had held a gold and silver scepter topped with a large rattle, and in his left hand, a smaller scepter of cast silver. In relief on the rattle, which was shaped like an inverted pyramid, were scenes of an elaborately dressed warrior subjugating a vanquished opponent. The sculpted head of the smaller scepter echoed this theme.

Working six days a week, it took us four months to document and safely empty the delicate contents of the tomb. As our original budget became exhausted, we received some partial funding from a brewery and a truckload of noodles donated by a pasta manufacturer. At one point we were paying the fieldworkers with a combination of cash and noodles. We eventually secured new support from the Research Committee of the National Geographic Society and were able to proceed with further excavation.

All the while we had been working and moving equipment around the coffin burial, we had been walking only inches above hundreds of ceramic vessels, two sacrificed llamas, a dog, and the burials of two men, three women, and a child of nine or ten. Although we do not know this for sure, the men and the child might have been buried as sacrifices to accompany the principal figures. The remains of the females, however, were partly decomposed at the time they were placed in the tomb,

as evident from the way the bones were somewhat jumbled. They had probably died years earlier and their remains maintained elsewhere until this final interment.

As we excavated the tomb and cataloged its contents, we couldn't help wondering who was the important personage buried there. The key to the answer was a major photographic archive of Moche sculpture and drawings at the University of California at Los Angeles. As the tomb was being excavated, photographs of the objects were sent to UCLA for comparative study.

Many of the objects in the coffin suggested the man buried there was a warrior. The archive of Moche art contains hundreds of depictions from which we can reconstruct a sequence of Moche militarism and ceremonial activity. We can see processions of warriors carrying war clubs, spears, and spear throwers, perhaps on their way to battle. We can see warriors in combat, apparently away from settled areas. The essence of Moche combat appears to have been the expression of individual valor, in which warriors engaged in one-on-one combat, seeking to vanquish, rather than kill, an opponent. The victor is often shown hitting his opponent on the head or upper body with the war club, while the defeated individual is depicted bleeding from his nose or losing his headdress or other parts of his attire. Sometimes the victor grasps his adversary by the hair and removes his nose ornament or slaps his face.

As far as we can tell, the Moche warriors fought with one another, not against some foreign enemy. Once an opponent was defeated, he was stripped of some or all of his clothing and a rope was placed around his neck. The victor made a bundle of the prisoner's clothing and weapons and tied it to his own war club as a trophy. After a public parading of the spoils, the prisoners were arraigned before a high-status individual and finally brought back to the Moche settlements or ceremonial precincts. There the priests and their attendants sacrificed them, cutting their throats and drinking the

blood from tall goblets. The bodies were then dismembered and the heads, hands, and feet tied individually with ropes to create trophies.

Many representations of the sacrifice ceremony exist in Moche art. Although they vary, not always depicting all personages in the ceremony, apparently three principal priests and one priestess were involved, each associated with specific garments and ritual paraphernalia. The most important was the "warrior priest," generally depicted with a crescent-shaped nose ornament, large circular ear ornaments, a warrior backflap, a scepter, and a conical helmet with a crescent-shaped ornament at its peak. A comparison of these and other details with the contents of the tomb convinced us that the individual buried there was just such a warrior priest.

When the sacrifice ceremony was first identified in Moche art, in 1974, no one could be sure it was a real practice, as opposed to a mythical event. Now we had archeological evidence that this was an actual part of Moche life. Here was one of the individuals who presided over the sacrifices. Further, because the limited numbers of objects salvaged from the looted tomb were similar to some of those we had excavated, we could conclude that the looted tomb also must have belonged to a warrior priest.

As if this were not enough, during the excavation of the warrior priest's tomb, we located another suspected tomb elsewhere on the pyramid. We held off excavation until work on the earlier find was nearly complete. The knowledge we gained made it easier to anticipate the sequence of excavation. Again we found the residue of a plank coffin containing the rich burial of a man between thirty-five and forty-five years old. Among his grave goods was a spectacular headdress ornament of gilded copper, in the form of the head and body of an owl from which arched long banks with suspended bangles, representing the feathered wings. Nearby we found the remains of four other individuals: a male between fourteen and seventeen years of age, two females in their late teens or early twenties, and an eight- to ten-year-old child. Buried with the child were a dog and a snake.

The contents of this tomb were only a little less lavish than those of the warrior priest. They suggest that the principal individual was another of the priests depicted in the sacrifice ceremony—one we call the "bird priest." The major clue was the large owl headdress. He was also buried with a copper cup near his right hand, similar in proportion to the cups portrayed in pictures of the sacrifice ceremony.

Having identified these individuals as participants in the sacrifice ceremony, we began to wonder if such ceremonies took place in Sipán itself. The answer was soon revealed when, about eleven yards from the bird priest's tomb, we found several small rooms that contained hundreds of ceramic vessels, human and llama bones, and miniature ornaments and implements, mixed with ash and organic

residues. Among the human remains were hands and feet, quite possibly the trophies taken from dismembered sacrificial victims. Altogether these looked to be the residue of sacrifice ceremonies, which the Moche apparently carried out at Sipán, as no doubt they did at their other centers.

The looted tomb, the two excavated tombs, and the sacrificial offerings all seem to date to about A.D. 290. While excavating the offerings, we found a fourth, somewhat earlier tomb containing the remains of a man between forty-five and fifty-five years old, also richly endowed with grave goods, including a necklace of gold beads in the form of spiders on their webs, anthropomorphic figures of a crab and a feline, scepters, an octopus pectoral with gilded copper tentacles, and numerous other ornaments and objects. Nearby we found the body of a young, sixteen- to eighteen-year-old woman next to a sacrificed llama. This tomb

may also have belonged to a warrior priest, but not all the identifying elements are there. Possibly, this is simply because it dates to an earlier period than the depictions we have of the sacrifice ceremony, which are all from after A.D. 300.

Moche civilization collapsed suddenly, probably as a result of one or more of the natural cataclysms that periodically devastate coastal Peru—earthquake, flooding, or drought. The Moche had no writing system, so they left no records we can hope to decipher. They disappeared before Europeans reached the New World and could leave us eyewitness accounts. Yet with the scientific excavation of these royal tombs, we have gained an intimate portrait of some of their most powerful lords. Work at Sipán continues, now at a promising location near the tomb of the bird priest. As we dig more deeply, we look forward to our next encounter.

Damming the Past

Are reservoirs destroying our archeological heritage? Scuba divers give us an answer

Daniel J. Lenihan

Trained as both a diver and an archeologist, Daniel J. Lenihan is chief of the National Park Service's Submerged Cultural Resources Unit. Recently his team mapped and photographed various American, German, and Japanese ships sunk in the 1946 atomic bomb testing at Bikini Atoll.

The movie light I hold in one hand plays over a graffiti-covered wall in the dark, concrete building. A scrawl in balloon letters, "The Lord Cometh," reminds me of spray-can wisdom I have seen on a hundred subway cars. I float slowly through the flooded hallway, walking on the index and middle finger of my free hand. Tiny clouds of silt puff up as I leave my odd paw prints. Another ghostly form, that of my diving partner, rises effortlessly toward the ceiling. He prepares to snap a picture of the illuminated words.

The building was probably a foundry. The Lord may have been here, but he's gone now. We linger for a second photo, then we too move on. Gently, silently but for the sound of our exhaled breaths splashing on the ceiling, we glide through a series of doorways devoid of doors and propel ourselves through a glassless window. On emerging, we are in the light of day, subdued by the twenty feet of water between us and the air above.

What does it take to cover sixty square miles of New Mexico desert with water? Sometimes, an act of God, but in this case it was the Bureau of Reclamation. In 1911, Burec cameth and made rise the waters of the Rio Grande to create the Elephant Butte Reservoir and Recreation Area. The Southwest is full of these improvements on nature. They harness indolent rivers for electrical power, allow people to live in flood plains, and convert desert scrub into profitable farmland. Regaining the surface, I am reminded that they also insure the popularity of the outboard engine. Protective of the student divers under my supervision, I make obscene gestures at boaters who come too close to our diver warning flags.

I have visited many of these watery worlds. From 1975 to 1980, I led a National Park Service study of major water-impoundment areas in the United States, mainly in the arid Southwest. Other researchers were charged with assessing loss of habitat and scenic values. My task was to determine if the federal money allocated for salvaging archeological sites was being prudently spent.

The dozens of large reservoirs built by the Army Corps of Engineers, Bureau of Reclamation, Tennessee Valley Authority, and others throughout the country impact river valleys, usually the locus of past human activity. The scope of this phenomenon is hard to convey. The combined surface area of just two of the artificial lakes on the Colorado River, lakes Mead and Powell, for example, is more than 500 square miles, or about half the size of Rhode Island. Sizable portions of these two lakes are deep enough to cover the Washington Monument. Beneath them now lie some 2,000 known sites of the Anasazi—the ancient ones—ranging from the ruins of pueblos to scatterings of stone tools. The sites identified in surveys before the valleys were flooded probably represent only a fraction of those actually present. Apart from the value archeologists attach to these remains, one can only imagine what living Indian peoples must feel when they see their heritage, including sacred sites and ancient landscapes, obliterated.

Even as the dams were being built, the American preservation community managed to impress upon Congress that archeological remains are irreplaceable. This sometimes elusive point was easiest to establish with politicians from regions where the loss of impressive ruins would be noticed by their constituents. One piece of legislation in the early 1970s authorized the spending of up to one percent of the entire cost of a new reservoir on salvage archeology. Large-scale excavations of the most dramatic sites in the deepest parts of the about-to-be lakes seemed the remedy of choice.

The result, however, was warehouses full of artifacts needing expensive curating, from sites dug for the wrong reasons. A reaction to this process was taking shape in the archeological profession about the time our study began, culminating in the formation of the American Society for Conservation Archeology. These archeologists argued for more focused use of available human and monetary resources—in essence, elegance of research design instead of energetic shoveling. Terms such as "partial-site excavation," "minimal impact archeology," and "problem-oriented research designs" started to replace "dig we must."

Were history and prehistory destroyed when covered by impounded river waters? Or were they preserved forever in an underwater data bank for future generations? Environmental impact statements authoritatively supported these two contradictory positions. With public funds going toward some very comprehensive and expensive archeological projects, federal reservoir managers wanted some definitive answers fast. The National Park Service was given the ball, and I, a diving instructor with a degree in anthropology, got to be quarterback. I moved to Santa Fe, where at the behest of Calvin R. Cummings, regional archeologist for the service's Southwest region, I assembled a team.

With more than a little dismay we realized that we had to define what was of archeological value before we could decide whether or not it was being destroyed. Is the stuff of archeology made up of only artifacts and bones and their relative locations? What about the texture and color of the soil they are found in—how does flooding affect such archeological clues? What of the soil chemistry, which helps to establish where humans performed different daily activities? What of the subtle properties of materials dated through arcane laboratory tricks? Heady fare for a handful of archeologists just out of graduate school, selected for the job largely because we could dive.

This foundry dive is a training exercise for a group of sport divers wishing to refine their underwater recording skills. As I struggle to remove my wet suit, however, I dredge up memories of reservoir dives past. My mind's eye takes me momentarily from the nearby shore of the placid Rio Grande to the mighty Colorado. It gives one pause to stand on the brink of Glen Canyon Dam and look down at the Colorado River on one side and Lake Powell on

the other. A raging river, a piece of raw wilderness, has been molded into a huge pond. At the bottom of the sixty-story concrete megalith, a reconstituted Colorado seems to shrug off the insult and strive to regain its personality. By the time it hits the Grand Canyon, it has become a serious river once more. Farther downstream it is dammed again to form Lake Mead, then Lake Mohave, and yet again to become Lake Havasu.

Hundreds of speedboats zooming in what seem to be long lanes of traffic give Lake Havasu the appearance of an aqueous turnpike. To cap the impression of some sort of surreal theme park, an entrepreneurial genius has placed the reconstituted London Bridge across a side channel of the impounded Colorado River. Moved stone by stone for the Thames, the bridge now stands as a monument to the general level of intelligence involved in our use of human energy and natural resources in the great American Southwest.

Below Lake Mead, released through the turbines of Hoover Dam, the Colorado rages through a narrow, steep canyon for several miles. For scuba divers, this is a challenging stretch. At Ringbolt Rapids the current drags divers down into a hole almost seventy feet deep before disgorging them back to the twenty-foot depth. Here, in the shallower reaches below the rapids, we tried to document the remains of an old river boat (such boats would winch themselves upriver using iron bolts set in the canyon walls). One of our group would try to take a photograph while holding on to the wreck with one hand, but if he relaxed his grip even slightly, the current would sweep him away, leaving behind only a swirl of sand and silt. And if he glanced back upstream, his mask would be ripped off. We eventually decided that a "preliminary evaluation" was sufficient, declared victory, and headed for more convenient sites to document.

The presence of historic shipwrecks in the desert is always cause for wonder. A few miles below Glen Canyon Dam, the *Charles H. Spencer* lies near Lee's Ferry, a popular point for rafters to begin their run through the

Grand Canyon. Near the ruins of the old mining camp, the craft lies in shallow water with most of its lower hull well preserved. At most water levels, the smooth, metal boiler is partly exposed, and Navajos fish from the perch it offers. Prefabricated in San Francisco, the *Spencer* was assembled at Lee's Ferry to carry coal to a gold mine. After the craft was launched more than a thousand miles from the ocean, its owners discovered it took more coal to fight the river than the vessel could carry as cargo. The craft was left to rot on the riverbank—a long-term proposition in this part of the world.

Newly impounded waters hold special surprises. I recall the hull of our small aluminum boat scraping over the tips of branches above Cochiti Dam, as Cochiti Lake filled just west of Santa Fe. These were the tops of ponderosa pines, their roots still embedded in the drowned soil sixty feet below us—New Mexico's high desert converted into an evergreen swamp. The Anasazi pueblos, which we had found on our foot survey through this valley years before, would know a strange requiem. While their descendants struggle to maintain an identity, selling their traditional wares on the plaza in Santa Fe, the Anasazi lie buried in earthen house floors, sleeping with the fishes.

Hiking along the ridgetops above Cochiti Dam, I have rested on smooth white logs hundreds of yards above the river. These convenient seats are driftwood, piled there when melts from heavy snowpacks in the Rockies raised the waters to levels unthinkable before impoundment.

During droughts in California's Folsom Reservoir, nature temporarily overrules the dam builders, as rivers fall to their original levels. Here, prehistoric house floors compacted from years of trampling resist the erosion of the receding waters better than the surroundings soils can. The curious result is that once-buried archaeological treasures are left pedestaled above the adjacent terrain. Stumps of oak trees stand beside them on their tap roots. Raccoons, nature's opportunists, have done their own excavating in the hardened house floors, placing snail shells and potsherds in neat piles outside their burrows. One suspects they are less interested in scientific analysis than in extracting the mollusks that took up residence in the house floors during inundation, but their precise digging technique would put some archeologists to shame.

Underwater in Texas, I have flutter-kicked through old ranch houses, cut my way through barbed-wire fences, trailed old railroad tracks into the depths, and followed asphalt highways (still feeling some compulsion to keep to the right of the yellow line). In some places I have even seen old dams that have been covered by the waters backed up by new dams. These reinforced concrete monsters that gobble up river valleys devour their own with equal indifference.

Several tense, cold winter days spent searching for a drowned diver in the submerged powerhouse of a dam near the Mexican border will stay with me always. A hundred feet below the surface, my colleague Larry Murphy and I entered through glassless windows much more forbidding than the ones in the Elephant Butte foundry and felt our way cautiously through murky water. Our tanks scraped against hazardous wires and steel bars hanging from the ceiling. Blinded by disturbed sediment that even our powerful lights couldn't penetrate, we felt our way down a flight of stairs, ran our hands over commodes, and searched restroom stalls. With equal caution we made our way back out before our double tanks emptied of their precious air.

We found the young man's body a day later, wedged in a corner between a glass partition and the electrical switch cage. Larry and I felt especially compelled to remove a fellow diver from this alien environment. Muttering words of encouragement to the lifeless form, we maneuvered him through the many obstacles to the surface.

The official conclusions of our National Reservoir Inundation Study, while voluminous, can be boiled down to a few general observations. The most surprising is that one of the lowest impact zones is in the bottom of a lake, particularly if it has been flooded quickly. Most of what has archeological value is preserved intact, except for soil chemistry, which loses its analytical use after inundation. Access, of course, is compromised, but the findings are reassuring, at least if the goal is to bank sites for future research.

The places worst hit turn out to be the zones where the water level varies up and down, subjecting sites to alternate wet and dry cycles. Little of archeological value survives that sort of treatment. In addition, this is where park goers have their greatest impact. As reservoir levels fluctuate seasonally or over the years, campers follow the beach line, parking their RVs side by side. At Roosevelt Lake in Arizona, for example, stones that marked the ancient house outlines of Hohokam and later Salado peoples for hundreds of years are piled helter-skelter by unknowing tourists to form campfire pits. Even areas outside the maximum flood pool are highly affected, as sites formerly exposed only to occasional visits of Native Americans and backpackers become available to anyone with a bass boat and a sixpack.

Our inundation project also taught us something about American values. Underlying the whole program was the premise that reservoirs were going to be built, archeological sites or endangered snail-darters notwithstanding. Society had already made its fundamental choices; we were providing answers that would improve the efforts to mitigate the impact.

Many reservoirs are beautiful places, although those who love wild rivers may find that hard to swallow. Some people, like the late writer and "eco-warrior" Edward Abbey, have such an intense hatred for dams that they would take satisfaction in seeing them blown up. The heroes of Abbey's *Monkey Wrench Gang* attempt just that, to the vicarious delight of many readers. They could just as well take solace, however, in contemplating the fragility of human-made structures. The ghosts of drowned rivers stir restlessly beneath the placid waters of reservoirs. In the eye-blink of a few thousand years, they will sweep away the concrete and earthen plugs that hamper their quest for the sea.

As I cram the last of the dive gear into our van at Elephant Butte, one of our students approaches me to ask a parting question. She points across the lake at the white line that runs along the steep shoreline just above the present water level—the bathtub ring common to many water impoundments. "What is that anyway?" she wants to know. I tell her it's blue-green algae bonded with calcium carbonate, and if she'd like a closer look, she can glance down at her feet, because she is standing in it. Like many of the things that affect us most, it isn't noticeable until we're removed enough to gain perspective.

Before the Deluge

Dam Construction in Turkey Threatens Invaluable Archaeological Sites

Karen Fitzgerald

The fifth-largest rock-and-earth dam in the world, the Ataturk is the third of 21 dams the Turkish government intends to build on the Tigris and Euphrates rivers. Supplying irrigation water and hydroelectricity, the dam promises to transform the vast dust bowl of southeast Turkey into a breadbasket that could feed all of the Middle East and Europe, too, according to Vassar College geologist Yildirim Dilek, who has studied the dam's impact.

But to make way for the future, pieces of the past must be sacrificed. The dam project has already flooded hundreds of archaeologically significant sites along the Euphrates and will affect hundreds more before completion. The clock is ticking for the archaeologists scrambling to excavate these potentially invaluable sites before the water rises. Much of the region is virgin territory to archaeologists.

Samsat, near the Euphrates, was one of the first victims of the dam project. A bustling city of 50,000 during the Roman Empire, Samsat goes as far back as the Neolithic Period. A rich site like this would normally take decades to excavate, but archaeologist Nimet Özgüç of the Turkish Historical Society and her team had only 11 years to work before the water came rushing in in the late 1980s.

Archaeologists from Ankara University, working under the direction of Olus Arik, have begun another emergency excavation at a town called Hasankeyf, due to be submerged upon the completion of the Tigris's Ilisu Dam in about six years. Many archaeologists consider Hasankeyf the most wrenching loss because of its striking buildings. "Hasankeyf is filled with masterpieces of Islamic architecture," says archaeologist Guillermo Algaze of the University of California, San Diego.

The dam region holds the only clues to the intersection of the Mesopotamian cultures to the south and the Anatolian cultures of ancient Turkey to the north, Algaze explains. Only four known sites record the incursion of the Sumerian culture of Mesopotamia into Anatolia, he says. The Carchemish Dam, planned for the Euphrates River, will put three of them under water.

Yet another threatened site, Kazane Hoyuk, may contain artifacts that overturn conventional notions of how and where civilization began. A tablet found there recently is written in cuneiform, the first system of writing, devised by the Sumerians. Some archaeologists consider it another example of Sumerian culture spreading into Turkey, but University of Virginia archaeologist Patricia Wattenmaker, a director of the excavation, says the artifacts found so far reflect a culture distinct from the Sumerians. The great size of the site—100 hectares—suggests it was a city of a population unheard of before the development of agriculture and civilization. Wattenmaker believes the prehistoric city was an independent seed of civilization, perhaps one of many independent city-states throughout the Middle East that nurtured cultural advances at about the same point in history.

Her team has excavated Kazane Hoyuk for only two summers, and only five to seven more years remain before irrigation construction concludes there. Then the land will be devoted to agriculture year round, making archaeological excavation too expensive to continue. Ironically, archaeologists would probably never have discovered the Kazane Hoyuk site if not for the large irrigation channel that now cuts through the modern town. During its construction, bulldozers kicked up prehistoric pottery that tipped off Wattenmaker to the importance of the site.

Although she knows her days at Kazane Hoyuk are numbered, Wattenmaker has only praise for the Turkish government's efforts to excavate the sites before flooding. She and other archaeologists point out that other countries, including the United States, do much less when technology encroaches upon archaeological material, a not-uncommon occurrence. "It happens literally every day everywhere in the world," Algaze says.

Regardless, the massive scale of the dam projects in a country so rich in antiquities makes Turkey's case particularly poignant. Turkey boasts more than 40,000 recorded archaeological sites, and half the country hasn't even been explored.

Dam construction imperils sites such as Kazane Hoyuk, which boasts pottery (above) dating back to 5000 B.C., and Harran, home of ancient Harran University (below).

Archaeology Meets the 104th Congress

Budget-cutting threatens a host of federal programs that manage and protect archaeological resources.

Loretta Neumann

Loretta Neumann is president of CEHP (Conservation, Environment and Historic Preservation) Inc., a consulting firm in Washington, D.C., that specialize in research, policy analysis, and government relations.

Last fall, before the congressional elections, a group of Republican candidates for the House of Representatives stood on the steps of the United States Capitol and, with broad smiles and great bravado, signed a "Contract with America." They talked of welfare and regulatory reform, tax cuts and balanced budgets. They promised to reduce the size and cost of the federal government. They did not, it is safe to assume, utter a word about archaeology. Since taking over in January, however, members of the 104th Congress in both the House and the Senate have pursued an agenda that could radically alter the way the federal government manages, funds, and protects archaeological resources.

Some of their proposals are quite direct, such as the termination of the National Endowment for the Humanities, a major source of funding for archaeological research, education, and interpretation, including support for museum exhibitions and grants for scholars and educators. The House passed legislation that would cut the NEH budget nearly in half—from $172 million in 1995 to $99.5 million in 1996—phasing it out entirely over the next three years. Similarly, the chair of the House Science Committee, Robert Walker (R, Pennsylvania), proposed abolishing a program in the National Science Foundation that is the biggest source of funding (about $4 million annually) for scientific research in prehistoric and classical archaeology. Although the Appropriations Committee subsequently voted to keep the program, its future remains in doubt. Meanwhile Senate Foreign Relations Committee Chair Jesse Helms (R, North Carolina) proposed legislation that would, among other things, eliminate the United States' $450,000 contribution to UNESCO's World Heritage Convention, which identifies natural and cultural resources of global significance that should be protected, including archaeological sites in the United States such as Mesa Verde National Park, Colorado; Cahokia Mounds State Historic Site, Illinois; and the Pueblo de Taos, New Mexico.

Other proposals would affect federally managed archaeological resources, such as legislation to transfer public lands in the West to the states and remove from federal management many historical and archaeological areas now administered by the National Park Service. One very controversial measure would allow the Forest Service to override environmental laws while accelerating the cutting of several billion board feet of timber from dead or dying trees. Timber cutting—and ancillary activities such as road construction—can cause severe damage to archaeological resources, as well as fish and wildlife. In another move, Don Young (R, Alaska), chair of the House Resources Committee, has proposed cutting all Bureau of Land Management funds for law enforcement, which would preclude enforcement of those laws that protect archaeological resources from looting and vandalism.

Some proposals would appear to have no relationship at all to archaeology, but would tie the hands of federal regulators whose jobs are to protect these resources. An example is legislation that passed the House that would place a moratorium on most new federal regulations. If enacted, the legislation could imperil a number of guidelines and rules relating to the management and protection of archaeological resources that the Secretary of the Interior and the Advisory Council on Historic Preservation are required by law to develop. Several measures would force federal agencies to make cash payments out of their operating budgets if their actions diminished the value of a private owner's property by even a small percentage; carried to the extreme, these could include payments to owners whose property declined in value because it was designated an historical landmark.

The question, then, is not whether archaeology will be affected by the Congress but to what extent. People who care about archaeology—enthusiasts and professionals alike—must pay more attention to what is happening in Washington and let their voices be heard when bills that could affect archaeology are being debated and voted on.

To understand what Congress is doing and how it can affect archaeology, it helps to know what Congress has done in the past. Federal programs for the management and protection of archaeological resources have a long and complex history. In the late nineteenth century Congress responded to public demand and set aside places on public lands in the West—such as Casa Grande Ruins in Arizona—to protect them from looting and vandalism. In 1906 it passed the Antiquities Act, which requires permits for excavation and imposes penalties for damaging historic or prehistoric ruins on federally owned land. During the 1930s the Roosevelt administration hired archaeologists and laborers to excavate some of the great prehistoric mounds of the Mississippi, Ohio, and Tennessee river valleys. In 1935 the Historic Sites Act launched the National Historic Landmarks program. In 1960 the Reservoir Salvage Act set in place procedures for conducting archaeological investigations and salvage before construction of federal dams and reservoirs; the program was expanded in 1974 to apply to all federal projects. The Archaeological Resources Protection Act of 1979 regulates the removal of archaeological resources from federal land. The 1983 Convention on Cultural Property Implementation Act creates a process to prohibit entry of looted antiquities into the United States, if requested by another country. The Abandoned Shipwreck Act of 1987 removes abandoned historic shipwrecks in U.S. waters from the jurisdiction of the admiralty courts and transfers title to the states. And the Native American Graves Pro-

tection and Repatriation Act of 1990 requires federal agencies to consult with and possibly repatriate to Indian tribes human remains and objects uncovered during federal projects.

Archaeology is also covered under the provisions of the National Historic Preservation Act (NHPA). Enacted in 1966 in response to the enormous destruction that federally funded urban renewal and interstate highway construction projects had wrought on historic properties throughout the United States, the NHPA has also helped to protect archaeological sites. Among other things, it directs the Secretary of the Interior, through the National Park Service, to maintain and expand the National Register of Historic Places, which includes "buildings, sites, districts, structures and objects significant in American . . . archaeology and culture."

Many archaeological programs depend on federal regulations and funding, and without great personal wealth or acclaim, individuals have a difficult time influencing Congress.

Key to the implementation of the NHPA is Section 106, which requires federal agencies to take into account the effect that their undertakings might have on historic properties and to provide the Advisory Council on Historic Preservation with an opportunity to comment on them. The Council, an independent federal agency, is composed of representatives of federal agencies, state and local governments, and private citizens. While it does not have a veto over federal projects, it does provide a public forum for balancing historic preservation concerns with federal project requirements. Over the years it has handled many complex problems, such as the proposed expan-

sion of the McKinley Coal Mine in central New Mexico; the planned construction of an interstate highway through Abbott Farm National Historic Landmark in New Jersey; the archaeological work during the cleanup of the *Exxon Valdez* oil spill in Alaska; and the successful resolution of the controversial excavation and study of the African Burial Ground in Lower Manhattan, a site that has since been designated a National Historic Landmark by the Secretary of the Interior (see ARCHAEOLOGY, March/April 1993).

Over the years, these programs have weathered changing political climates and overcome the vagaries of different administrations. Today, however, they face a different set of circumstances. Many former Democratic supporters in Congress are gone or find their powers significantly weakened. Even Republican supporters—archaeology has always enjoyed bipartisan support—are feeling pressure to walk in lockstep with their party in its quest to shrink the federal government. Yet many archaeological programs depend on federal regulations and funding, and their survival depends on support from both parties.

The task ahead is daunting. Without great personal wealth or acclaim, individuals have a difficult time influencing Congress. It is usually easier to work through groups that share a common cause. Several professional organizations the Society for American Archaeology, the Society for Historical Archaeology, and the Society of Professional Archeologists—have long track records in working to affect legislation. They frequently join forces with organizations including the National Conference of State Historic Preservation Officers, Preservation Action, the National Trust for Historic Preservation, and the U.S. Committee of the International Council on Monuments and Sites.

The battle to save the Advisory Council on Historic Preservation provides a good example of how groups work on these issues. Earlier this year a new organization, the American Cultural Resources Association (ACRA), was formed to address the concerns of businesses working in cultural resource professions—archaeology, history, architecture, and landscape architecture. In mid-June members of ACRA were alarmed to learn that the House Interior Appropriations Subcommittee planned to eliminate the Advisory Council in its fiscal 1996 bill that provides funds for the Department of the Interior and Related Agencies. "Related agencies" include the Advisory Council and the NEH, as well as others such as the Smithsonian Institution and the Institute for Museum Services. The federal government's fiscal year goes from October 1 to September 30. The subcommittee proposed to cut the Council's funding by two-thirds, from $3 million to $1 million, the remaining funds to be used to close it down.

The nation's archaeological record is finite and nonrenewable, and there is still an essential federal role in archaeological research, resource management, and protection.

With only a few days' warning before the subcommittee was scheduled to meet, ACRA sent out pleas for help over the Internet and faxed information to its members and other groups. They found a champion in David Skaggs, (D, Colorado), a member of the subcommittee who offered an amendment to restore some of the Council's funding. He lost on a voice vote. Only one other congressman, former subcommittee chairman Sidney Yates (D, Illinois), spoke on its behalf. Because Skaggs' amendment would have taken the funding from the Park Service's construction budget, many committee members—including some who usually support preservation—

did not vote for it because they had projects in their districts that would have lost funds.

The bill went to the full Appropriations Committee the following week. Skaggs planned to offer a simple amendment to strike the provision eliminating the Council, without adding any additional funds. The theory was that it would leave the issue open when the bill went to the Senate. ACRA again asked other organizations to help. They drafted a joint letter to each of the members of the Appropriations Committee urging them to save the Council. They sent out more alerts on the Internet and faxes to people throughout the country. They received dozens of letters from constituents of the committee members, which were hand delivered the day before the scheduled vote. Many people also telephoned their representatives. Yet when Skaggs offered his amendment, only one other committee member expressed support, Jack Kingston (R, Georgia). By contrast, the chairman of the Interior Appropriations Subcommittee, Ralph Regula (R, Ohio) spoke against it, and the amendment was solidly defeated on a voice vote.

ACRA learned afterwards that the committee's Republicans had agreed ahead of time to support the chair on the bill as a matter of toeing the party line. Only one amendment (and many were offered) was passed over the chair's objections—to reinstate a moratorium on offshore oil leasing, which gained support from several coastal-state Republicans. The vote against Skaggs' amendment was not necessarily a blanket vote against all federal archaeology and historic preservation programs. Many provisions in the bill that support preservation remained untouched: $18.5 million for the National Register programs in the National Park Service and $34.4 million for grants to state historic preservation offices, Indian tribes, and historically black colleges. Although the grant to the National Trust for Historic Preservation was cut from $7 million to $3.5 million, an effort in the committee by

Tom DeLay (R, Texas) to eliminate federal funding for the Trust was defeated.

In its report accompanying the bill the committee claimed that it was eliminating the Advisory Council, but not doing away with its functions:

The action of the Committee to terminate federal support for the Council in no way negates the legal requirement for all federal agencies to continue to identify, evaluate, and consider in good faith the impacts of proposed actions on properties included in or eligible for inclusion in the National Register of Historic Places. It is the Committee's intent that the advisory functions shared by the Council and Secretary of the Interior should now be carried out through the Park Service in cooperation with the State Historic Preservation Offices. (H.Rpt 104–173).

While the subcommittee's language is encouraging, it shows a basic misunderstanding of the need for an independent voice, such as the Advisory Council's, that can balance historic values with other important public needs. It is not a function that can be handed over to the Secretary of the Interior or the states, which have complementary but different missions. In fact in 1976 Congress removed the Council from the Interior Department to give it the independence it needed to regulate other agencies, including the Interior Department itself, which controls the bulk of federally owned land in the United States.

Fortunately for the Advisory Council, Bernie Sanders (I, Vermont) offered an amendment on the House floor to restore its funding to the full $3.06 million requested in the President's budget. With only one day's notice of Sanders' intentions, ACRA led a major campaign in support of the amendment, making phone calls to nearly all of the 435 members of the House, hand delivering letters to them, and using the Internet and faxes to alert their constituents. The amendment passed by a vote of 267 to 130. The final outcome, however, will not be known until after the Senate acts and any differences are resolved by a joint House-Senate conference committee, which may not occur until late September.

Meanwhile, other legislative battles loom. Congress operates in two-year sessions, and the 104th Congress is not even half over. Many bills are pending that could affect archaeology directly or indirectly. Action on legislation will

continue well into the fall of 1995 and could pick up in 1996, an election year.

People who care about archaeology need to voice their concerns to the Congress—not just in reaction to a crisis over a particular piece of legislation, but also to remind them that citizens throughout the United States care about these resources. The nation's archaeological record is finite

and nonrenewable, and there is still an essential federal role in archaeological research, resource management, and protection. Historic preservation is a partnership among many entities—the federal government as well as state and local governments, American Indian tribes, educational institutions, and the private sector. Now is the time to improve, not destroy, that partnership.

Saving Our World's Heritage

Ellen Hoffman

On a potholed, dusty road a few miles south of the Mayan ruins of Tulum on Mexico's Caribbean coast, a crudely executed wall painting of a turtle advertises a primitive seaside bungalow camp. *PESCA, BUCEO, PATRIMONIO UNIVERSAL,* it says in Spanish. In English, its "FISHING, SKIN DIVING, WORLD HERITAGE." The causal tourist might never focus on or question the meaning of "WORLD HERITAGE." But to the diligent travel researcher or member of the eco-cognoscenti, that phrase signals a specific message: You are in or near a natural or cultural site "of outstanding universal value to mankind." In this case, the site a few miles down the road is the Sian Ka'an Biosphere Reserve, a 1.3-million-acre landscape of tropical forest, savannas and mangrove, and coastal and marine habitats that abound with white ibis and roseate spoonbills, manatees and monkeys, sea turtles, and the living corals of the world's second largest reef system.

Several hundred miles away, in the dense, vine-clogged jungle of Mexico's Chiapas state, the imposing stone temples of the Mayan city of Palenque attract thousands of visitors every year. But unless they search out the now-closed museum on the fringe of the site and read the plaque attached to the facade, they might never know that here—as in Sian Ka'an—they are in the presence of a monument that belongs to an elite club whose other "mem-bers" include the Great Wall of China, the Tower of London, Africa's Victoria Falls, and our Statue of Liberty.

The "club" is the World Heritage List, created by the World Heritage Convention, an international treaty approved in 1972 and since then signed by 134 of the world's 188 nations. The List consists of natural and cultural sites and monuments that meet specific criteria designed to verify their "outstanding universal value."

To get on the List, a site or monument must meet at least one of several criteria that emphasize both uniqueness and superlative qualities. A natural site, for example, might qualify because it is an "outstanding example" of a stage of the earth's evolutionary history or the habitat for an important threatened animal or plant species. A man-made site or monument, such as a building or a group of buildings, might make the List because it is a "unique artistic achievement" or because it represents a civilization that has disappeared.

"If we want to protect the world for future generations so they can enjoy the benefits of the work of nature, of millennia, the diversity of plants and species, the World Heritage List can help us do that," says Bernd von Droste, a German ecologist who directs the program from the World Heritage Centre at UNESCO headquarters in Paris.

A sedate, systematic bureaucrat on the podium when he was conducting business at the World Heritage Committee's annual meeting in Santa Fe, New Mexico, last December, in an interview von Droste revealed himself as a passionate advocate for the World Heritage Convention as a tool for nothing less than saving the world.

"Why do we need diversity of species? Of culture?" He answered his own question. "We need them for human survival. Since we don't know about the future, it's better to keep all the knowledge we have about how to adapt."

One purpose of the Santa Fe meeting was to celebrate 20 years of the World Heritage Convention—which the delegates did at a series of festive receptions and dinners sponsored by local officials and cultural institutions. But they also heard a clarion call from von Droste, who reported, "This year many more World Heritage sites are severely damaged or under threat than ever before in the history of the Convention," and cited examples including earthquake damage to the pyramids and other Egyptian monuments and war damage to the medieval city of Dubrovnik.

Population growth, widespread poverty and lack of education, global warming and acid rain ("It creates stone degradation that affects monuments"), climate change, the rising of the sea level—von Droste ticked off a series of physical threats to sites on the List. "If we believe what most scientists are saying," he said, "conservation will be in for a hard time."

To understand not just the physical but also the thorny political and finan-

LIST OF ENDANGERED PLACES

The following World Heritage sites have been inscribed on the Danger List because of threats to or deterioration of the characteristics for which they were placed on the List. The date signifies the year the site was placed on the List.

Benin: Royal Palaces of Abomey; damaged caused by tornado (1985).

Bulgaria: Srebarna Biosphere Reserve; drainage of wetlands has damaged the ecosystem and threatened bird habitats (1992).

Cambodia: Angkor; the former Khmer capital has suffered severe war damage and lacks a comprehensive plan for rehabilitation (1992).

Croatia: Plitvice Lakes National Park; near the border with Serbia, left without a comprehensive management structure and, due to the war, a total loss of tourism income (1992).

Ecuador: Sangay National Park; heavy poaching of wildlife, illegal livestock grazing, and a proposed road-construction project (1992).

Guinea and Cote d'Ivoire: Mount Nimba; lack of effective management, possible uncontrolled mining, and an influx of refugees from Liberia (1992).

Hashemite Kingdom of Jordan: Old City of Jerusalem; concern over the archaeological methods used to document the Old City and its walls (1982).

India: Manas Wildlife Sanctuary; damage to park infrastructure from invasion of Bodo tribespeople, including "illegal cultivation" (1992).

Mali: Timbuktu; enroachment of desert sand (1990).

Niger: Aïr-Ténéré National Nature Reserve; fighting between government forces of Niger and the Tuareg rebels. Six members of the park staff were held hostage for more than a year and a half. Four were released; two were killed (1992).

Oman: Bahia Fort; general deteriorating conditions and poor restoration practices (1988).

Peru: Chan Chan Archaeological Zone; damage from excavation work and plundering (1986).

Poland: Wieliczka Salt Mine; deterioration of salt carvings (1989).

Yugoslavia: Kotor and its Gulf; earthquake damage (1979). Old City of Dubrovnik; war damage to city walls and old buildings, especially their roofs (1991).

Zaire: Garamba National Park; alarming reduction in population of northern white rhinoceros (1984).

---

cial threats the sites on the List face, it's necessary to understand how the World Heritage Convention works. Individual governments nominate sites within their borders. They must convince the 21-member international World Heritage Committee (the group that met in Santa Fe) that each proposed site meets the criteria of "universal value to mankind," and pledge to conserve it.

'There is no way to ensure that sites are protected from environmental degradation, war, neglect, tourism, urbanization, and development.'

The Committee accepts or rejects nominations to the List on the basis of information supplied by two nonprofit organizations: the International Council on Monuments and Sites (ICOMOS) in the case of cultural or manmade sites, and the World Conservation Union

(IUCN) in the case of natural sites. Although neither of these groups is an official organ of UNESCO, their role is written into the Convention's guidelines.

Twenty years after its creation, the still-growing List consists of 378 sites. With an annual budget of around $2 million to implement the Convention, some sites have been named to the List without even being visited by impartial evaluators. And, although it's being discussed, there is no routine program of monitoring to ensure that all sites are protected from threats of environmental degradation, war, urbanization, tourism, and "development."

Once on the List, a site or monument the Committee believes faces "serious and specific dangers"—such as war damage, as in Dubrovnik, or in the case of Sangay National Park in Ecuador, "suffering from heavy poaching of wildlife, illegal livestock grazing, and encroachment"—may be placed on the World Heritage In Danger List, signifying the need for dramatic intervention or major financial or technical assistance. As of press time, the Danger List consisted of 15 sites, including six added at the December meeting.

The United States has 18 World Heritage sites, including Grand Canyon and Yellowstone national parks, Independence Hall in Philadelphia, and the Everglades. They are managed by the National Park Service and supported by tax dollars as well as admission fees. But many sites are in the developing world, where there is less tourism and a commitment to conservation poses wrenching decisions. "When people are living hand to mouth" as they do in some African game-reserve areas, for example, "you can't expect them not to poach," says Jim Thorsell, who evaluates natural sites for IUCN.

The Committee spends some of its funds on technical cooperation and training—restoring earthquake-damaged sites in Egypt or training natural-park managers, for example—but lacks the resources to support large-scale conservation projects.

During the week-long Santa Fe meeting, the delegates—some clad in colorful African robes or gauzy saris, others in the more severe attire of international diplomacy—attended marathon sessions in a hotel ballroom. UNESCO staff hurried up and down the aisles, distributing a blizzard of French- and English-language documents while the Committee discussed reports, guidelines, and budgets and made decisions via simultaneous translation, which were offered in French and English.

In addition to expanding the Danger List, the Committee added 21 new sites to the World Heritage List, including the Kasbah of Algiers and Angkor, the ancient Khmer capital of Cambodia. The tone of these sessions was primarily bureaucratic and politely diplomatic. Yet throughout this twentieth-anniversary meeting, there was a persistent undercurrent of urgency—of concern about the future of the World Heritage List. "The Convention is at a crossroads," said Andy Turner, who is involved with the World Heritage program in Australia. "It has got to deal with the difficult issues."

By the end of the week, the Committee's discussions had illuminated not only the physical threats facing the monuments, but also some of the thorny philosophical, political, and financial issues clamoring to be resolved. For example:

• How can the List be more "balanced"? Only 88 of the 378 sites are natural; 291 are cultural. Europe has a heavy concentration of sites, while other continents have only a few. The Committee has begun to address this by encouraging all countries that have signed the treaty to inventory sites they believe are eligible and want to nominate and by offering some funding to help prepare the nominations.

• Should the List even distinguish between natural and cultural sites? Too often, von Droste says, "culture and nature are artificially separated. They belong together. If you destroy the tropical forest, you also destroy the culture of the people who live there." To address this issue, the Committee has been trying to define a new category of sites called "cultural landscapes," which would recognize "combined works of nature and man."

• How can the World Heritage Centre find the resources to offer protection to so many sites? Publications sales and voluntary contributions by countries or individuals add to the budget, but von

Droste reported that as needs for both emergency funds and regular monitoring and technical assistance grow, the "overall budget at the disposal of the Committee is stagnating or even decreasing in real terms." A key reason for the decrease is that many countries lag far behind in their mandatory contributions. Argentina, for example, owed more than $65,000 for the years 1986 through 1993 as of last December.

Given these limitations, does the World Heritage Convention really have an impact on the future of the earth's most important, often threatened, monuments, natural habitats, and cultural sites? What has it accomplished? What challenges does it face, and what are its prospects for the future?

IUCN's Thorsell has compiled a list of 22 cases in which World Heritage Committee intervention, he says—through political pressure, funding, technical assistance, and the like—has helped protect or improve threatened sites. The success stories include Ecuador's Galápagos islands, where "tourism-control policies were introduced," and Tanzania's Ngorongoro conservation area, which received equipment needed for park management and was removed from the Danger List.

But these accomplishments seem like a drop in the bucket when compared with the size and needs of the entire List and von Droste's gloomy appraisal of the current state of World Heritage efforts.

One case in point—discussed at length in Santa Fe because of the difficulty of agreeing on what to do about it—is that of Mount Nimba, a natural reserve that straddles the borders of Guinea and Ivory Coast in West Africa. In 1980, Mount Nimba—which is described in a book about World Heritage as a "beautiful and isolated environment," the habitat of "rare species of bats, lichens, and other plants and animals"—was put on the List.

Twelve years later, at the Santa Fe meeting, the Committee placed Mount Nimba on the World Heritage In Danger List, citing two major threats to its integrity: a proposal by the Guinea government to open an iron mine adjacent to the site, and the presence of as

many as 60,000 "extremely poor Liberian refugees" in the region, who, von Droste told the Committee, "if not helped, will destroy the whole area."

Despite diplomatic conversations and meetings, technical missions to the reserve, and extensive debate at Santa Fe and previous meetings, the Committee can't even agree on the boundaries of the World Heritage site—and whether the proposed mine really is inside them. The Guinea government's delegate told the Committee in Santa Fe that the proposed mine—which the government has been developing for more than 20 years—"was never protected under World Heritage" because, he said, it was outside the site.

At the same time it put Mount Nimba on the Danger List, the Committee decided to send another mission to study the boundaries, determine the impact of the threats to its "universal values," and work toward development of a management plan to protect the reserve. The mission was successful. Participants generally agreed on new boundaries for the site. The Mount Nimba example illuminates several dilemmas that the World Heritage Convention confronts in its role as protector of our collective future:

• The Convention has lofty principles, but the Committee has limited ability to enforce them. Sites are put on the list because they're considered to be of great value and because individual governments agree to protect them. But, other than mobilizing world opinion, the Committee can do little to protect a site that's threatened by a government policy, such as the proposed iron-mine development, or by unforeseen events, such as the turmoil that led so many Liberians to seek refuge in another country. The case of Mount Nimba illustrates the difficult political and financial issues the Convention faces: The potential value of the iron mine to the country of Guinea is approximately $8 billion—money that could be spent to build an infrastructure and resolve pressing social problems.

• The Convention has lofty operational goals but few resources for implementing them. Even if contributions were paid up, the budget cannot support thorough investigation of proposed nominations or regular monitoring of 378 sites, let alone keep pace with demands generated by adding to the List. This dilemma also emerged in debates on whether to add sites to the Danger List. As long as the Committee cannot provide funds for conservation programs or compensate governments for what they see as an economic loss—not mining in the Mount Nimba reserve—placement on the Danger List appears more like a reprimand than a positive call for protection.

•The structure for implementing the Convention is sensitive to political pressures. The World Heritage Centre is physically located in UNESCO headquarters and receives some funding and other support from the agency. The Convention and the Committee, however, are independent of UNESCO. (The director of the World Heritage Centre reports to and is responsible to the director general of UNESCO.) The entire Committee, which takes action on all nominations as well as makes program policy decisions, meets only once a year. As the Mount Nimba case illustrates, development and enforcement of effective conservation plans may require a long-term perspective as well as technical knowledge. But many delegates who attend the Committee meetings are diplomats rather than substantive experts—with a short-term assignment.

Despite the structural issues confronting the Convention and the continuing problems surrounding Mount Nimba, halfway around the world from West Africa, Australia offers a different, more positive model of the World Heritage system: an example of how environmentalists used the international treaty to safeguard sites in their own country and to stimulate public debate and awareness of environmental issues.

"Australians have a history of fighting in public about these things," says Andrew Turner, then-assistant secretary of the Commonwealth's (federal government's) Nature Conservation Branch, over breakfast one morning before the Committee went into session.

When the government proposed a logging ban in the Wet Tropics of Queensland, a World Heritage site, he recalled, "You couldn't walk into a pub without someone picking a fight about it, with someone else or with you."

Australia's constitution gives land-management power to the states, not to the central government. "In the early 1980s," Turner recounted, "the Tasmanian Hydroelectric Commission wanted to build a dam that would have flooded the valley of the Gordon River, including a lot of aboriginal caves with evidence of early habitation." The proposed dam was in the Tasmanian Wilderness, a World Heritage area that now encompasses about 10 percent of the state.

The Australian High Court set an important precedent in the 1980s in two decisions when it cited the national government's commitment to an international treaty—the World Heritage Convention—as grounds for approving the Commonwealth government's power to impose the logging ban in Queensland and prohibiting the proposed dam project in Tasmania.

Unlike most countries, the Australian government publishes a regular monitoring report on all of its World Heritage sites, describing the nature of the property; current issues, such as proposed construction or tourism growth; management plans; and the number of people who visited the site.

Most observers and participants in the World Heritage process agree that an important key to its future effectiveness is increasing awareness of the concept and the reasons for protecting natural and cultural monuments.

The United States played a key role in creating the Convention and makes the largest contributions to the program budget. But it took the meeting of the Committee in Santa Fe, 20 years after the formation of the treaty, to spur the National Park Service to commit itself to providing information about World Heritage to the millions of people who visit our sites every year.

In contrast, Spain, which has 15 sites, ranging from the prehistoric caves of Altamira to a twentieth-century Barcelona house designed by architect Antonio Gaudí, publishes a glossy, illustrated pamphlet describing each site and the purpose of the World Heritage Convention.

It may or may not be coincidental that one of World Heritage's most passionate advocates is a Spaniard, Federico Mayor, who is UNESCO's director general. "Each citizen of the world should become a defender of our world heritage," he said. "I like to imagine that the World Heritage message is a message of solidarity, of sharing, but that must come from the world level to the national and municipal levels."

Mayor said he's encouraged by the publicity given to conservation of the environment by the Rio conference and the possibility of increasing funding through the new Global Environmental Facility starting in 1994.

His vision for a vigorous, effective World Heritage program a decade from now emphasizes education and public awareness: "In Paris, at UNESCO headquarters, we have a clearinghouse for information, with publications from all over." In addition to the Paris Centre, he hopes to see five or six regional centers and national non-governmental organizations, which would actively promote an understanding of the Convention and suggest actions to help preserve World Heritage sites. "In children's textbooks, World Heritage would be a symbol of sharing and general awareness of what is precious in one's own and other cultures."

'Will our grandchildren be able to visit the Taj Mahal or the Galápagos Islands? The rock churches of Ethiopia or the lagoon of Venice?'

The person most on the spot now to shape the future of World Heritage is Centre director Bernd von Droste, who became director in May of 1992. Equipped with his meager budget and the energy that comes from knowing you're right, von Droste has begun to address issues of public awareness and funding by negotiating for a major television series on World Heritage and seeking private-sector funding.

Von Droste also has a sheaf of dreams for the future. Stressing that these are his personal ideas, not official UNESCO or Committee policies, he offered the following vision of an effective World Heritage program 20 years down the road:

• A World Heritage Fund of $2 billion or more, with new mechanisms to fund it, such as an energy tax.

• Formation of an academy of "the world's leading personalities—beyond any suspicion—to see that World Heritage is defended on the highest levels."

• Communication networks that will spread the World Heritage message.

• Proper management of tourism at all sites so that they continue to be protected at the same time that they contribute to economic development.

Will our children or grandchildren be able to visit and appreciate the sublime architecture of the Taj Mahal? Will they see the blue-footed boobies of the Galápagos? The rock churches of Ethiopia? The lagoon of Venice or the monoliths of Stonehenge? Or will they only be able to read about them in books?

In an ideal world, where we all recognize and appreciate natural phenomena and the achievements of humankind, where resources abound and protection of the planet is a shared value, our progeny would visit, learn from, and enjoy all of these World Heritage sites—and more. In the real world, points out IUCN's Thorsell, "World Heritage is a small player, taking in a small portion of the world's protected areas and the world's problems." But, he emphasizes, it's worth doing. "One thing that this world needs is more bridges. World Heritage helps build bridges."

Proving Ground of the Nuclear Age

The mangled artifacts and lunar landscape of the Nevada Test Site are a vivid testament to the advent of atomic weaponry.

William Gray Johnson and Colleen M. Beck

William Gray Johnson, assistant research professor with the Desert Research Institute, is in his third year of investigating the Nevada Test Site's historic structures. Colleen M. Beck, associate research professor at the Institute, has published on prehistoric and historic cultures in the Andes and the western United States. The authors would like to thank the U.S. Department of Energy for funding the research that made this article possible.

The desert flats of central Nevada offer an eerie landscape of twisted I-beams, bent towers and deformed bridges, frame buildings ripped apart, and stretches of land scarred by craters—one so vast it rivals depressions on the moon. Welcome to the Nevada Test Site, 1,350 square miles of landscape indelibly marked by hundreds of atomic bomb experiments. Here, for some 40 years during the Cold War between the West and the former Soviet Union and its allies, scientists experimented with various forms of nuclear weaponry.

Today, with moratoriums on both underground and aboveground testing, the Test Site is a silent wasteland, its devastation a legacy of that time.

We work for the Desert Research Institute (DRI), a branch of the University of Nevada system set up in 1959 to investigate arid land problems such as water availability and air quality. Since then our focus has broadened to include past environments and archaeology. Working for the United States Department of Energy (DOE), which owns the Test Site, and for state and private agencies in Nevada, we also regularly study Native American cultures as well as early settlements of miners and ranchers. The Native American ruins span some 10,000 years and include scatters of stone artifacts and pottery, occasionally associated with rock-shelters, caves, and rock outcrops decorated with petroglyphs and pictographs. Most of the mining and ranching occurred between 1905 and 1940, and claim markers and shafts can be seen in the hilly regions nearby, where springs, stone and wood cabins, outhouses, corrals, and fencing still remain.

We began recording these sites in 1978 in an effort to help the DOE comply with the National Historic Preservation Act of 1966, which directs federal agencies to inventory archaeological and historical property under their jurisdiction and to determine the effects of their activities—in the DOE's case the testing of nuclear weapons— on these properties. It soon became clear that what remained of the testing program itself was the most important component of the archaeological record. Like most artifacts left unused on the landscape, the Test Site structures and associated debris have begun to disappear. Weathering, recycling of items, and the need to reuse areas for other activities are slowly stripping the landscape of its Cold War artifacts. In 1982 Nevada's State Historic Preservation Office acknowledged the years of testing as an important period in the state's history and recommended that specific artifacts be preserved as testaments to the nuclear bomb experiments spawned by the Cold War.

In 1988 we proposed to the DOE that we survey the area. The proposal was well received, and in 1991 we were asked to evaluate two structures, a 1,527-foot tower used in a study of

Reprinted with permission from *Archaeology* magazine, May/June 1995, pp. 42-49. © 1995 by the Archaeological Institute of America.

Preserving a Cold War Legacy

Ricardo J. Elia

Military sites associated with the Cold War are scattered throughout the United States and abroad—in deserts, on farmlands, within suburbs, and beneath the ocean. While they may lack the evocative power of historical flashpoints like Gettysburg, Normandy Beach, or Pearl Harbor, these sites—atomic testing grounds and missile defense barriers—make up the Cold War landscape that helped define the second half of the twentieth century. Many of these installations have already been destroyed or lie in ruins. Others are being preserved to commemorate the period. Some examples:

• In the Blue Hills Reservation, a nature preserve south of Boston, are the well-preserved remains of Nike Ajax Missile Battery B-55, a surface-to-air missile launching facility that was operational between 1954 and 1965. Battery B-55 was equipped with missiles, a launch silo, radar tower, fallout shelter, generator building, mess hall, and protective earthen berm. The battery's control point was set atop a nearby hill where its radar could search the skies for hostile aircraft. Served by eight officers and 100 enlisted men, the facility was intended to protect Boston from Soviet bomber attack. By the 1970s, however, any Soviet assault would have been delivered by intercontinental ballistic missiles (ICBMs). Obsolete Nike batteries were soon replaced with ICBM installations designed to withstand a Soviet first strike and retaliate in kind. Battery B-55 was decommissioned and turned over to the Metropolitan District Commission (MDC), a state agency that manages the Blue Hills Reservation. According to Thomas Mahlstedt, MDC's chief archaeologist, the agency hopes to restore its buildings and open the installation to the public.

• One of the first American ICBMs was the Titan II. Of the 54 Titan II complexes that were built, only one survives. Known as Missile Site 8, the Green Valley, Arizona, installation is listed on the National Register of Historic Places because it is "the sole survivor of a weapon system built to survive a nuclear attack and then be available for retaliation if so ordered." Last year it was also declared a National Historic Landmark, indicating its national historical importance. The site contains a three-story underground launch center whose silo door, weighing 740 tons, was built to withstand a nuclear blast of up to 20 megatons.

• Among the eeriest sites of the Cold War are the sunken remains of American, Japanese, and German warships destroyed by nuclear bombs as part of an atomic testing program called Operation Crossroads. The tests were conducted in the Bikini Atoll Lagon of the Marshall Islands in July 1946, less than a year after the bombing of Hiroshima and Nagasaki. Among the 21 vessels sunk in the lagoon were the USS *Saratoga,* damaged by Japanese bombs off Iwo Jima in 1945, and the *Nagato,* flagship of the Imperial Japanese Navy at the time of the attack on Pearl Harbor. In 1989 and 1990 underwater archaeologists with the National Park Service surveyed the Operation Crossroads site. Divers documented the condition of several sunken vessels, including the *Saratoga,* which was found to be largely intact despite having been blown 30 to 40 feet in the air and 800 yards away from its original position. James Delgado, one of the archaeologists who participated in the survey, believes the site is more than a relic of atomic testing. Now executive director of the Vancouver Maritime Museum, Delgado says that the deliberate destruction of Japanese ships, especially the *Nagato,* amounted to a "symbolic, ritual killing of the enemy's ships."

Studies are under way to determine the feasibility of an underwater park at Bikini Lagoon, to be run by the Marshall Islands, which owns the sunken vessels.

Elsewhere, military planners and preservationists are grappling with the question of what to do with the surviving heritage of the Cold War. Should anything from the era be preserved? If so, what and how much? Such questions are being examined by the Department of Defense (DOD) Legacy Resource Management Program, established by Congress in 1991. Its mandate includes a provision "to inventory, protect, and conserve the physical and literary property and relics of the Department of Defense, in the United States and overseas, connected with the origins and development of the Cold War. . . ." The initiative calls for property management, a review of documentary records and oral histories, and a survey of selected historical properties. Funding for the Legacy program remains uncertain. Fifty million dollars were appropriated for the current fiscal year, but the new Congress is now reexamining DOD programs. Meanwhile, some states, including Louisiana, Pennsylvania, and Oklahoma, seem reluctant to consider Cold War sites for preservation because their histories are so recent. That view is shortsighted, according to Air Force historian Rebecca Cameron, who manages the Legacy project. The time to start planning for preservation is now, she asserts, otherwise "there is the likelihood that these resources will just disappear, and we will have no way to recapture what has been one of the lengthiest and liveliest periods in American history. The measure of any civilized country is the extent to which it protects its heritage."

Ricardo J. Elia teaches archaeology at Boston University.

radiation released from an unshielded reactor, and an underground parking garage tested for possible lateral and vertical displacement in a nuclear blast. We felt both were eligible for the National Register of Historic Places, the official list of the nation's cultural resources deemed worthy of preservation. Soon after we were asked to inventory all Test Site structures to determine their eligibility for the National Register. This program continues today. Surprisingly, many of the artifacts and even some of the structures we have researched are not recorded in any official documents. Instrumentation stands and temporary storage bunkers, for example, were important for the instruments they held or stored, but were not considered worth documenting.

To enter the Test Site, one takes U.S. Highway 95 north from Las Vegas to Mercury, a complex of scientific laboratories and warehouses, a building that houses radiation monitoring equipment and staff, dormitory-style housing, a cafeteria, a post office, a fire station, a hospital, a bowling alley, and a chapel. This is where scientists and support staff lived and worked during the nuclear testing period, which began January 27, 1951, with an air-drop event code-named Able. Aboveground testing ended in 1963 with the Limited Test Ban Treaty, which prohibited atmospheric, underwater, and outer-space nuclear testing. The current moratorium, which includes underground testing, took effect October 2, 1992. It has been extended twice, most recently to October 1995. Scientists still work here, but their efforts are focused on tracking residual radiation in the environment and cleaning it up. Mercury is still closed to the casual tourist, and a gate is manned by guards 24 hours a day. The DOE began conducting public tours in the early 1980s in recognition of the need to communicate the nature and extent of the testing program and in acknowledgment of the taxpayers' contributions to the program. Monthly tours continue to be available to individuals and groups.

Those who visit the site follow the Mercury Highway north. A sign indicates that cameras are not allowed in the forward areas. Another warns workers to be cautious of posted radiation areas. Driving through Checkpoint Pass, a guard station no longer used, one enters Frenchman Flat, a dry lake bed surrounded by rolling hills leading to distant mountains. Blownout buildings and twisted metal litter the landscape. Fourteen aboveground nuclear devices were detonated here; Grable, Priscilla, and Met were the code names of three. The largest, Priscilla, left most of the wreckage. Bunkers, motels, and homes, grouped at different distances from ground zero, were subjected to a blast equivalent to 37,000 tons of TNT. A steel-reinforced, concrete-sided bank vault at the center of the blast survived pressures of 600 pounds per square inch. We have recommended that the entire area be considered a historic district.

Continuing north, the highway cuts through Yucca Pass and a collection of gray windowless buildings that once served as the Test Site's electronic Control Point. Nearby, a faded sign on a boulder-covered hill identifies the site of News Nob, "where on April 22, 1952, the American press and radio first covered, and the nation first viewed by the medium of television, the firing of a nuclear device known as 'Operation Big Shot.' " At the foot of the hill are 11 rows of weather-beaten benches where reporters and dignitaries observed multiple explosions, some as close as 14 miles away.

Yucca Flat, whose cratered surface resembles the surface of the moon, witnessed more aboveground and underground tests than Frenchman Flat. One huge crater, known as Sedan, measures 320 feet deep and 1,280 feet across, and is a regular stop on the DOE tours. It was created in the Plowshare Program, a project designed to find peaceful uses for nuclear bombs, such as large-scale excavation. (A redigging of the Panama Canal was under consideration at the time.) Sedan Crater was listed on the National Register last year, the first Test Site area to be so designated.

Yucca Flat bears the remains of two-story houses located 6,600 and 8,000 feet southeast from ground zero of a test code-named Apple II. They were part of "Survival Town," a 1955 Civil Defense exercise designed to study the durability of typical civilian buildings subjected to nuclear weapons. Test targets also included industrial buildings and shelters, electrical power systems, communications equipment, a radio broadcasting station, trailer homes, fire equipment, cars, and food supplies placed at varying distances from ground zero. The force of the blast was the equivalent of 29,000 tons of TNT. Only the two-story houses and the frames of a few ranch-style homes survived.

Yucca Flat was also the site of radiation experiments. Bare Reactor Experiment, Nevada, or BREN, was part of Operation Ichiban, a program intended to determine radiation exposures experienced by the survivors of the Hiroshima and Nagasaki bombings. In these tests an unshielded reactor was placed in an elevator that rode up and down a 1,527-foot tower. The reactor released radiation on a mock Japanese village whose frame houses contained dosimeters for measuring exposure. Raising or lowering the reactor enabled scientists to change the angle and range of the radiation. Ichiban data allowed scientists to determine relationships between radiation doses and health problems associated with radiation sickness. Though the tower was moved to another part of the Test site in 1965, our research at the Japanese village and the relocated tower has determined that both are National Register candidates. Also eligible is an experimental dairy farm designed to study the effects of radioactive fallout on the fodder-cow-milk food chain. A number of small dairy farms were located downwind from the Test Site, and there was concern at the time that children drinking milk from these dairies might be affected by the fallout.

Farther north, Rainier Mesa rises 7,000 feet above sea level. Underground nuclear testing began here in

Nevada Test Site

PAHUTE MESA

RAINIER MESA

Dairy Farm

Y U C C A F L A T

Japanese Village

Survival Town

Control Point

News Nob

Yucca Pass

Nuclear Rocket Development Area

FRENCHMAN FLAT

BREN Tower

Checkpoint Pass

Mercury

NEVADA

Test Site

Las Vegas

10 Miles

Bette Duke

1957. Code-named Rainier, the first blast shook the mesa and surrounding areas with the force of 1,700 tons of TNT. Rainier Mesa and its neighbor, Pahute Mesa, were the sites of numerous underground tests. Some nuclear devices were placed in long shafts, others in tunnels. We know of underground bunkers, similar to bomb shelters, and we have heard about structures shaped like submarines with periscoping elevators. What condition are they in today? We hope to find out. Elsewhere there are remarkable structures associated with nuclear rocket development. We believe they too are significant.

Is this archaeology? We think it is. Our instincts lead us to believe that these artifacts of the Cold War are historically important and need to be studied. Can anyone honestly call them nonarchaeological? Scholars traditionally time-trek through millennia. Casually discussing similarities between the migrations of hunters and gatherers of 50,000 years ago and the peopling of the New World at the end of the last Ice Age some 10,000 years ago, they have grown accustomed to thinking in large blocks of time. It is the short blocks of time, especially our own, that we have difficulty understanding.

Sentinels of Stone

Rooted in ancient tradition, Inuit signposts find a new life in art

Text and photographs by Fred Bruemmer

I spent summer and fall of 1967 on Coats Island in northern Hudson Bay with some scientists studying polar bears. Our camp was near the remains of a settlement of the now extinct Sadlermiut, arctic inhabitants who had died out early this century from a disease introduced by whalers. One day, contemporary Inuit walrus hunters passing our camp in their Peterhead boat gave me a lift to the north tip of Coats Island and left me there to observe the great murre colonies.

I was fifteen miles away from camp and anticipated an arduous walk along a coast cut by many steep-sided valleys. While still puzzling what route to take, I noticed a cairn, or pile of stones, on a nearby ridge. I walked over and saw another cairn inland, due south and half a mile away. From it, I saw the next cairn and a long line of them, strategically placed, leading me to camp by the easiest and most direct route possible. By luck, I had come upon an ancient trail that had linked the Sadlermiut's homes with the murre colonies, which were to them well-stocked larders of birds and eggs.

In Inuktitut, the language of the Inuit, the cairns I had stumbled upon are known as *inukshuit* (singular *inukshuk*), which means "something acting in the capacity of a man." (*Inuk* is the singular for *Inuit*). In an empty land, an inukshuk seen in silhouette can look startlingly like a human. Some consist of only a few stones and are three or four feet tall, while others exceed twelve feet in height. Traveling northward in 1834 toward the Arctic Ocean on the

George Hakungak, of Bathurst Inlet, wields his rifle in a shooting pit that was built by earlier bow-and-arrow hunters. His father, Ekalun, met some of the explorers who visited the Arctic early this century.

river that now bears his name, Captain George Back, of Britain's Royal Navy, was amazed to see "a man" looking down from a high hill. Closer inspection revealed it to be a stone man "placed there by the Esquimaux."

"Cairns of this type, which from a distance look like a man, are often found deep in the interior," wrote Heinrich Klutschak, a member of the American 1878–80 expedition across the Canadian Barrens. "They serve [as] signposts for the natives." Such inukshuit, however, often had hidden meanings that eluded white explorers.

Simeonie Aulaqiaq, an Inuk from Pangnirtung on the east coast of Baffin Island, recently explained that "in the Baffin region, the traditional meaning of an inukshuk has to do with direction. . . . An inukshuk on land with two arms and two legs means there is a valley, and at the end of the valley, you are able to go in two directions." An inukshuk with no arms but both legs points toward a single-pass valley, while an inukshuk without arms and legs "is simply a guide for a . . . hunter . . . when you stand beside one of them, you should be able to see the same kind of inukshuk somewhere in the distance."

Similar stone pillars guided Inuit seafarers traveling by umiak or kayak along the complex coasts of their realm. In the 1940s, while working in northernmost Labrador, the Canadian archeologist Douglas Leechman saw inukshuit "on many headlands . . . gazing steadfastly out to sea. Their principal purpose is to serve as landmarks, and an Eskimo knows the shape and color of every one in his district. Should he be overtaken by fog or bad weather he will often be able to save himself from going astray by the timely sight of a familiar cairn."

The north shore of Hudson Strait seems designed for the destruction of boats. Sheer-cliffed headlands jut out into the sea, and a maze of islands and skerries bars the way. Storms are frequent, tidal currents fierce, and "The Weather for the most Part, a stinking Fog," as the exasperated British explorer Captain Thomas James put it succinctly in 1631.

In his long lifetime of travel, the Inuk Ooloopie Killiktee, at whose camp I spent the summer of 1979, had mastered the intricacies of this complex and dangerous coast. Inukshuit helped. There were hundreds of them on strategic capes and mountains, and he seemed to know the position and meaning of each one. Some, he said, were made by the Tunit (the Inuit name for a prehistoric people known to archeologists as the Dorset Culture) and may have been built more than a thousand years ago. Others were relatively new; Killiktee remembered who had built them and why. And some he had constructed himself: to identify the entrance to an inlet where soapstone for seal oil lamps could be quarried, to indicate a safe passage between two islets, or simply to mark a place where he had camped.

Crossing Hudson Strait in skin boats was risky and the Inuit thought it wise to appease the spirits of sea and wind. "A long time ago near Cape Dorset [on southern Baffin Island] there was a special inukshuk," the Inuk Peter Pitseolak told historian Dorothy Eber. "In the old days people from our side who were going to cross [Hudson Strait] used to go to the inukshuk and give presents. They would say 'I give you this. I wish to return again.' "

In 1965, Kiakshuk, the oldest man in Cape Dorset (he died in May 1966), told Brian W. Lewis, then principal of the Cape Dorset school, that "when men were about to make a long sea voyage they always made an inukshuk for good luck; invariably they left an offering to the sea spirits to insure their safety on the water."

Among their most important uses, inukshuit were aligned to funnel migrating caribou toward hidden hunters. Some of these alignments are extremely ancient. Curiously, these inukshuit are often just small mounds of stones, and it would take a very vivid imagination to see in them any resemblance to humans. Yet they worked, their efficacy based on the clever use of topography and expert, nearly intuitive knowledge of caribou behavior.

"The driving is started by the men giving long howls in imitation of wolves," wrote the explorer Vilhjalmur Stefansson. "This generally makes the caribou restless and starts them moving slowly" toward the long line of inukshuit "set up from fifty to a hundred and fifty yards apart, according to the character of the topography."

Frightened by the howling and the sudden appearance of humans, Stefansson noted, the caribou's "imagination appears to turn all the little monuments into a line of people. It seems absurd that two stones, one on top of the other, reaching an elevation of only a foot, should be feared as much by the caribou as actual persons, but that appears to be the fact. It seldom happens that the animals break through the line and usually they are driven at a speed from five to eight miles per hour toward the ambush."

Among the precontact Inuit "discovered" by the 1913–18 Stefansson-Anderson expedition was a ten-year-old boy named Ekalun. Fifty-four years later, I lived at Ekalun's camp in the Bathurst Inlet region of arctic Canada, sharing his tent for six months and, when he was in a reminiscent mood, his immense knowledge of Inuit life and hunting techniques.

Caribou were essential to Inuit. They provided food and, most important, the best fur for arctic clothing. Seven skins were required to dress a man, a woman re-

A distinctively shaped inukshuk high above Hudson Strait served as a landmark for Inuit navigators traveling by umiak or kayak.

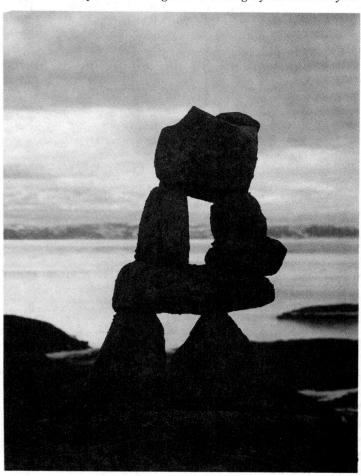

quired six, and a child four. The Inuit made every effort to kill caribou for winter clothing in August and early September, when the fur was of optimum quality.

This was also when the caribou that had spent the summer on far-north tundra pastures began their southward migration, which brought some herds to elaborate inukshuk systems that channeled the flow of animals toward waiting hunters armed with bows and arrows or with lances. One such inukshuk system, similar in concept and design to several others I have seen in the Arctic, was twenty miles inland from Ekalun's coastal camp, and he had hunted there for many years, as a boy driving the caribou and, later, as a man and hunter waiting for them in shooting pits.

The traditional ambush required three main elements. The first was an extensive area of lush arctic meadow where migrating caribou naturally bunched and browsed. From there two long rows of inukshuit were arranged to lead the caribou for many miles, converging at some natural defile—a narrow pass where the caribou would be forced to proceed uphill in a thin line. And finally, shallow shooting pits with low rims of rocks were prepared for the hunters, usually at the top of the defile.

The hunt began, said Ekalun, with boys and young men circling the herd and driving it slowly, cautiously toward the entrance between the two inukshuit alignments. Once in the pillar-flanked passageway, the caribou were kept trotting forward and uphill. Whenever they veered toward one side, women and children, hidden behind some of the inukshuit, jumped out, waved their arms, flapped long strips of white caribou belly fur, and screamed. " 'Hoo-hoo-hoo,' they howled, just like wolves," Ekalun recalled. To make the inukshuit more realistic, people placed lumps of sedge-covered sod on the tops of many of them to give them a mop-headed appearance.

Terrified by the people, the howling, and the lines of stone men, the caribou rushed forward toward apparent safety: the open defile with its hidden hunters. The men waited, tense with excitement, until the caribou were within a few feet, then shot them with their bows or speared them with lances.

The weakness of the Inuit bow made the inukshuit-directed caribou drive essential. Made of pieces of driftwood, brittle and fragile, the Inuit bow was ingeniously carved and pegged together, backed with plaited sinew cord to give it spring, and lashed with caribou or seal leather to give it strength. But it remained an ineffectual weapon compared with bows of other regions where suitable wood was available. The longbow made of yew used by English archers to win the battle of Crécy in 1346 was deadly at 200 yards and more. The Inuk bow, said Ekalun (who was married before he had his first rifle), killed from no farther than thirty paces.

Since the stone men and their purpose remained immutable, such ambush systems were used for centuries and belonged, in Inuit fashion, to all the people. Anyone could use it. When I asked Ekalun (who found the white man's mercenary ways deplorable) who could use the system, he said sarcastically: "Anyone who paid $500!" In the 1960s, the Canadian archeologist William E. Taylor, Jr., examined an "elaborate inukshuk system . . . extending over an area of about two square miles" on southern Victoria Island in the Canadian Arctic. Much of it had been built more than a thousand years ago by Dorset Culture hunters. It was subsequently used by Thule Culture people and "by recent Copper Eskimo people."

Both Taylor and the American archeologist Moreau S. Maxwell, who studied "inukshuit drives" on southern Baffin Island, speculate that this type of hunt, apart from procuring food and furs in their prime, also had social importance. Inuit camps in Canada, from the remotest past until the 1950s, consisted usually of about twenty-five to thirty individuals, presumably an optimum number for mutual support. Men normally hunted alone or occasionally in pairs. But the caribou drive, Taylor observed, required the "co-operative action of a sizeable number of people meeting at least annually." It was a time, said Maxwell, when "a number of bands may form a virtually structureless aggregate of 100 or more people."

That was roughly how Ekalun remembered it: a joyous get-together of many bands from an area about half the size of Belgium, the exchange of stories and gossip of an entire year, the thrill of the hunt followed by marvelous feasts. Once Inuit acquired guns, however, caribou drives were abandoned. Most Inuit moved into villages and towns, and the meanings and messages of inukshuit that once served as guides and beacons were gradually forgotten. The stone men stood alone in an empty land.

A squat inukshuk, below, stands near an old campsite on Somerset Island.

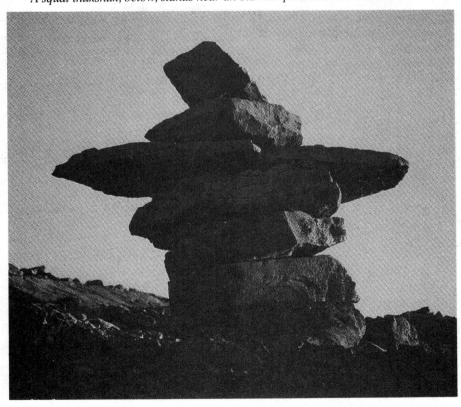

7. CONTEMPORARY ARCHAEOLOGY

Since Canadian law forbids the disturbance of archeological sites and the removal of ancient artifacts from the North, inukshuit have rarely been damaged or destroyed. Their very size and weight discourages pilfering and smuggling. But in recent years, outsiders have coveted these stone men as objects of art. Such a concept is alien to the Inuit. Puzzled but pragmatic, they have nevertheless begun to build inukshuit for money.

The first big commission came from the Toronto airport (now the Lester B. Pearson International Airport). Since, as a plaque states, "these stone figures are among the oldest transportation symbols" of humankind, they seemed an appropriate link between the Stone Age and the jet age. Three inukshuit, made of Baffin Island granite, were assembled on Cape Dorset in the early 1960s under the direction of Kiakshuk. They were marked stone by stone, photographed, and then shipped to Toronto for reassembly. The main figure, with an upraised arm and a powerful cubistic face that Picasso or Braque would have loved, was described by the British art expert Charles Gimpel in 1967 as "the best Canadian sculpture I have seen."

Many public and private commissions followed and inukshuit now stand on elegant urban properties and near many public buildings. One stone man stands in a strangely sylvan setting at the Ontario Science Centre in Toronto. Another, made by Kellypallik Pishuktie of Iqaluit on Baffin Island, was placed at the entrance to an exhibition entitled "Contemporary Inuit Masterworks," first displayed at the United Nations in New York and then at the Earth Summit in Rio de Janeiro during the summer of 1992.

Once guides to Inuit travelers, the rugged stone men of the Arctic are now the *dernier cri* in elegant *salons d'art*.

An inukshuk commissioned as a sculpture for the international airport in Toronto links the Stone Age to the jet age.

Ekalun, my old friend and mentor, who only knew inukshuit in the wild, would have been amused, but I think also pleased by this transformation.

The Boom in Volunteer Archaeology

Richard A. Wertime

Richard A. Wertime is a Contributing Editor to ARCHAEOLOGY.

Americans of all ages and from all walks of life suddenly want to get involved in archaeology. In a poll of more than 50 federal, state, and local organizations, ARCHAEOLOGY has found a dramatic surge in volunteer participation coast to coast. One federal initiative, the Forest Service's "Passport in Time" program, which oversees volunteer archaeology in 107 of the 125 national forests, reports a 550 percent increase in volunteer applications since its original two-state program went national in 1991.

State "Archaeology Week" initiatives, which help garner volunteer support

for statewide archaeological projects through museum exhibits, tours of active sites, and demonstrations of ancient practices, report major increases in amateur involvement in the past two years: up 300 percent in Virginia, 30 percent in Texas, and 100 percent in California. Urban-centered programs also report surprising growth in volunteer participation—since 1992, up 200 percent in Fairfax County, Virginia; 75 percent in Portsmouth, New Hampshire; 30 percent in St. Augustine, Florida. Whatever induces people to get involved in archaeology—and there is a host of intriguing motives—one thing is certain: amateur participation couldn't come at a better time, for there are far too few professionals to deal with all of the sites that are being discovered or that need to be protected.

What do amateur archaeologists do? What kinds of training and supervision do they get? And why has their interest in digging into the past blossomed so suddenly in so many parts of the country?

Some of the answers to these questions lie in the scores of federal, state, and local programs that both feed and benefit from the public's hunger for archaeology. Major national organizations like the Archaeological Institute of America, the Society for American Archaeology, and the Society of Historical Archaeology have created independent and sometimes interlocking programs that seek to educate the public about proper methods of archaeological investigation as well as site management and protection. In an effort to broaden public awareness and support, some 30 states now have an annual "Archaeology Week," and some, like Arizona and Virginia, an "Archaeology Month." Local enterprises like Alexandria Archaeology in Alexandria, Virginia, and Strawbery Banke in Portsmouth, New Hampshire, provide a wealth of opportunities for the avocational archaeologist, as do study centers such as the Crow Canyon Archaeological Center in Cortez, Colorado; the Four Corners School of Outdoor Education in Monticello, Utah; and the

Center for American Archaeology in Kampsville, Illinois.

The federal government has long been a leader in site protection and preservation. In 1892 it set aside for preservation the prehistoric ruins at Casa Grande in Arizona. The 1906 Antiquities Act specified the protection of antiquities on all lands owned or controlled by the government and required permits to excavate them. More recent federal efforts have focused on public archaeology. Visionary professionals like Charles R. McGimsey, III, and Hester Davis in Arkansas helped steer through Congress the Archaeological Resources Protection Act (ARPA) of 1979 and its 1988 amendments, including Section 10(C), which mandates that federal agencies develop programs to increase public awareness about cultural resource significance and protection.

The Bureau of Land Management, the Forest Service, the National Park Service, the Army Corps of Engineers, the Fish and Wildlife Service, and the Bureau of Reclamation today administer some 700 million acres of public land. In response to ARPA these federal agencies and others have developed an array of research and stewardship programs designed to involve the public in the management of archaeological sites on these lands. The National Park Service's "Volunteers in the Parks" embraces a range of initiatives and volunteer possibilities, as does the Bureau of Land Management's "Adventures in the Past." The Forest Service's "Passport in Time" program, started in 1989 in four national forests in Wisconsin and Minnesota, was conceived by archaeologists Gordon Peters, Christy Caine, and Mark Bruhy, who needed help with site surveys, excavation, and lab work. They began recruiting volunteers under what was then the agency's cultural resource management program. "At the time," recalls Bruhy, "the program was a well-kept secret. We had no inkling that it would become a nationwide effort by 1991."

But for all the federal government's involvement in public archaeology, it is the regional, state, and grassroots efforts that constitute the wellspring of nonprofessionals in archaeology. Avocational societies across the United States identify, study, and protect sites; conduct public outreach programs; publish newsletters, scholarly bulletins, and monographs; and oversee museum collections. They are often headed by deeply committed nonprofessionals who may have spent years studying the archaeology of their region. David A. Andreozzi of Barrington, Rhode Island, and Kathleen Joyce-Bassett of Roanoke, Virginia, are cases in point. Andreozzi, a cabinetmaker, has been president of the Narragansett Archaeological Society for five years. "People are amazed that Precolumbian activity occurred in our area," he says. "They're especially amazed by the lithics, and want to become more involved."

In the fall of 1992, while walking near a kettle hole (a symmetrical depression left by an ancient glacier) in the wooded part of a local golf course, Andreozzi spotted three stone flakes, each about the size of a dime. The kettle hole, 25 feet deep and 100 feet across, contained two to three feet of water. "It seemed an ideal prehistoric water source for the big game that Stone Age inhabitants relied on," he recalls. "I suspected that there might be a lithic workshop nearby and proposed to the board of governors of the Rhode Island Country Club that we excavate it. The board approved and we went out and found four Late Archaic hearths at least 4,500 years old with a wealth of lithics. We had hit the nail right on the head." The C-shaped hearths were well preserved, and stuck professional archaeologists who visited the site as unique. The excavation became the subject of the largest story the local newspaper had ever run, and Andreozzi began to hear from area teachers who wanted to bring their students to the site. "One hundred and eighteen students hiked over from Barrington Middle School," he remembers with pride. "We set up tables for the artifacts and even had some students participate in the fieldwork by digging and sifting for lithics." Before long, he developed a slide show for students who could not visit the site. Now, he says, "I've turned on 1,200 to 1,400 kids. We let them form their own teams, and they are helping us excavate test pits."

Andreozzi has just received a $2,000 grant from a Rhode Island philanthropist to pay for carbon dating and aid his outreach effort. About one-fiftieth of the potential site area has been excavated with the assistance of Paul Robinson, Rhode Island's state archaeologist; Barbara Hall, curator of the Haffenreffer Museum of Anthropology at Brown University, and her assistant David Gregg; and Carol Barnes Fidler and E. Pierre Morenon, Rhode Island College anthropologists. Material recovered at the site is being held by the Narragansett Society. After it is analyzed and cataloged, a representative collection will be presented to the country club. The remainder will be kept by the society and periodically made available to the public at the Barrington Preservation Society Museum.

Kathleen Joyce-Bassett, who works for the Virginia Department of Corrections, is president of the Archaeological Society of Virginia (ASV), which has 15 chapters statewide. "One of the most important concerns of our group," she says, "is providing education about preservation issues and about archaeology, both historic and prehistoric." Accordingly, the society publishes a quarterly bulletin, which contains articles by professionals and nonprofessionals, and recently received an award from the Society for Historical Archaeology for publishing seminal work. The society has also cosponsored with the Council of Virginia Archaeologists a series of symposia on Virginia archaeology, and is now engaged in an ambitious fundraising program known as the ASV 2000 Development Fund, whose objective is to raise $250,000 to establish an ASV center with a library and exhibitions. "Right now," says Joyce-Bassett, "everybody in our organization is a volunteer. The work we're doing has gotten so extensive that we

How to Volunteer

The National Park Service offers an informative brochure, *Participate in Archeology,* that lists titles of books, movies, television programs, and videos on archaeology, as well as a selection of titles for people who need a basic introduction to the discipline. Write: Publication Coordinator, Archaeological Division, National Park Service, P.O. Box 37127, Washington, DC 20013-7127.

The Forest Service publishes *PIT Traveler: Passport in Time Newsletter,* which lists volunteer opportunities. Write: Jill Schaefer, Volunteer Services Manager, Passport in Time Clearing House, P.O. Box 183664, Washington, DC 20036 (telephone: 202-293-0922; fax 202-293-1782).

The broadest annual listing of volunteer opportunities is the *Archaeological Fieldwork Opportunities Bulletin,* published by the Archaeological Insti-

tute of America. Write: Kendall/Hunt Publishing Company, Order Department, 4050 Westmark Drive, Dubuque, IA 52002 (telephone: 800-228-0810). The cost is $9.00 for AIA members, $11.00 for nonmembers. It also contains the names, addresses, and phone numbers of all state archaeologists and historic preservation officers, as well as regional societies of the Institute.

Earthwatch, published bimonthly by Earthwatch and sent to its members, also lists volunteer opportunities. Write: Earthwatch Membership Service, P.O. Box 8037, Syracuse, NY 13217 (telephone: 800-776-0188; fax 617-926-8352).

Nonprofessionals interested in opportunities available through private organizations and archaeological study centers should write directly to them. These include Crow Canyon Archaeological Center, 23390 County Road K, Cortez,

CO 81321 (telephone: 800-422-8975); Center for American Archeology, Department B, Kampsville Archeological Center, P.O. Box 366, Kampsville, IL 62053 (telephone: 618-653-4316); Four Corners School of Outdoor Education, East Route, Monticello, UT 84535 (telephone: 801-587-2156); Anasazi Heritage Center, Bureau of Land Management, 27501 Highway 184, Dolores, CO 81323 (telephone: 303-882-4811); University Research Expeditions Program, Department J-4, University of California, Berkeley, CA 94720 (telephone: 415-642-6586); Foundation for Field Research, P.O. Box 2010, Alpine, CA 91001 (telephone: 619-445-9264); and The Smithsonian Institution, Smithsonian National Associates, Research Expedition Program, Suite 4210, 490 L'Enfant Plaza SW, Washington, DC 20560 (telephone: 202-357-1350).

—R.A.W.

need an executive director to handle all of the paperwork."

In many state societies avocational archaeologists work closely with professionals. In Texas, for example, archaeological societies are open to both professionals and amateurs. Thomas Hester, director of the Texas Archaeological Research Laboratory and a two-time president of the Texas Archaeological Society says, "the tie between avocationals and professionals goes back to the 1920s when the society was organized. There were not many professionals at that time, and the few that we had worked closely with the amateurs." Texas is distinguished from many other states by the sheer number of its avocational archaeologists and by the independence of its 32 regional societies, which are not to be confused with the ten regional

chapters of the statewide archaeological organization. Many members of the regional groups also participate in state chapter activities. Cities like El Paso, Fort Worth, Houston, and Dallas have their own societies.

In 1962 the Texas statewide organization started a summer field school that annually attracts 450 to 500 participants and moves around the state to endangered sites or locations where professionals need help with long-range regional studies. The field school is run by professionals, but is organized and managed by avocationals, who, says Hester, "provide the crew chiefs and the training." Texas, along with Arizona, has one of the oldest and best managed "site steward" programs in the country. Site stewards are avocationals who monitor and maintain sites, reporting damage or looting

when it occurs. The stewards are appointed and administered by an advisory board representing the state's archaeological community, including academic and contract archaeologists as well as amateurs.

Nonprofessionals are attracted to archaeology for a number of reasons. Some want escape from their daily routines, others like the experience of new places, the mingling with new people, the challenge of the work. Affording as it does a material record, archaeology also offers *tangible* evidence of the past. Museum of Florida History educator KC Smith observes: "While the thrill of unearthing or working with ancient objects initially may draw volunteers to archaeological projects, they quickly appreciate that sites and artifacts are the keys to unlocking the past. Inevitable, their excited focus on 'things' evolves into an intense curiosity about the people who made those things."

Just as the motives vary, so do the talents that nonprofessionals bring to the field. Jill Osborn, who coordinates "Passport in Time" in Washington, D.C., insists that the central function of public archaeology is not to furnish professionals with free labor, but rather to enfranchise the public in the task of preserving the nation's heritage. Avocationals bring an array of talents to their work: skills in organization, management, and public relations; technical training in draftsmanship, cartography, and photography; and curatorial abilities.

Perhaps the most precious resource that people bring is curiosity. Janel Kerby was a 17-year-old high-school student from Canyon, Texas, when she traveled to Tallahassee to participate in a two-week program called "Florida Findings." Sponsored by the Girl Scout Council of Apalachee Bend and the Museum of Florida History, the program introduces newcomers to the field of archaeology. What led Janel to Florida is instructive: "When I was younger," she says, "my dad and grandfather would take me arrowhead hunting down in Plains, Texas. They were interested in the past—nothing scientific—they'd just talk about how things used to be." When she was 15, Janel joined the Panhandle and Texas archaeological societies. She learned about "Florida Findings" through the Girl Scout Wider Ops (for "wider opportunities") Program, which affords scouts the chance to participate in enrichment programs across the country. In Tallahassee, she worked on land and underwater sites. What made the experience so special? "There was something different to it," she says. "Other teachers I'd known knew the answers to questions they asked. In Florida, we helped find the answers."

Alexander Munton of Portsmouth, New Hampshire, is a 78-year-old retired expert in industrial hygiene, a field, he says, in which "accurate measurement is extremely important." To his volunteer work at Strawbery Banke

in downtown Portsmouth, Munton brought his passion for precision. To measure the bases and rims of ceramics, he devised an ingenious transparent plexiglas measuring board with a series of concentric circles and a rule on it. The device measures pots, even large ones, quickly and accurately. He also devised excavation data sheets and drew maps recording various excavations at the site.

The first settlers to sail into Portsmouth Harbor in the early seventeenth century encountered an embankment covered with strawberry plants. Now a ten-acre historic urban neighborhood, Strawbery Banke encompasses a part of the old waterfront known as Puddle Dock (largely silted in by the turn of the century and land filled today), and nine furnished houses dating from 1695 to the 1950s. Munton got involved with Strawbery Banke in 1981, when he joined "Project Discovery," a program that trained volunteers for exploratory excavations at an historic home. In 1990 he joined his teenage grandson in a field school at another historic site. To his surprise, his grandson was "treated as one of the volunteers—as an adult" by director Martha Pinello. "We were blessed at having an opportunity to be involved in an archaeological project together," says Munton. "It's not always easy to find sites available to amateurs." What hooked the senior Munton on archaeology? "Several things," he says. "Strawbery Banke has a high caliber of staff. They're very professional, very friendly. They take a lot of time with you. They're not set in their ways; they're anxious to progress. It's just an exciting place to be!" His first excavation, he said, "was like being a child at the seashore." His expertise has deepened with time. An archivist of considerable experience, he is writing an article for the New Hampshire Archaeological Society on deeds, probates, and early maps of Portsmouth.

Where is avocational archaeology headed? Most observers agree that the full potential has barely been tapped. The Forest Service, for one, plans to incorporate people with disabilities

into its outreach programs. Special needs participants in the "Passport in Time" programs will have the same spectrum of challenges available to them as people without disabilities. Says Jill Osborn, "People with disabilities want those levels of challenge. A person in a wheelchair may want to push himself to the limit" in tackling archaeology in a wilderness setting. While she says that there are no plans to try to make all programs and sites accessible to people with disabilities, it is the government's intention to create avocational opportunities for them wherever they are reasonable. "It makes good business sense," says Osborn. "Forty-three million Americans have a permanent disability, and they are more active today than at any time in the past. If 30 percent of the total population is interested in heritage, 30 percent of the population with disabilities is also interested. In addition, Passport in Time is a family activity. If the experience excludes one person in the family with a disability, chances are, the rest of the family won't participate either."

This past September, the Society for American Archaeology convened its second "Save the Past for the Future" conference in Breckenridge, Colorado. As they had done five years earlier at a gathering in Taos, New Mexico, conferees representing federal, state, and local agencies issued a plea for intensified efforts to educate the public about the widespread looting of sites and the need for greater public participation in site maintenance and protection. "Public education increases the public's understanding of and appreciation for the past," says George Smith, a National Park Service archaeologist based in Florida and a co-chairman of the conference. "This translates into more volunteers and more effective site stewardship. The more people we can get involved the better the chance we will have to get this looting crisis under control."

Public archaeology is in some ways a uniquely American phenomenon. KC Smith believes "Americans have inherited something from their el-

Educating the Volunteer

There are dozens of field schools and certification programs that train non-professionals, but how well-trained do they need to be? Many archaeologists feel that close supervision and a low ratio of professionals to amateurs are crucial to effective training. David Starbuck, who has directed or participated in at least 25 field schools, believes that one professional for every six amateurs is about right. He offers no formal certification, in part because "it is impossible to tell from a certificate whether someone is well trained." How does one tell? "Call up the previous instructor and simply ask him or her whether the trainee knows what to do," says Starbuck.

Others who work with volunteers take an even more flexible approach. "There are many jobs that untrained people can do," says KC Smith, a Museum of Florida History educator experienced in introducing archaeology to the lay public. "You can train people to do basic field-assistance activities—screening, washing of artifacts—in two hours, and that satisfies them perfectly. Not everybody needs extensive training."

Texas state archaeologist Robert J. Mallouf believes "professionals must accept the fact that it may not always be possible to instill professional attitudes in avocationals to the degree that one is comfortable turning them loose on a problematic undertaking. Most avocationals can reasonably be expected to fall short of expectations when it comes to the difficult, tedious requirements of scientific reporting."

In some states archaeologists do offer certification programs aimed at turning nonprofessionals into highly skilled colleagues. One such program is run by the Arkansas Archaeological Survey under the direction of state archaeologist Hester Davis. Widely emulated by states such as Kansas, South Carolina, New Mexico, Oklahoma, New Jersey, and Virginia, the program affords the nonprofessional a multitiered training experience, with everything from a two-and-one-half week program of lectures, lab, and fieldwork to opportunities to assist archaeologists in labs around the state. The strength of the Arkansas program is in the number of professionals who participate, as many as one archaeologist for every six volunteers. Kay McCarron, Fairfax County archaeologist in northern Virginia, has adapted the Arkansas model to serve the needs of the Washington, D.C., region. McCarron's program offers a technician certification upon completion of one year of lab work, excavation, and fieldwork, and a paraprofessional certification requiring at least three years of study.

The cost of archaeological training for avocationals is also an issue much discussed among professionals. For its teenage summer camp, which lasts two weeks, Alexandria Archaeology charges $475 per person per week, and acknowledges that it uses the money to support ongoing work. Similarly, the Colonial Williamsburg "Learning Weeks in Archaeology" program costs $550 for a two-week session. The Andover Foundation for Archaeological Research in Andover, Massachusetts, requests a hefty tax-deductible donation of $1,600 from those who volunteer to work at its rock-shelter site in southwestern New Mexico. By contrast, the Fairfax County, Virginia, certification programs costs $30 for technician certification and $50 for papaprofessional certification. Richard Boisvert, New Hampshire deputy state archaeologist and coordinator of the State Conservation and Rescue Archaeology Program, offers an innovative program for adults in archaeological recording, management, and education that is funded by the state's Historic Preservation Fund and hence costs nothing—although the program accepts donations for the rental of porto-potties. "The public has a responsibility for its heritage," says Boisvert, "and archaeology has an obligation to include the public where it's appropriate. It's a two-way street. A great deal of archaeology can be taught to anyone who is reasonably intelligent and reasonably healthy." On the other hand, he adds, "If archaeology is available only to people who can afford it, that's wrong. It shouldn't become an exclusionary thing."

The cost of training goes hand in hand with the question of program quality. Not every avocational is satisfied with the preparation he or she receives. A case in point is the mixed experience of Joseph Illick, a professor of history at San Francisco State University. In 1991, Illick responded to an ad for volunteers in the Sierra Club magazine. He traveled to the mountain town of Blanding, Utah, to help locate, map, and photograph Anasazi Indian sites in the Abajo Mountains under a program jointly sponsored by the Sierra Club, the Bureau of Land Management, and the Forest Service. Having paid several hundred dollars for the privilege, he joined some 30 other volunteers mapping vast stretches of territory for days at a time. While his first day was devoted to a "reasonably comprehensive" series of orientation sessions, he felt that "there wasn't sufficient follow-up once we got out there," and that he and his fellow participants were covering a lot of territory "with only occasional glimpses of what this was all about." His frustration was compounded when the entire project was later abandoned, apparently because of disagreements among the project sponsors. Illick says he would volunteer again, but would check more carefully the manner in which participants were prepared and kept in touch with the general goals of the project. "I accept the fact that volunteers are expected to carry out the most mundane tasks," he notes, "but that labor should be accompanied by daily, or nightly, discussions of topics that elevate the experience. After all, that's why we contribute ourselves."

—R.A.W.

ders—a congenital fascination with people, places, events, and things of the past." As an observer of the archaeological scene for a generation, this writer would add his own perspective: archaeological activity—particularly that of unearthing what has been buried—affords citizens an especially potent metaphor for self-realization. Indeed, the pull that archaeology exerts seems almost mystical, inasmuch as it affords an opportunity to become grounded in the past. For Native Americans, this becomes an act of recovery, an reclaiming of ancient identity; for Americans with immigrant pasts, it is a strengthening of cultural and national affiliation.

Archaeology can be hot, cold, tedious, frustrating, unglamorous, and dirty work. For volunteers, the privilege of participating can be an expensive one. What draws people into such work? Archaeology is a field of great diversity. By virtue of its mission—recovering the past and articulating it to the present—it embodies the concept of the common good. Archaeology is a mirror held up, not to nature, but to humanity. To excavate the past is to polish that mirror, that we may better see ourselves and know more clearly who we are.

The Preservation of Past

Conservators are racing to save monuments threatened by development, pollution, looting and neglect. In the process, they are transforming the field of archaeology into a new science

Marguerite Holloway

Staff Writer

Just before sunset, the stones of Pueblo Bonito in Chaco Canyon, New Mexico, glow golden, and their varied patterns stand out like friezes. The ruin—an elaborate city built and inhabited by Anasazi Indians between A.D. 850 and 1150—becomes empty of the day's tourists, and the cold of the desert night begins to settle in the shadowy rooms and kivas, circular ceremonial centers sunken in the ground. The small vents and tapered doors grow black.

One of these dark entrances—a high, squat door sitting at the junction of two walls—captures the attention of Dabney Ford, an archaeologist with the National Park Service who has worked at and studied Chaco Canyon for more than 10 years. She explains that the opening is aligned to catch sunlight only on the winter solstice. On that day, rays of light reflect on a specially built wall corner on the opposite side of the room. Although archaeologists understand relatively little about Anasazi culture, some have recently come to believe that the design of Pueblo Bonito—like that of Teotihuacan in Mexico, Machu Picchu in Peru and many other ancient cities—reflects astronomical cycles. The door is just one example of an architecture oriented by solar and lunar fluxes—one that perhaps embodies Anasazi political and social hierarchy.

"Architects and archaeologists have had a hard time perceiving the complexity of this society," Ford notes, as she moves through tiny doorways, pointing out wood beams that have survived intact for hundreds of years. Chaco Canyon "is pretty humbling."

It is also falling apart. Being able to reinterpret Anasazi culture (if one is an archaeologist), visit the site (if one is a tourist) or pray in the sacred kivas (if one is a tribal descendant) depends on the walls' not buckling or collapsing as water seeps into the aging rocks and mortar. It depends on preventing salt crystals from growing in the stones and breaking them apart, vandals from digging up artifacts and visitors from climbing on walls or wood beams, splintering in minutes what endured for a millennium. Preserving Chaco Canyon entails solving a series of problems posed by archaeological sites around the world.

These concerns have, in the minds of many archaeologists, art historians and preservationists, reached crisis proportions. All 440 places designated by UNESCO as World Heritage Sites (including Chaco Canyon) are threatened, explains Bernd von Droste, director of the World Heritage Center in Paris. Angkor in Cambodia, the Pyramids in Egypt, the Parthenon in Athens, the old city of Dubrovnik in Croatia, the earthen bas-reliefs of the Royal Palaces of Abomey in Benin and the homind fossil footprints found by archaeologist Mary Leakey in Tanzania

are among hundreds of cultural and anthropological icons in danger of destruction. "In another 20 years, most of the archaeology of Egypt is going to be in museums," remarks Fred Wendorf of Southern Methodist University, who has been working in Egypt since 1962. "Everything else is going to be covered by water or plowed up in fields or coated with asphalt."

The principal threats to archaeological sites are the same ones cited by environmentalists as endangering biodiversity: development, population growth, tourism, illegal traffic, air pollution, war, neglect and, in some cases, botched efforts at conservation. Nevertheless the dangers stalking the world's cultural patrimony have not catalyzed any grassroots campaign to rival that of the green movement. (Some archaeologists speculate that, despite the public's fascination with Indiana Jones, roofless buildings do not have the same appeal as baby seals. Degradation also can be too slow to engage general interest: the fading looks of a sculpture may be seen only by comparing a contemporary photograph with one taken 30 years ago.)

Within the archaeological community, however, the growing perils are fostering a reevaluation of the entire field. "The whole attitude of archaeologists has been to plunder, then leave," notes Pamela Jerome, a professor at Columbia University, who is teaching one of the first courses exclusively on site conservation given at a graduate school. Typically archaeologists have excavated and then moved on—sometimes covering ruins over again to preserve them, a process called backfilling. Their training has not included work in conservation. That effort has instead been the province of museum-trained conservators, who restore only portable artifacts and collected objects. The two groups have often been at odds, Jerome says: one trying to push ahead with a dig, the other saying slow down, save this.

WASTING AWAY

But field archaeologists are now facing many of the challenges that have always confronted object conservators: disintegration and loss. They "have begun to realize that the rate of site destruction is pretty sizable and that archaeology is a nonrenewable resource. They have become more interested in preserving sites in situ," describes Francis P. McManamon, an archaeologist at the National Park Service. "That awareness has been reinforced by the recognition that you still have to take care of all the material that was excavated." Park Service collections alone hold an estimated 24.6 million objects, of which 16.8 million have not yet been catalogued. (Renovating facilities to care for these artifacts properly, something required under 1990 regulations, could cost more than $59.8 million.) The staggering amount of material that has been amassed worldwide has led some researchers to call for moratoriums on excavations until collections have been thoroughly researched; in many cases, recovered objects waste away in dusty vaults, unstudied and ill cared for.

The artifact crisis and the site crisis together have led to a new ethic and science. Borrowing from the wealth of knowledge about conserving artifacts and from materials science, scientists at several institutions—including the Getty Conservation Institute (GCI) in Marina del Rey, Calif., the International Centre for the Study of the Preservation and the Restoration of

Cultural Property in Rome, the International Council on Monuments and Sites in Paris, UNESCO, the World Monuments Fund in New York City and various laboratories and universities—are formalizing the discipline of site conservation. Symposiums and courses such as Jerome's are beginning to appear. The International Institute for Conservation of Historic and Artistic Works will hold its 1996 meeting on archaeological preservation. A journal, *Conservation and Management of Archaeological Sites,* to be published in London, is slated to start this year.

The primary goal of this burgeoning area of research is to slow deterioration. Buried ruins can survive for eons because they reach equilibrium with their stable surroundings. When dug out of sand or a mat of jungle growth or opened to air, their components

begin to fall apart. "You are exposing it to sun, to rain, to dewfall, to oxygen, to all these things," describes Neville H. Agnew, associate director of programs at the GCI. "You catalyze a whole assemblage of degeneration that just springs into action—sometimes even within hours of excavation you can see deterioration starting." Some protective strategies being investigated include determining how to backfill ruins correctly, how to monitor caves or tombs for changes in humidity that could cause wall paintings to flake off, how to treat stones of tropical ruins with biocides and how to protect adobe, or earthen, buildings from the ravages of earthquakes.

Although backfilling has been practiced casually by archaeologists for years, it has never been tested rigorously. Conservationists view reburial as the best solution for many places,

YUNGANG GROTTOES in China are threatened by pollution, arid climate, and water seepage. These factors are causing the 1,500-year-old sculptures to deteriorate, as is evident in a comparison of the same statue in 1933 (*below, left*) and in 1991 (*below, right*). Conservators are working to drain water from the site and to construct shelters to protect certain caves.

HEDDA MORRISON, *courtesy of Getty Conservation Institute*

MARGARET G.H. MAC LEAN *Getty Conservation Institute*

but the procedure remains controversial because researchers want their sites left uncovered so they, or the public, can wander around. This concern is evident at Chaco Canyon, where the GCI is collaborating with the Park Service on a backfilling experiment. Every year the park receives 80,000 visitors, who, presumably, want to see most of the site.

Even in Chetro Ketl, one of the great houses of Chaco, it is clear that some effort is needed to stanch further deterioration. The effects of wind, rain and a failed attempt at stabilization are all apparent. Heavy cement applied to the top of walls in the 1960s to keep out moisture has broken the lighter, underlying stone. Erosion around the base of many walls has destabilized them to the verge of collapse. Water has entered the crowns of other walls, frozen and subsequently forced apart the stones below. And water has caused salt to effloresce, or leach out, from the structure. Once such saline crystals form, they grow or shrink depending on the availability of moisture—and when they grow, they, too, push apart the stones, ultimately crumbling them.

Ford points out the white salt stains along the walls as she walks through the building, explaining the setup. Only 10 of 60 targeted rooms at Chetro Ketl have been backfilled, because reburying

the rest would cost about $150,000—the annual maintenance budget for the entire 10-mile-long section of canyon and its thousands of ruins. Some rooms have been refilled only a few feet, with drains installed to pull moisture away from the walls and out of the site into drainage ditches. In other places, troughs buried in the center of the chambers collect and evaporate water.

In one room with wood beams, back-filling has been quite extensive and includes what are called geosynthetic materials—in this case, a sheet of black knotted plastic, which holds the soil firmly in place. Keeping the soil stable and getting the damp away are crucial so that the reburied wood does not rot, Ford says, and this test is being carefully monitored. She scrambles over to a nearby kiva and gestures toward a lunar probe lookalike standing, ungainly, in the middle of the sacred space, recording fluctuations in moisture and temperature.

Although the experiments are not finished, in some chambers the system seems to be stabilizing the walls. In other places, the attempts are not so successful, and the right strategy remains elusive. "It may be a real mess," Ford shrugs, "but, hey, that's science."

Unforeseen results are inevitable because every location is different and because site conservation technology

NEFERTARI'S TOMB in Egypt houses wall paintings that were damaged when the site was entered in 1904 (*left*). To preserve the recently cleaned and protected murals, researchers argue that tourism should be limited. A virtual-reality guide could offer visitors an alternative (*below*).

is just emerging. Agnew of the GCI recalls being called in to help preserve fossilized dinosaur tracks in Lark Quarry, a remote region of Australia. A shelter designed to protect the prints had also protected kangaroos from the hot sun, and so they would congregate there, cooling off and defecating, which did little to help preserve the tracks. Agnew concludes that the best approach if one does not have the resources needed to maintain a monitoring crew—which Lark Quarry management did not—is just "to rebury the site until that time when it can be opened for public display."

That lesson is being applied to fossil footprints in Tanzania that are more than 3.5 million years old. The GCI is evaluating how best to cover the famous Laetoli tracks that established bipedalism in hominids of that era. Although Leakey covered the site with dirt in 1979, tree roots have destroyed part of the trackway. Researchers are now considering how water flows in and around the site, whether they should use biocides to control the growth of weeds and trees, how they should signal future excavators that these levels of dirt and other materials are not original, how deep the prints should be buried and what kinds of geosynthetic materials should be incorporated. Once covered, it is unclear when, or if, the prints will be unearthed—or how it would be determined that experts should reinterpret the site or that the public should view the prints.

"There are challenges at many levels—they are not just scientific and technological," Agnew remarks. "We have to understand the mechanisms of deterioration of material and sites from a scientific point of view; that is critical. But it goes well beyond that as well." The issue of access, for instance, is pivotal. Archaeologists have the privilege of excavating places that belong to all of humanity. But what if strangers love the site to death?

The Egyptian Antiquities Organization is grappling with that concern at Nefertari's tomb in the Valley of the Queens. Originally opened in 1904, the tomb of the favorite wife of Ramses II houses magnificent wall paintings de-

JET PROPULSION LABORATORY/NASA

ANGKOR BY SATELLITE offers a fresh perspective for archaeologists studying the ancient Khmer city in Cambodia. Conservators hope data on vegetation growth and hydrology can aid them in protecting the site from further degradation and, perhaps, in restoring some of the original canals and reservoirs.

picting Nefertari's voyage to the afterlife. The luxurious red, yellow, white and green murals were destabilized during discovery and after the introduction of desert air: plaster was damaged, and salts crystallized, sometimes an inch thick, pushing off the mud plaster and growing through the pigment. Before the 1980s it was clear that the paintings would not survive much longer. Between 1988 and 1992 some of the paintings were painstakingly removed and cleaned, and flakes of paint were reattached. The paintings were then put back in place.

The past two years have been devoted to monitoring humidity and changes in temperature to see how stable the internal environment is and whether it could support visitors. Shin Maekawa, head of environmental sciences at the GCI, tried to determine what the original state of the tomb was before it was opened because that condition had preserved the paintings perfectly for about 3,200 years. Through a series of experiments he found that the tomb had been quite humid through the centuries. In fact, humidity probably reached 50 percent in the summer months.

"Until that time, people thought that in order to conserve wall paintings it had to be drier, but that is not true," Maekawa explains. What turns out to be most critical is keeping such levels stable, something that can be achieved only if the number of visitors is strictly limited. "It took the tomb three days to recover from having 20 people inside for half an hour in the summer," Maekawa reports. Other popular tombs—such as Tutankhamen's, which already shows extensive deterioration—may have more than 3,000 visitors a day. "Despite all that effort we put in, if unregulated numbers of tourists are allowed into the tomb again, the wall paintings will be placed in danger," Maekawa warns.

Nevertheless, the government is under great pressure to open it. Tourism brings Egypt about $3 billion annually, and the reopening of Nefertari's tomb could boost the number of visitors. Indeed, although it can be beneficial, tourism is cited as one of the gravest threats to sites everywhere. According to von Droste of UNESCO, there were 500 million international tourists in 1994; about 40 percent of them traveled to see monuments such as the

Sphinx, the Mayan temples of Tikal in Guatemala or the city of Petra in Jordan. Unfortunately, von Droste says, tourism often produces money for operators outside the countries being visited, so "revenues rarely go to the protection of the site." To address this problem, the GCI and others are trying to devise sustainable site management plans—as well as plans for historic centers within cities—that involve the local community, scientists, the government and the tourist industry.

In some cases, replicas can serve as proxies, protecting originals from the touch of tourists. The cave paintings of Lascaux in France were nearly destroyed by visitors brushing up against the walls. So the government built a replica nearby. The original caves are now viewed only by scholars, and the facsimile has become so popular that the number of tourists has to be limited. The GCI and Infobyte in Rome developed a virtual-reality guide to Nefertari's tomb—an alternative to visiting the real thing that may become common. But such solutions do not convey the power of a place. Nor do they resolve the question of who has the right to visit a site, whether sacred places should be left untouched or whether something should be preserved if no one can see it.

LIMITED ACCESS

It is worth saving sites, even if no one can get in there other than a few select scholars and other people," Agnew states energetically. "Of course, one does not like to be elitist and exclude the visiting public, but in fact, 90 percent of most tourists are not interested in art history. They come ill prepared: they wander in, and they wander out. Those people can go see other tombs in Egypt or other sites that are not threatened. I do not believe everyone has an inalienable right to see everything they want to see, any more than everyone can get into a Pavarotti concert—there are a limited number of seats. That is the reality of life."

Most preferable to conservators would be to extract archaeological information without touching the site at all. Consequently, researchers are increasingly using remote sensing—that is, recording information with cameras, radar, magnetometers—in short, any technology that will reveal aspects about a site from afar. "We are trying to develop the tools for conservation," says Farouk El-Baz, director of the Center for Remote Sensing at Boston University. El-Baz and his colleagues have used one of the techniques to determine how moisture was entering Nefertari's tomb as well as to extract air from a sealed chamber at the base of the Great Pyramid of Giza and to photograph the room's contents.

Remote sensing by satellite was recently used to map Angkor in Cambodia, and conservators are attempting to figure out how to apply the information. Angkor was the capital of the Khmer Empire from the ninth until the 15th century. Because each king would build a new capital, Angkor has more than 60 major monuments. The site is overgrown, stones have fallen out of place and the details of many sculptures have faded. Teams from several countries are working on various temples, each following its own distinct approach.

Preserving monuments in tropical environments is an unruly task because the jungle keeps taking over. Conservators have to decide whether to use biocides to kill vegetation and whether to shelter sites. Angkor gets 12 feet of water a year. "That much water is going to support plant growth, no matter what you do," says John Stubbs of the World Monuments Fund, which is preserving the compound of Preah Khan.

Stubbs has decided not to use biocides. Instead the team is removing heavy plant growth by hand, documenting many of the statues and performing anastylosis—replacing stones from where they have landed on the ground to what is assumed to be their original position in the ruin. On the whole, the World Monuments Fund approach is hands-off and reflects the growing consensus among archaeolo-

gists that sites should not be reconstructed, because that activity entails a potentially incorrect reinterpretation of the past.

Nevertheless, Stubbs does favor a certain kind of reconstruction and hopes to use the satellite data from the National Aeronautics and Space Administration to that end. "I would like to restore water features because I am quite convinced that the architecture was supposed to be seen in reflection," he explains. "The whole culture is about capturing and manipulating water." The image shows the reaches of the estuary, which covers the area from the Mekong River up to Angkor during the rainy season. The information could help conservators understand the region's hydrology, knowledge that could, in turn, help them determine how and whether to drain parts of the site to preserve it.

Stubbs's biggest fear about Angkor—and he is not alone—is that looting will leave it barren. "The popularity of the site, the new access, the hunger for Khmer art and the lawlessness of the place are all a recipe for pillaging," he notes. Stubbs says he has visited shops in Bangkok, inquired about buying Khmer antiquities and been shown pictures of objects taken from Preah Khan—and even some photographs of statues still in place.

Many archaeologists single out looting as the major threat to ancient sites and objects. It is impossible to get good numbers on the value of the stolen objects, but estimates run from $2 billion to $6 billion annually. From 80 to 90 percent of antiquities, including those sitting in museums, are considered "hot." The scale of seizures intensified in the mid-1980s, when people began to look at antiquities as investments, explains Ricardo J. Elia of Boston University. All the more horrible, he fumes, is that an artifact obtained as a spoil of plunder, at the expense of a destroyed site, comes to be seen as an art object when it is bought by a wealthy collector and ends up in a museum: "It starts out real dirty and ends up real clean."

For conservators, stopping illicit traffic and using science and technology to protect monuments and ruins are, in many ways, easier tasks than answering questions that are raised about saving sites. Given limited resources and conflicts of interest, what should be saved? "It used to be that time made the choice," reflects Miguel Angel Corzo, director of the GCI. "War came, and people used houses and monuments as quarries. It was just the natural evolution of things that brought us to where we are today. But now we have an extraordinary capacity to save whatever we want; the technology is there. What are we going to leave behind? Are we going to take the same attitude, 'Time will tell'? Or are we going to be people of the 21st century and say, 'This is who we are going to be remembered as'?"

It is tragically clear that wiping out a site can wipe out cultural identity—something that happens when ethnic groups clash, each trying to obliterate the culture of the other. China's razing of the monasteries of Tibet is but one example. The interpretation of archaeological remains powerfully shapes the outlook of an entire people, as can be seen in the evolving view of the Great Zimbabwe, a series of majestic granite structures constructed between A.D. 1400 and 1600. British colonialists claimed that the circular compound could not have been built by native Africans: northern invaders from either Greece, Egypt or the Middle East

must have swept down and built the sophisticated enclosure. It has been established, however, that it was the ancestors of regional Shona people who built the Great Zimbabwe. The cultural identity and independence of Zimbabwe (formerly Rhodesia) are closely linked to this monument.

African countries, in particular, could lose a profound part of their cultural identity if their sites are not conserved. The continent has a dearth of native archaeologists, and many places have not yet been excavated. According to a 1992 World Bank conference report, *Culture and Development in Africa,* there is only one archaeology program in 11 central African countries, and the total annual budget for the entire region is $20,000.

Despite the vast challenges and many unresolved ethical questions, the archaeological community is developing a philosophy of conservation. This shift could be seen in the response to the recent discovery of some 300 Cro-Magnon paintings in a cave near Avignon, France. Immediately after its discovery, the cave and its 20,000-year-old masterpieces were sealed off. "The cave should be left as it is. It must be studied, of course, but bearing in mind that the collecting of the information must not be destructive," says Jean Clottes, a prehistorian and adviser to the French Culture Ministry.

"It is out of the question to start excavating all over the place." As Clottes points out, ever smaller samples of materials are needed to date paintings, and so the investigations of archaeologists present may seem like ravages to those to come. Furthermore, "theories change," Clottes notes. "Everyone believes in one for 10 or 15 years, then there is another theory."

It is for the sake of these theories and for the awe of place and time that people want to hold on to their past. Multiculturalism—the celebration of any culture, no matter how small—as well as the movement toward the next millennium may be contributing to a growing nostalgia or, as some archaeologists put it, a need to reconnect with history. For others, though, the attempt to hold on to everything makes little sense. We Westerners tend to feel that it is massively important to preserve," comments Marian A. Kaminitz, a conservator at the National Museum of the American Indian. Others "have a strong sense of allowing things to return, of not holding on to them."

In the gathering dark of Chaco Canyon, Pueblo Bonito returns to the desert. An absolute stillness settles around the ruins. "It is beneficial that they are protecting it," says Petuuche Gilbert, a descendant of the Anasazi. But we could also let it go, he adds: "It would be part of the natural cycle."

Credits/ Acknowledgments

Cover design by Charles Vitelli

1. About Archaeology
Facing overview—American Museum of Natural History photo.
35—Courtesy of the Library of the University of Virginia.
36—Courtesy of Jeff Hantman. Map source: David Bushnell, "The Five Monacan Towns in Virginia, 1607," Smithsonian Miscellaneous Collections, Vol. 82, No. 12, 1930. A reprint of a section of the 1624 original. 39—Courtesy of the McNitt Collection/State Records Center and Archives, Santa Fe. 40-44—Photos by Terrence Moore.

2. Thinking Like an Archaeologist
Facing overview—Photo Researchers photo. © 1985 by David Weintraub.

3. Problem-oriented Archaeology
Facing overview—United Nations photo by Rothstein.
69-71—Photos by Neal Brown. © 1993 by The Walt Disney

Company. Reprinted by permission of Discover magazine.
80—Courtesy of Bruce and Kenneth Zuckerman/West Semitic Research Project. 93—History Today map by Joe LeMonnier.

4. Experimental Archaeology
Facing overview—United Nations photo. 114-116—Photos by Michel Lorblanchet.

5. History and Ethnoarchaeology
Facing overview—United Nations photo. 132-133—History Today maps by Joe LeMonnier.

6. The New Politics of Archaeology
Facing overview—York Archaeological Trust photo.

7. Contemporary Archaeology
Facing overview—United Nations photo. 205—History Today map by Joe LeMonnier.

PHOTOCOPY THIS PAGE!!!*

ANNUAL EDITIONS ARTICLE REVIEW FORM

■ NAME: _____ DATE: _____

■ TITLE AND NUMBER OF ARTICLE: _____

■ BRIEFLY STATE THE MAIN IDEA OF THIS ARTICLE: _____

_____

■ LIST THREE IMPORTANT FACTS THAT THE AUTHOR USES TO SUPPORT THE MAIN IDEA:

_____

_____

_____

_____

_____

_____

■ WHAT INFORMATION OR IDEAS DISCUSSED IN THIS ARTICLE ARE ALSO DISCUSSED IN YOUR
TEXTBOOK OR OTHER READING YOU HAVE DONE? LIST THE TEXTBOOK CHAPTERS AND PAGE
NUMBERS:

_____

_____

_____

_____

_____

_____

_____

■ LIST ANY EXAMPLES OF BIAS OR FAULTY REASONING THAT YOU FOUND IN THE ARTICLE:

_____

_____

_____

_____

■ LIST ANY NEW TERMS/CONCEPTS THAT WERE DISCUSSED IN THE ARTICLE AND WRITE A SHORT
DEFINITION:

_____

_____

_____

_____

_____

*Your instructor may require you to use this Annual Editions Article Review Form in any number of
ways: for articles that are assigned, for extra credit, as a tool to assist in developing assigned papers, or
simply for your own reference. Even if it is not required, we encourage you to photocopy and use this
page; you'll find that reflecting on the articles will greatly enhance the information from your text.

ANNUAL EDITIONS: ARCHAEOLOGY 96/97
Article Rating Form

Here is an opportunity for you to have direct input into the next revision of this volume. We would like you to rate each of the 45 articles listed below, using the following scale:

1. **Excellent: should definitely be retained**
2. **Above average: should probably be retained**
3. **Below average: should probably be deleted**
4. **Poor: should definitely be deleted**

Your ratings will play a vital part in the next revision. So please mail this prepaid form to us just as soon as you complete it.
Thanks for your help!

Annual Editions revisions depend on two major opinion sources: one is our Advisory Board, listed in the front of this volume, which works with us in scanning the thousands of articles published in the public press each year; the other is you—the person actually using the book. Please help us and the users of the next edition by completing the prepaid article rating form on this page and returning it to us. Thank you.

Rating	Article	Rating	Article
	1. The Quest for the Past		22. Red Feathers from the South, May 1970
	2. The Golden Marshalltown: A Parable for the Archeology of the 1980s		23. Post-Mortem at the Little Bighorn
	3. How Archaeology Works		24. The Past as Propaganda
	4. The Enlightened Archaeologist		25. Murders from the Past
	5. 'Reverse Archaeologists' Are Tracing the Footsteps of a Cowboy-Explorer		26. Bones and Bureaucrats: New York's Great Cemetery Imbroglio
	6. Kentucky Memoir: Digging in the Depression		27. The Earth Is Their Witness
	7. Epistemology: How You Know What You Know		28. Colorful Cotton!
	8. The Mysterious Fall of the Nacirema		29. Living through the Donner Party
	9. Rhinos and Lions and Bears (Oh, My!)		30. The Antiquities Market
	10. Coming to America		31. Who Owns the Spoils of War?
	11. The Politics of First-Century Judea: Searching for Jesus		32. Politics and Archaeology
	12. Dead Sea DNA		33. An Anthropological Culture Shift
	13. Egil's Bones		34. When My Grandmother Is Your Database: Reactions to Repatriation
	14. Find Suggests Weaving Preceded Settled Life		35. Archeology Division
	15. Ancient Odysseys		36. Indians, Archaeologists, and the Future
	16. Thailand's Good Mound		37. Tales from a Peruvian Crypt
	17. Yes, Wonderful Things		38. Damming the Past
	18. Moving the Moai—Transporting the Megaliths of Easter Island: How Did They do It?		39. Before the Deluge: Dam Construction in Turkey Threatens Invaluable Archaeological Sites
	19. Paleolithic Paint Job		40. Archaeology Meets the 104th Congress
	20. Bushmen		41. Saving Our World's Heritage
	21. Ancient Indians Sought Shadows and Ice Caves		42. Proving Ground of the Nuclear Age
			43. Sentinels of Stone
			44. The Boom in Volunteer Archaeology
			45. The Preservation of Past

(Continued on next page)

ABOUT YOU

Name _____ Date _____
Are you a teacher? ❑ Or student? ❑
Your School Name _____
Department _____
Address _____
City _____ State _____ Zip _____
School Telephone # _____

YOUR COMMENTS ARE IMPORTANT TO US!

Please fill in the following information:

For which course did you use this book? _____
Did you use a text with this Annual Edition? ❑ yes   ❑ no
The title of the text? _____
What are your general reactions to the Annual Editions concept?

Have you read any particular articles recently that you think should be included in the next edition?

Are there any articles you feel should be replaced in the next edition? Why?

Are there other areas that you feel would utilize an Annual Edition?

May we contact you for editorial input?

May we quote you from above?

ANNUAL EDITIONS: ARCHAEOLOGY 96/97

BUSINESS REPLY MAIL

First Class   Permit No. 84   Guilford, CT

Postage will be paid by addressee

Dushkin Publishing Group/
Brown & Benchmark Publishers
Sluice Dock
Guilford, Connecticut 06437